BRAIN TRAINING PUZZLES

BRAIN TRAINING PUZZLES

ISBN: 978-1-78888-808-0
AD006781NT

Printed in China

2 4 6 8 10 9 7 5 3 1

Contents

LEVEL 1

1 Can you place the hexagons into the grid, so that where any hexagon touches another along a straight line, the number in both triangles is the same? No rotation of any hexagon is allowed!

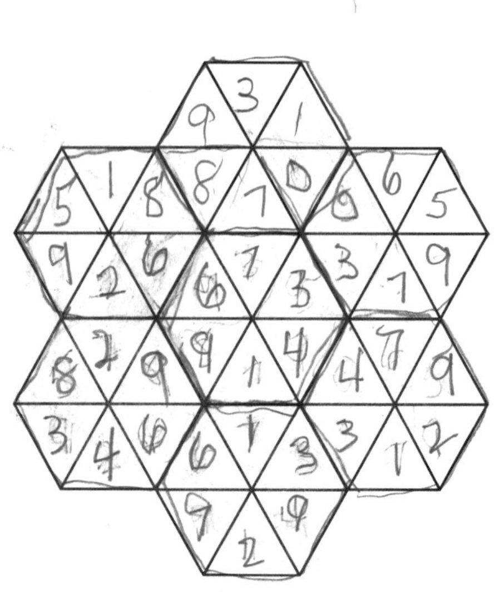

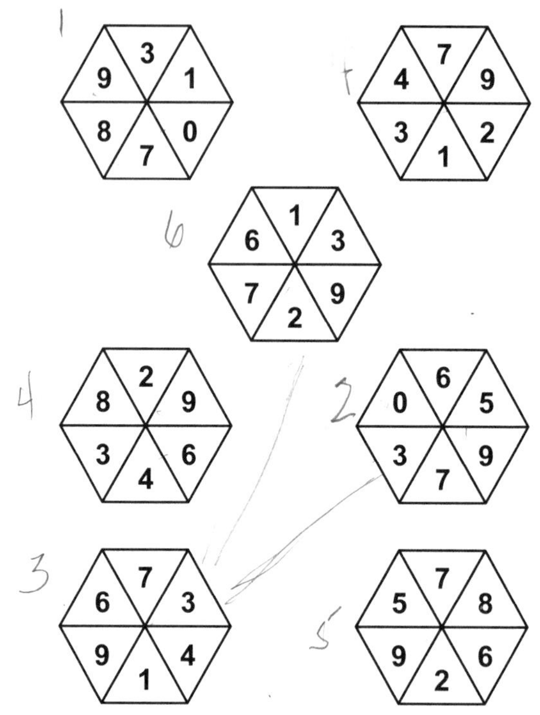

2 Can you place the vessels into the diagram? Some parts of vessels or sea squares have already been filled in. A number to the right or below a row or column refers to the number of occupied squares in that row or column.

Any vessel may be positioned horizontally or vertically, but no part of a vessel touches part of any other vessel, either horizontally, vertically, or diagonally.

Empty Area of Sea: ≈

Aircraft Carrier: ◀■■▶

Battleships: ◀■▶ ◀■▶

Cruisers: ◀▶ ◀▶ ◀▶

Submarines: ● ● ● ●

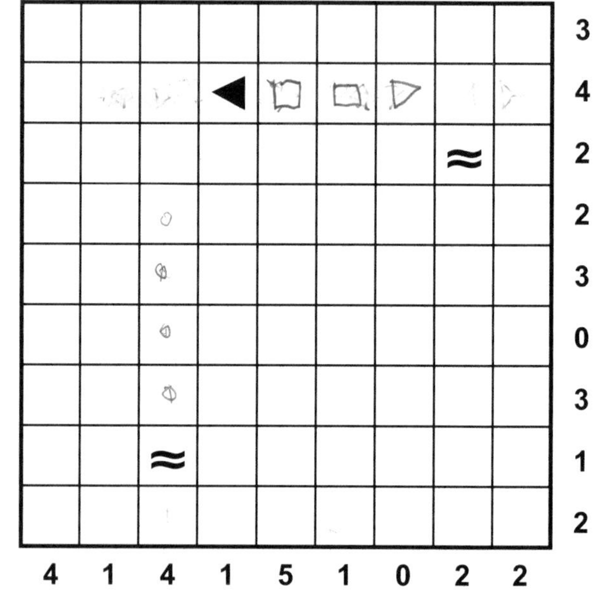

3 Each horizontal row and vertical column should contain different shapes and different numbers.

Every square will contain one number and one shape, and no combination may be repeated anywhere else in the puzzle.

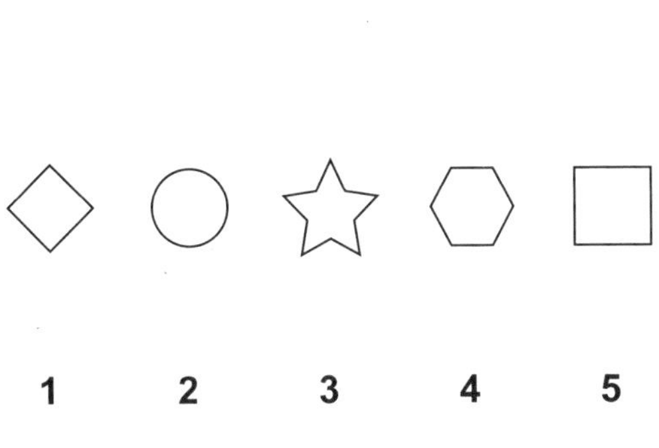

			3	
4	3	5		
	5			4
	2	1		
	4	3		

4 In the diagram below, what number should replace the question mark?

5

126 6

?

45 9

18

LEVEL 1

5 Every brick in this pyramid contains a number which is the sum of the two numbers below it, so that F=A+B, etc.

Just work out the missing numbers!

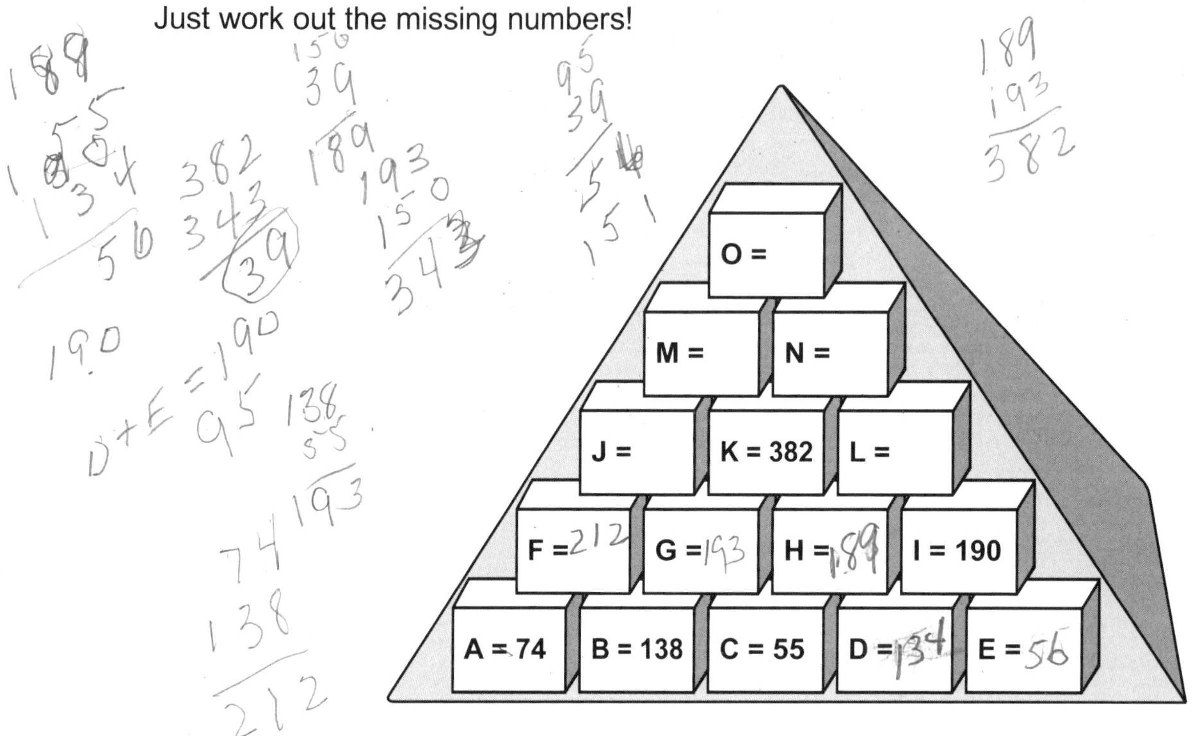

6 In this puzzle, an amateur coin collector has been out with his metal detector, searching for booty. He didn't have time to dig up all the coins he found, so has made a grid map, showing their locations, in the hope that if he loses the map, at least no-one else will understand it…

Those squares containing numbers are empty, but where a number appears in a square, it indicates how many coins are located in the squares (up to a maximum of eight) surrounding the numbered one, touching it at any corner or side. There is only one coin in any individual square.

Place a circle into every square containing a coin.

	1		0		2		2		1
		0					2		
	2	1			3		2	1	
3	3			2					
				2				0	
						1	0	0	
2		4				3	2	2	
		3	1	2					
2	2	2		3	4	6		4	
							3		

LEVEL 1

7 Given that the letters are valued 1-26 according to their places in the alphabet, can you crack the mystery code to reveal the missing letter?

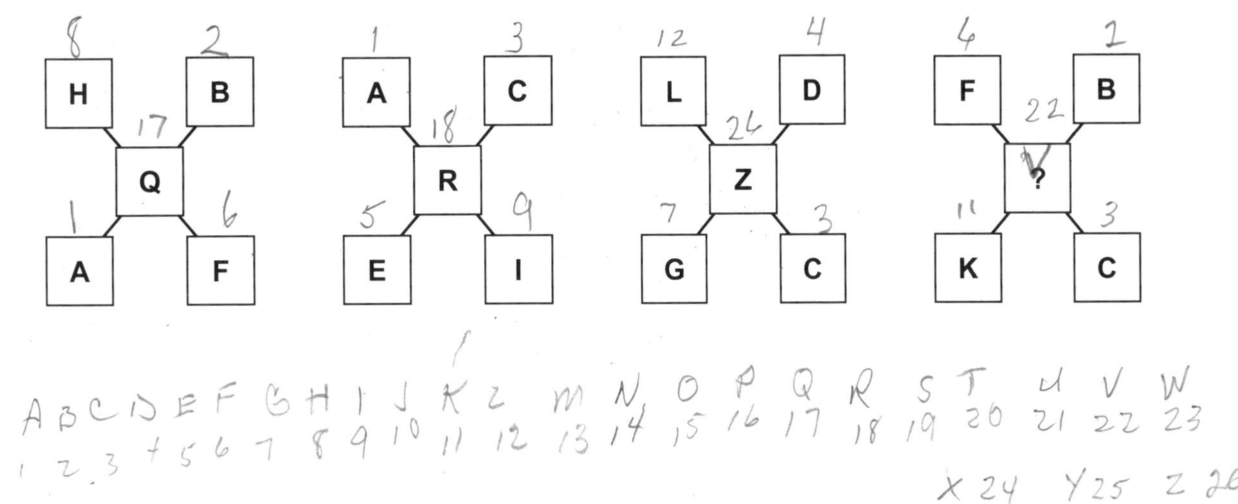

8 Place all twelve of the pieces into the grid. Any may be rotated or flipped over, but none may touch another, not even diagonally. The numbers outside the grid refer to the number of consecutive black squares; and each block is separated from the others by at least one white square. For instance, "3 2" could refer to a row with none, one or more white squares, then three black squares, then at least one white square, then two more black squares, followed by any number of white squares.

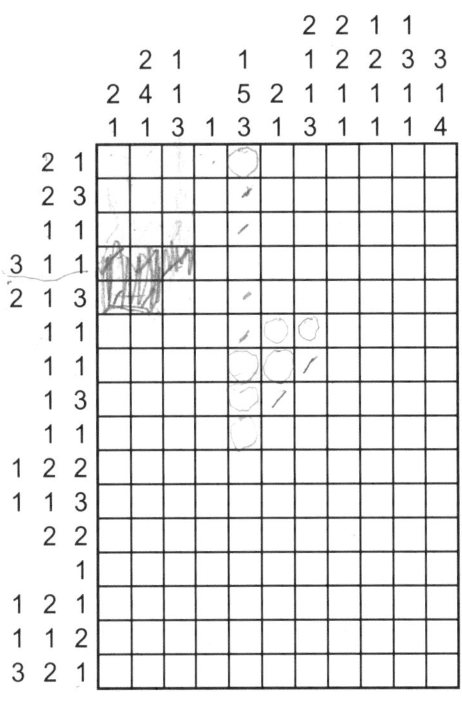

LEVEL 1

9 Each of the eight segments of the spider's web should be filled with a different number from 1 to 8, in such a way that every ring also contains a different number from 1 to 8.

The segments run from the outside of the spider's web to the middle, and the rings run all the way around.

Some numbers are already in place. Can you fill in the rest?

LEVEL 1

10 Every row and column in this grid originally contained one heart, one club, one diamond, one spade, and two blank squares, although not necessarily in that order.

Every symbol with a black arrow refers to the first of the four symbols encountered in the direction of the arrow. Every symbol with a white arrow refers to the second of the four symbols encountered in the direction of the arrow.

Can you complete the original grid?

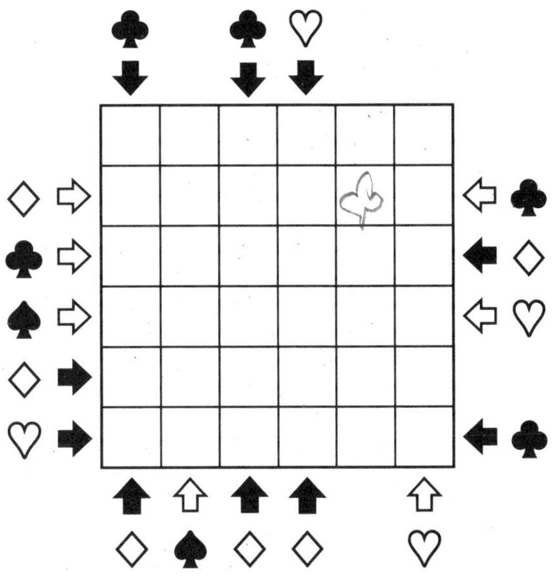

11 Fill the grid so that every horizontal row and vertical column contains the numbers 1-5. Any arrows in the grid always point toward a square that contains a lower number.

	5		2	
	3			
4		2		
				3

LEVEL 1

12

With the starter already given, can you fit all of the remaining listed numbers into this grid? Take care, this puzzle may not be as easy as it looks!

12	411	2469	6349	87745
13	429	2734	6499	94847
16	459	2910	6734	179070
25	544	2996	7760	192492
55	555	3189	7791	253300
71	619	3265	8102	376623
72	689	3299	8494	530548
84	714	3697	8904	659995
92	842	4228	23960	684513
93	853	5541	27769	687148
110	1234	5837	71907	934936
314	1356	6297	75659	990058

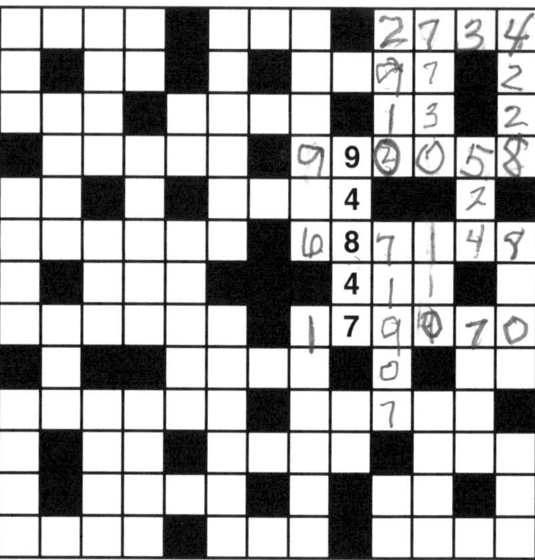

13

The grid should be filled with numbers from 1 to 6, so that each number appears just once in every row and column.

The clues refer to the digit totals in the squares, e.g. A 1 2 3 = 6 means that the numbers in squares A1, A2 and A3 add up to 6.

1 C 3 4 = 11
2 D 2 3 4 = 12
3 E 3 4 = 6
4 F 3 4 = 5
5 D E F 1 = 9
6 E F 2 = 5
7 A B 3 = 4
8 A B 4 = 10
9 C D 5 = 8
10 B C 6 = 5
11 A 5 6 = 7

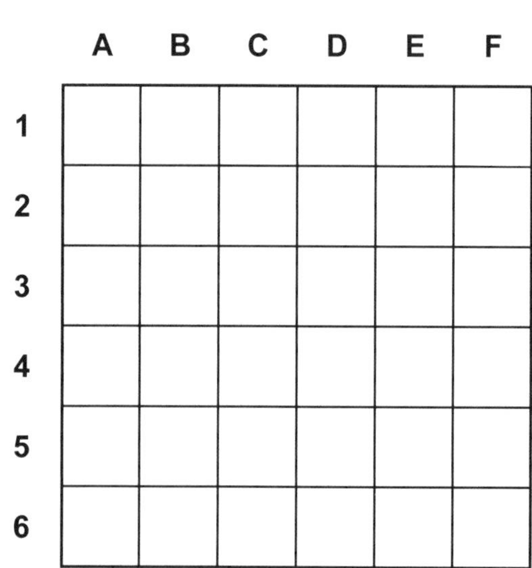

LEVEL 1

14 The object of this puzzle is to trace a single path from the top left corner to the bottom right corner of the grid, moving through all of the cells in either a horizontal, vertical, or diagonal direction.

Every cell must be entered once only, and your path should take you through the numbers in the sequence 1-2-3-4-5-6-1-2-3-4-5-6, etc.

Can you find the way?

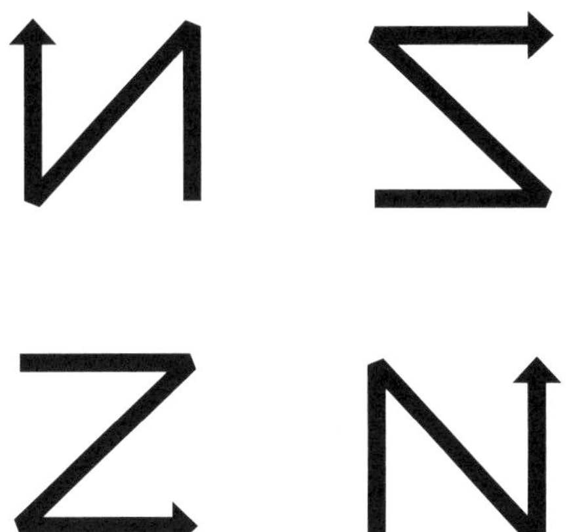

1	2	2	3	4	5
5	3	4	1	6	6
4	6	1	5	1	2
3	2	1	2	3	3
3	2	6	1	4	4
4	5	6	5	5	6

15 A standard set of 28 dominoes has been laid out as shown. Can you draw in the edges of them all?

The check-box is provided as an aid and the domino already placed will help.

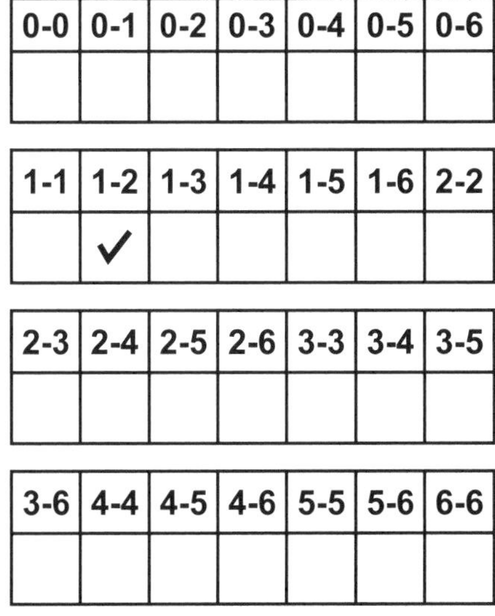

0-0	0-1	0-2	0-3	0-4	0-5	0-6

1-1	1-2	1-3	1-4	1-5	1-6	2-2
	✓					

2-3	2-4	2-5	2-6	3-3	3-4	3-5

3-6	4-4	4-5	4-6	5-5	5-6	6-6

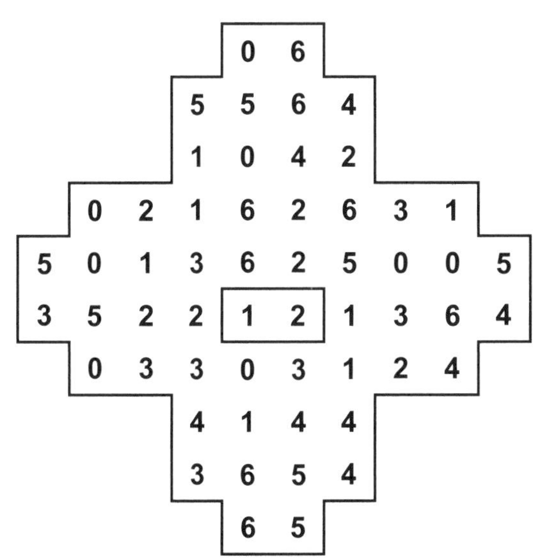

LEVEL 1

16

Draw a single continuous loop, by connecting the dots. No line may cross the path of another.

The figure inside each set of any four surrounding dots indicates the total number of surrounding lines.

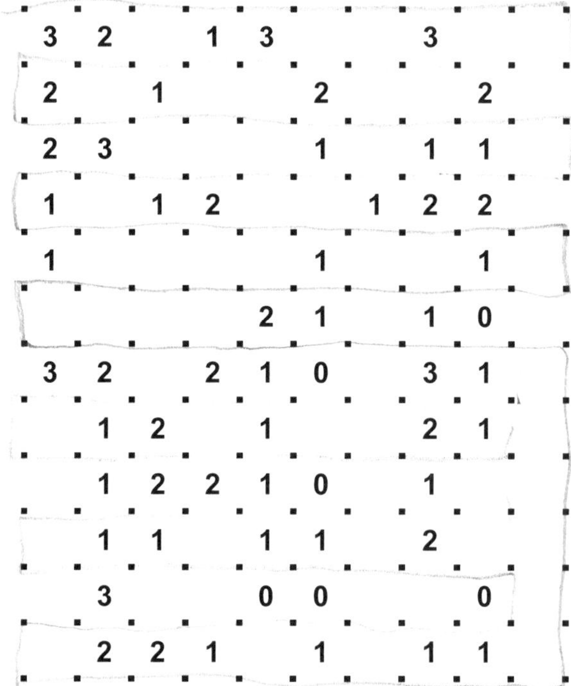

17

Place the eight tiles into the puzzle grid so that all adjacent numbers on each tile match up.

Tiles may be rotated through 360 degrees, but none may be flipped over.

3	4
3	2

2	1
2	1

2	2
3	4

1	1
3	2

2	4
3	1

4	2
1	2

3	2
2	2

4	3
4	4

1	3				
4	4				

LEVEL 1

18 Every oval shape in this diagram contains a different letter of the alphabet from A to K inclusive.

Use the clues to determine their locations. Reference in the clues to "due" means in any location along the same horizontal or vertical line.

1. The A is next to and north of the D, which is next to and east of the E.
2. The C is due east of the B, which is due north of the G.
3. The F is next to and south of the E, which is due south of (but not next to) the H.
4. The I is next to and west of the H, which is next to and south of the K.

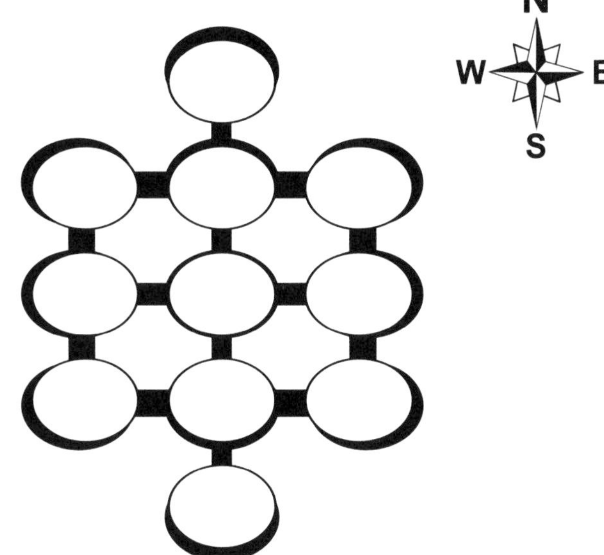

19 Draw walls to partition the grid into areas (some walls are already drawn in for you).

Each area must contain two circles, area sizes must match those numbers shown next to the grid, and each "+" must be linked to at least two walls.

3, 4, 5, 6, 7

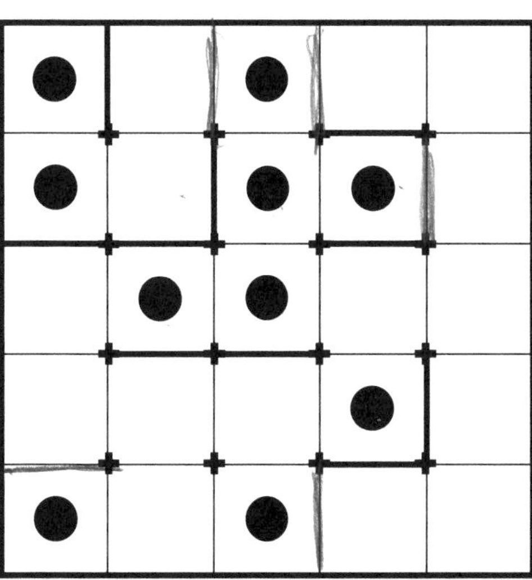

20 Twelve L-shapes need to be inserted in the grid, and each L has one hole in it.

There are three pieces of each of the four kinds shown here, and any piece may be turned or flipped over before being put in the grid. No pieces of the same kind touch, even at a corner.

The pieces fit together so well that you cannot see any spaces between them; only the holes show.

Can you tell where the Ls are? One piece is already in place.

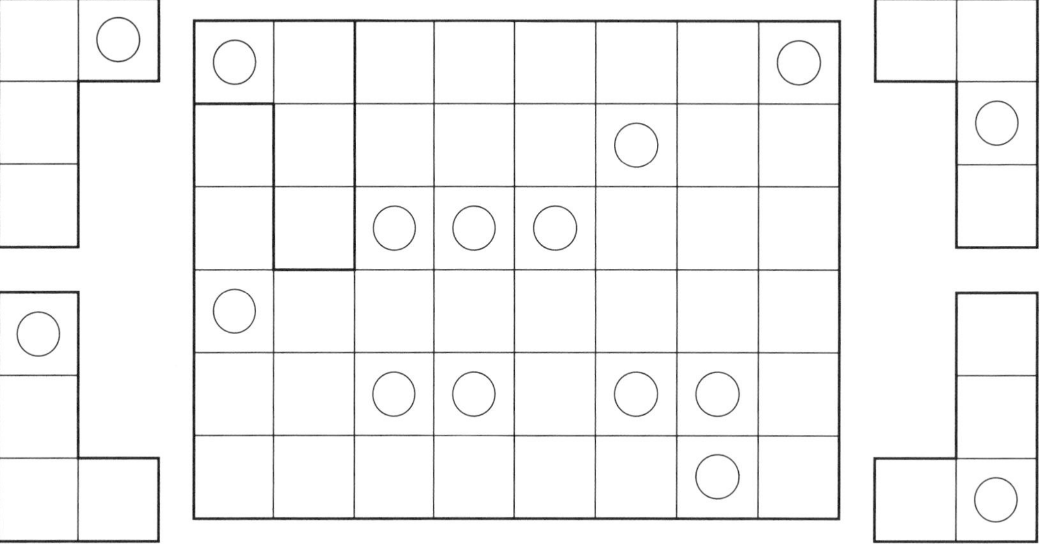

21 Fill the three empty circles with the symbols +, –, and x in some order, to make a sum that totals the central number. Each symbol must be used once, and calculations are made in the direction of travel (clockwise).

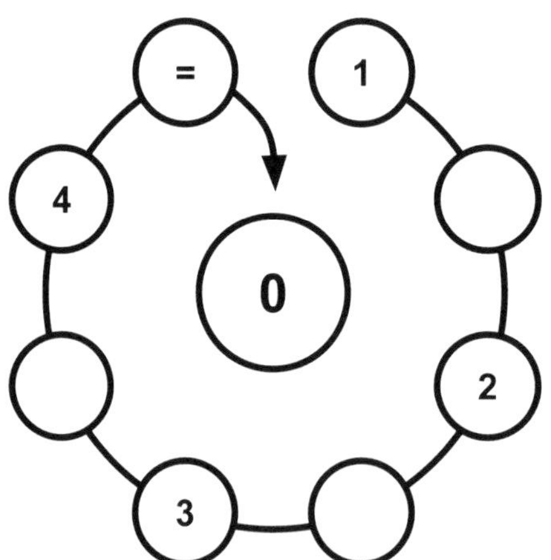

LEVEL 1

22

Each of the small squares in the grid below contains either A, B, or C. Each row, column, and diagonal line of six squares has exactly two of each letter. Can you tell the letter in each square?

Across

1 No two letters the same are directly next to each other
2 The Cs are further right than the Bs
3 The Bs are next to each other
4 The Bs are next to each other
5 The Bs are further right than the Cs
6 No two letters the same are directly next to each other

Down

1 Each C is directly next to and below an A
2 No two letters the same are directly next to each other
3 No two letters the same are directly next to each other
4 No two letters the same are directly next to each other
5 The As are next to each other
6 Each C is directly next to and below a B

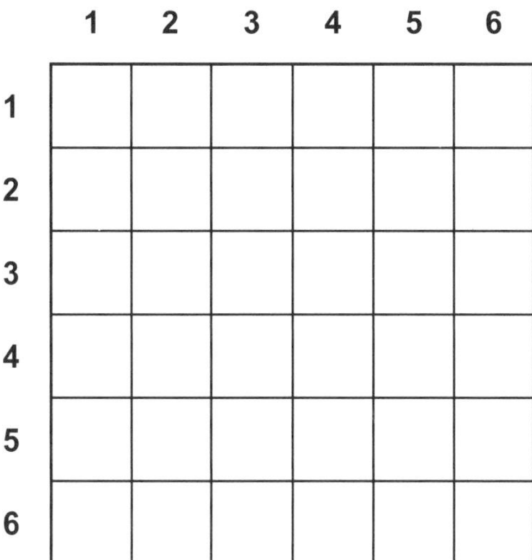

23

Using the numbers below, complete these six equations (three reading across and three reading downwards).

Every number is used once.

1 2 3 4 5 6 7 8 9

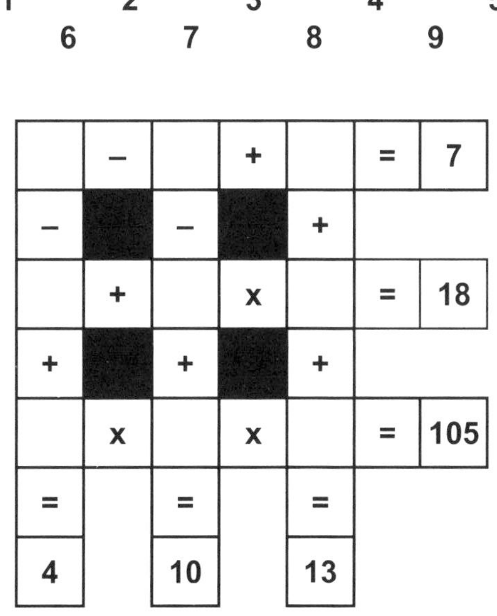

LEVEL 1

24 The chart gives directions to a hidden treasure behind the central black square in the grid. Move the indicated number of spaces north, south, east, and west (eg 4N means move four squares north) stopping at every square once only to arrive there. At which square should you start?

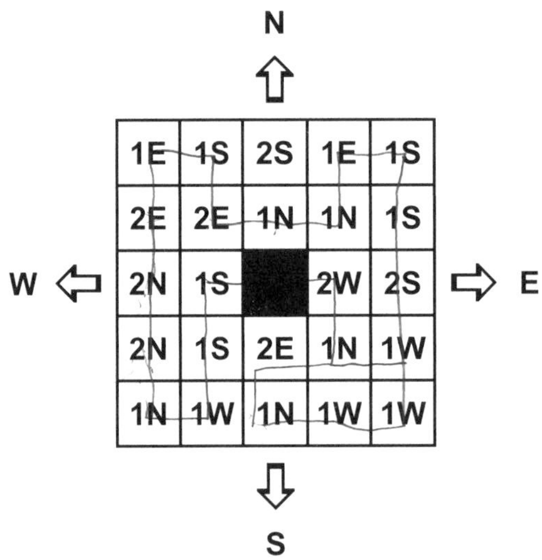

25 The numbers at the top and on the left side show the quantity of single-digit numbers (1-9) used in that row and column. The numbers at the bottom and on the right show the sum of the digits. A number may appear more than once in a row or column, but no numbers are in squares that touch, even at a corner.

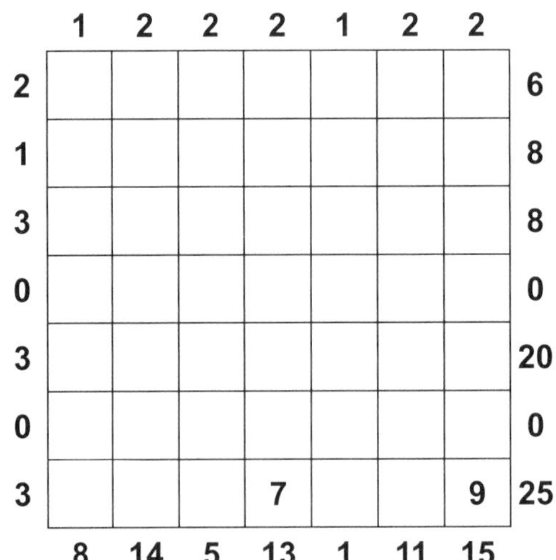

LEVEL 1

26 In the square below, change the positions of six numbers, one per horizontal row, vertical column, and long diagonal line of six smaller squares, in such a way that the numbers in each row, column, and long diagonal line total exactly 137. Any number may appear more than once in a row, column or line.

31	6	11	31	47	8
22	22	35	31	27	23
23	13	22	24	14	23
26	39	27	20	9	24
21	26	16	34	18	27
22	13	11	20	27	29

27 The blank squares below should be filled with whole numbers between 1 and 30 inclusive, any of which may occur more than once, or not at all.

The numbers in every horizontal row add up to the totals on the right, as do the two long diagonal lines; while those in every vertical column add up to the totals along the bottom.

							93
13	5	27			6	16	89
9	11		20		10	4	97
		22	21	17		3	84
15	25	20		14	29	5	110
30	26	2	4	9			107
17	19		6	5	3		94
		2	1	30	14		96
112	103	121	68	102	83	88	72

LEVEL 1

28

Can you place the hexagons into the grid, so that where any hexagon touches another along a straight line, the number in both triangles is the same? No rotation of any hexagon is allowed!

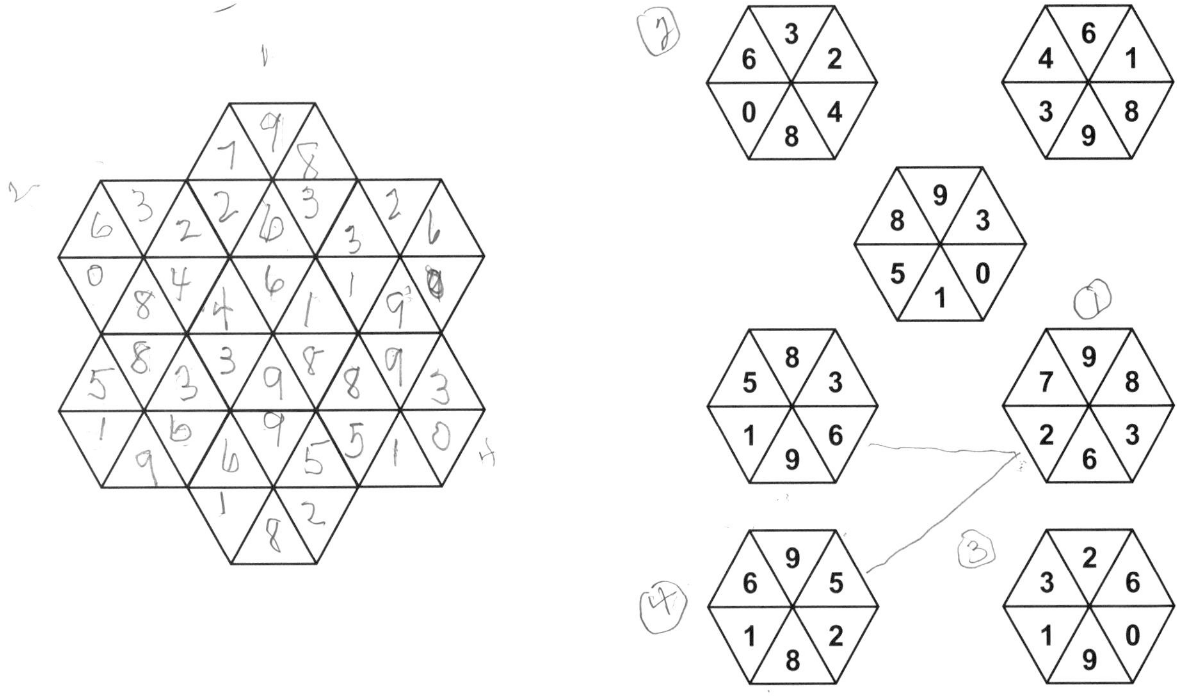

29

Can you place the vessels into the diagram? Some parts of vessels or sea squares have already been filled in. A number to the right or below a row or column refers to the number of occupied squares in that row or column.

Any vessel may be positioned horizontally or vertically, but no part of a vessel touches part of any other vessel, either horizontally, vertically, or diagonally.

Empty Area of Sea: ≈

Aircraft Carrier: ◀■■▶

Battleships: ◀■▶ ◀■▶

Cruisers: ◀▶ ◀▶ ◀▶

Submarines: ● ● ● ●

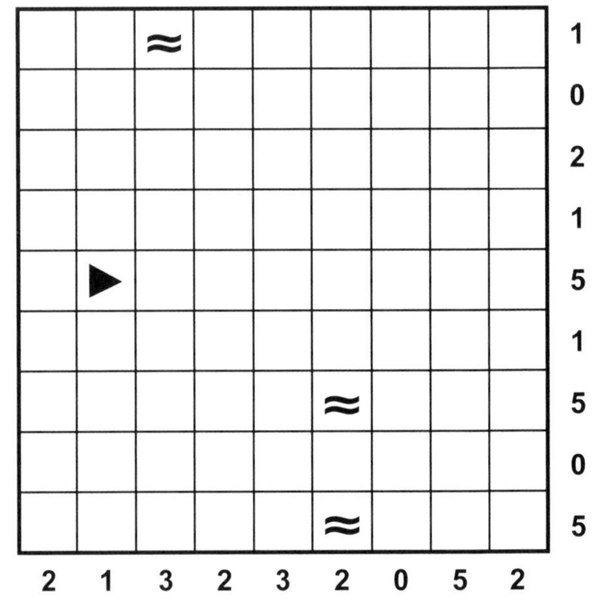

LEVEL 1

30 Each horizontal row and vertical column should contain different shapes and different numbers.

Every square will contain one number and one shape, and no combination may be repeated anywhere else in the puzzle.

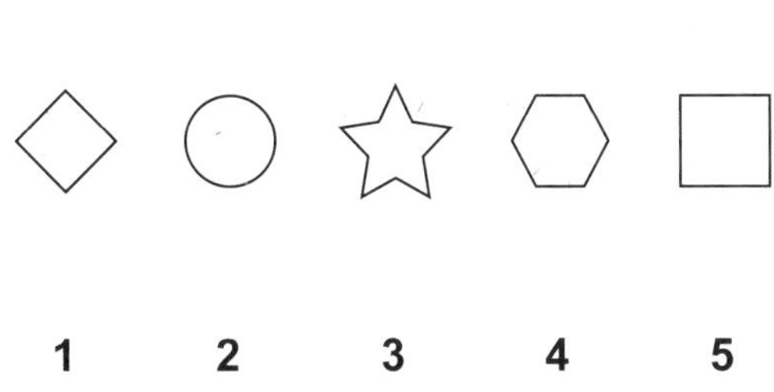

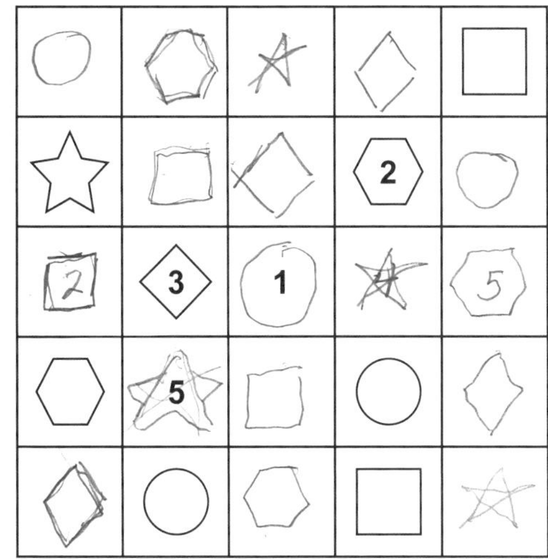

31 Which of the four lettered alternatives (A, B, C or D) fits most logically into the empty square?

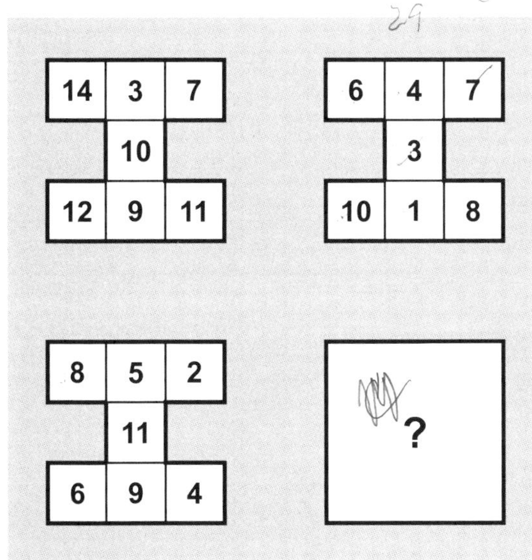

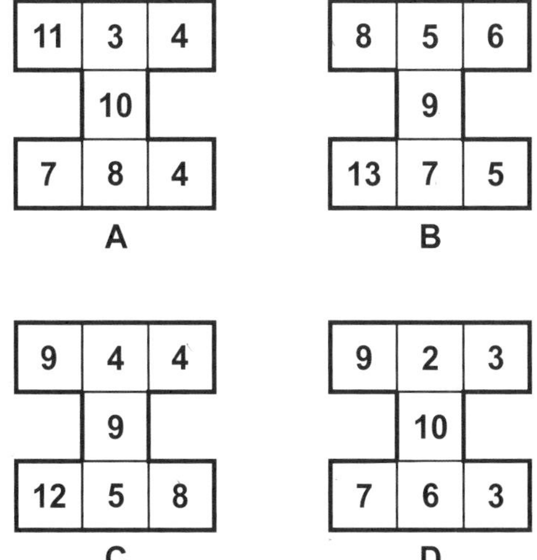

LEVEL 1

32

Every brick in this pyramid contains a number which is the sum of the two numbers below it, so that F=A+B, etc.

Just work out the missing numbers!

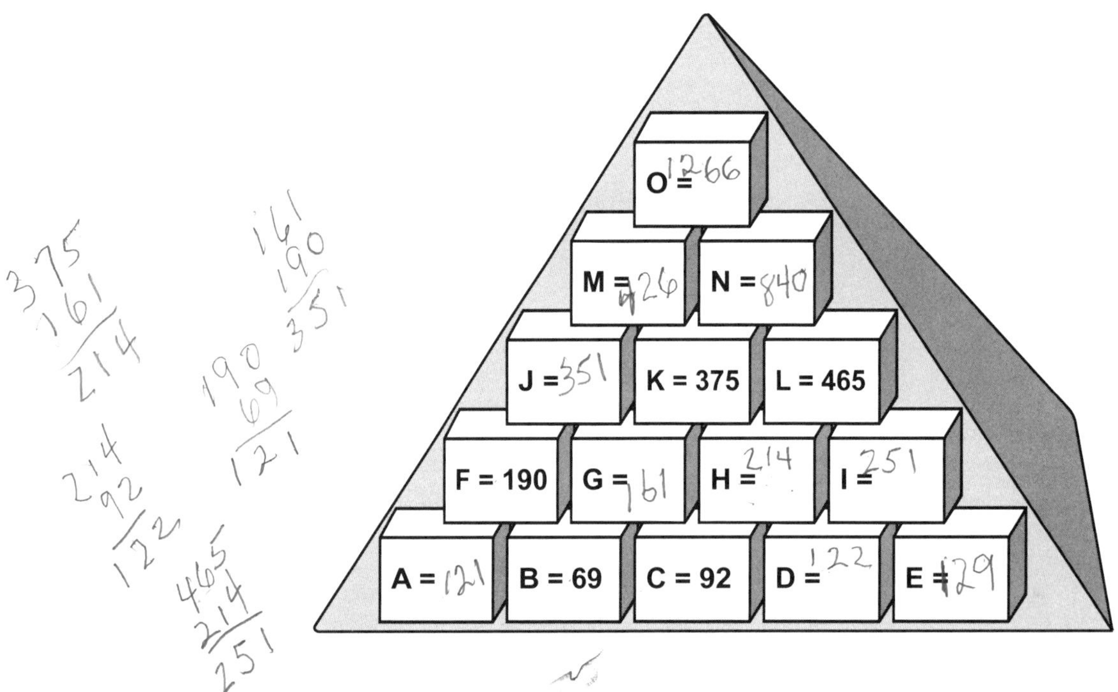

33

In this puzzle, an amateur coin collector has been out with his metal detector, searching for booty. He didn't have time to dig up all the coins he found, so has made a grid map, showing their locations, in the hope that if he loses the map, at least no-one else will understand it…

Those squares containing numbers are empty, but where a number appears in a square, it indicates how many coins are located in the squares (up to a maximum of eight) surrounding the numbered one, touching it at any corner or side. There is only one coin in any individual square.

Place a circle into every square containing a coin.

2			1	1			2		
		3		2				2	
1		1			2		0		0
		2			2	1			
		3					1		
	4		3					3	2
		2	3		3			2	
1		2			4	3		1	
	2	2		3					0
	1						1		

LEVEL 1

34 Given that the letters are valued 1-26 according to their places in the alphabet, can you crack the mystery code to reveal the missing letter?

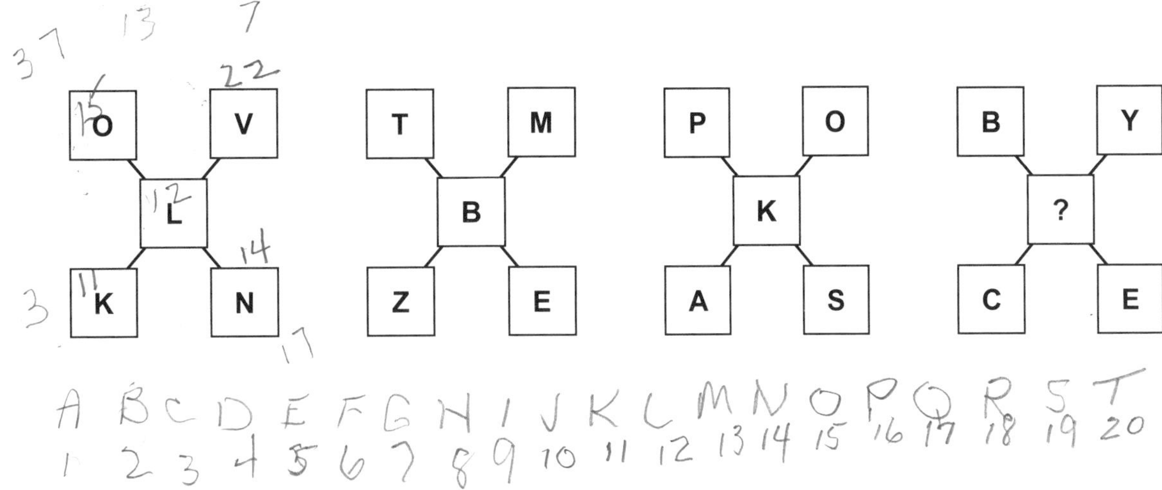

35 Place all twelve of the pieces into the grid. Any may be rotated or flipped over, but none may touch another, not even diagonally. The numbers outside the grid refer to the number of consecutive black squares; and each block is separated from the others by at least one white square. For instance, "3 2" could refer to a row with none, one or more white squares, then three black squares, then at least one white square, then two more black squares, followed by any number of white squares.

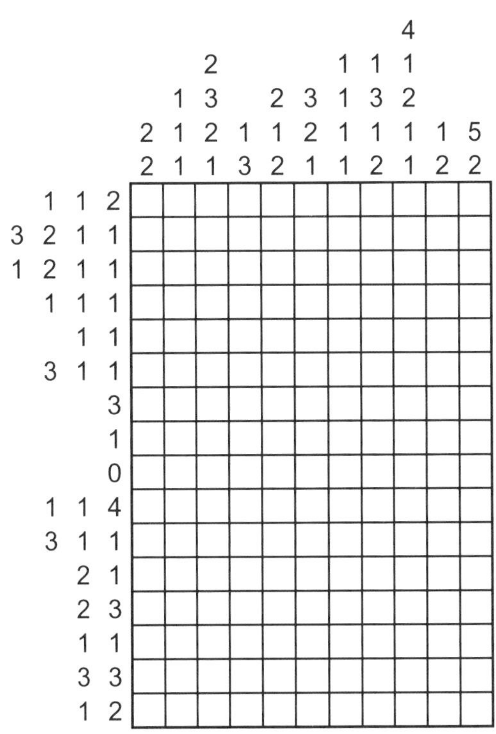

LEVEL 1

36 Each of the eight segments of the spider's web should be filled with a different number from 1 to 8, in such a way that every ring also contains a different number from 1 to 8.

The segments run from the outside of the spider's web to the middle, and the rings run all the way around.

Some numbers are already in place. Can you fill in the rest?

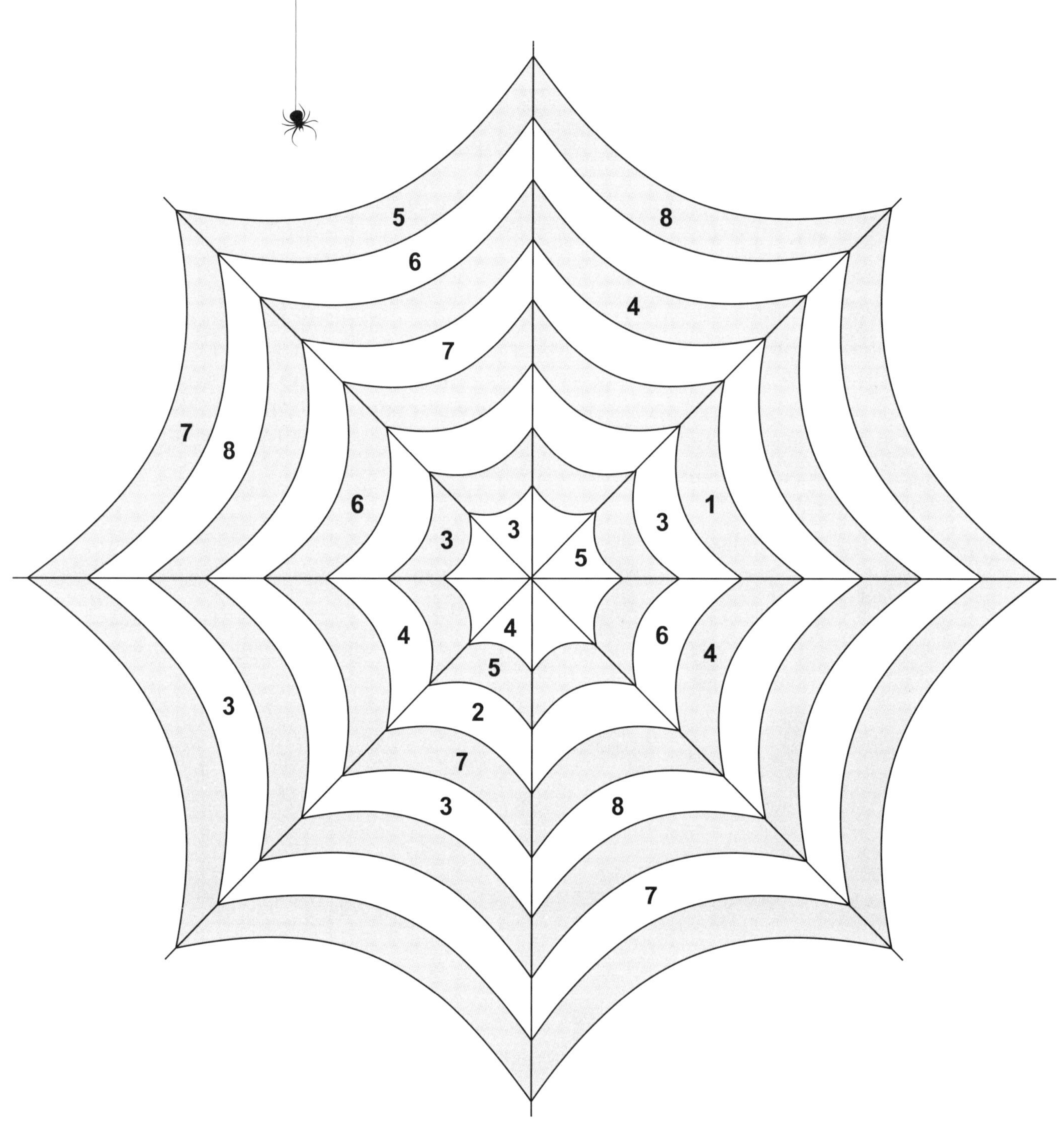

37

Every row and column in this grid originally contained one heart, one club, one diamond, one spade, and two blank squares, although not necessarily in that order.

Every symbol with a black arrow refers to the first of the four symbols encountered in the direction of the arrow. Every symbol with a white arrow refers to the second of the four symbols encountered in the direction of the arrow.

Can you complete the original grid?

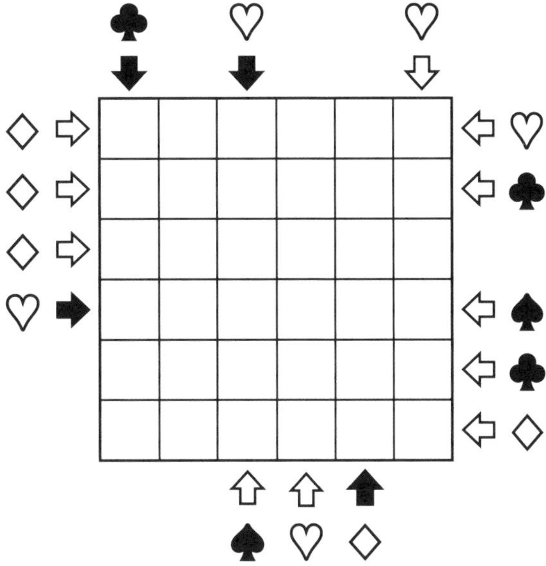

38

Fill the grid so that every horizontal row and vertical column contains the numbers 1-5. Any arrows in the grid always point toward a square that contains a lower number.

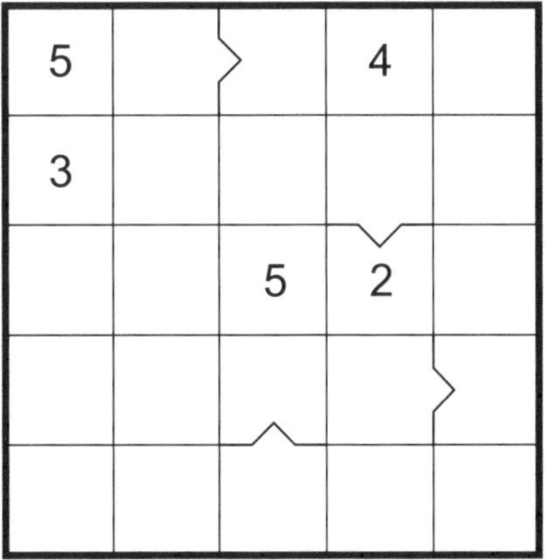

39

With the starters already given, can you fit all of the remaining listed numbers into this grid? Take care, this puzzle may not be as easy as it looks!

16	294	617	4397 ✓	47623
18	353	621	6234	72360
20	368	774	6596	73276
33	393	844	9282	82450
45	396	899	15590	164487
46	423	929	24306	321344
72	429	943	25352	608163
89	433	976	31566	618900
209	440	1039	35431	735764
268	584	1501	37119	844578
275	612	2734	42696	4188924
291	614	4364	47294	6000664

40

The grid should be filled with numbers from 1 to 6, so that each number appears just once in every row and column.

The clues refer to the digit totals in the squares, e.g. A 1 2 3 = 6 means that the numbers in squares A1, A2 and A3 add up to 6.

1 E 1 2 = 3
2 F 5 6 = 6
3 A B 1 = 9
4 A B 2 = 5
5 E F 3 = 10
6 B C 4 = 9
7 C D 5 = 7
8 C D 6 = 8
9 A 4 5 6 = 6
10 B 5 6 = 10
11 C 1 2 3 = 12

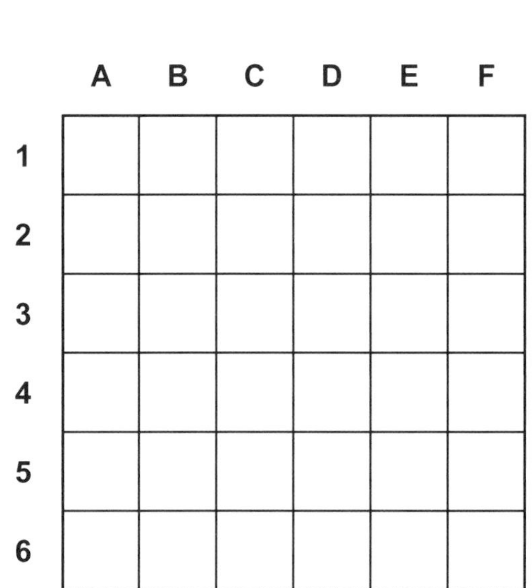

41 The object of this puzzle is to trace a single path from the top left corner to the bottom right corner of the grid, moving through all of the cells in either a horizontal, vertical, or diagonal direction.

Every cell must be entered once only, and your path should take you through the numbers in the sequence 1-2-3-4-5-6-1-2-3-4-5-6, etc.

Can you find the way?

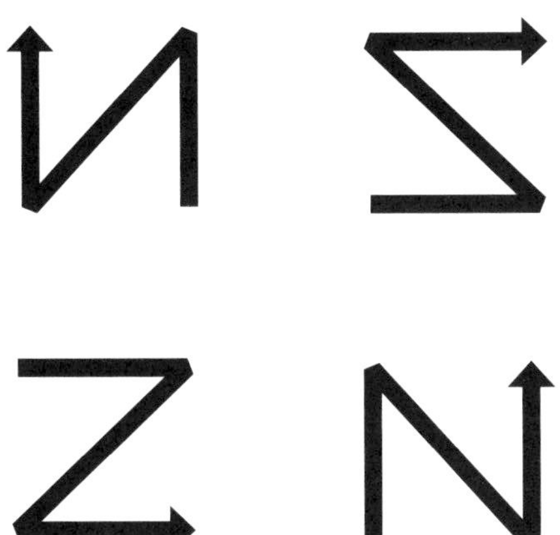

1	2	5	4	5	6
3	4	3	6	1	1
2	6	5	3	2	2
1	4	4	4	3	3
6	5	3	5	2	4
1	2	6	1	5	6

42 A standard set of 28 dominoes has been laid out as shown. Can you draw in the edges of them all?

The check-box is provided as an aid and the domino already placed will help.

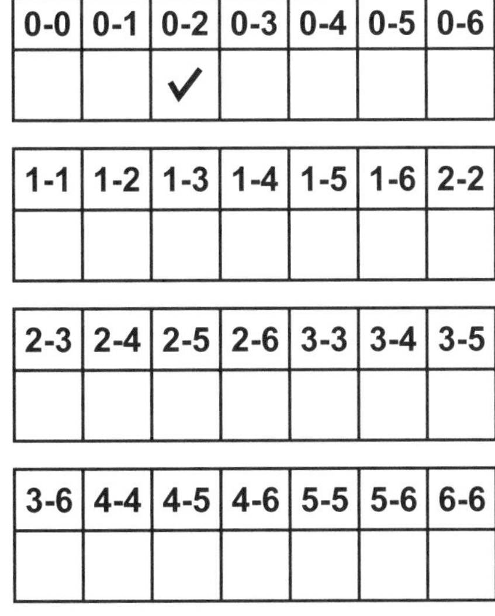

0-0	0-1	0-2	0-3	0-4	0-5	0-6
		✓				

1-1	1-2	1-3	1-4	1-5	1-6	2-2

2-3	2-4	2-5	2-6	3-3	3-4	3-5

3-6	4-4	4-5	4-6	5-5	5-6	6-6

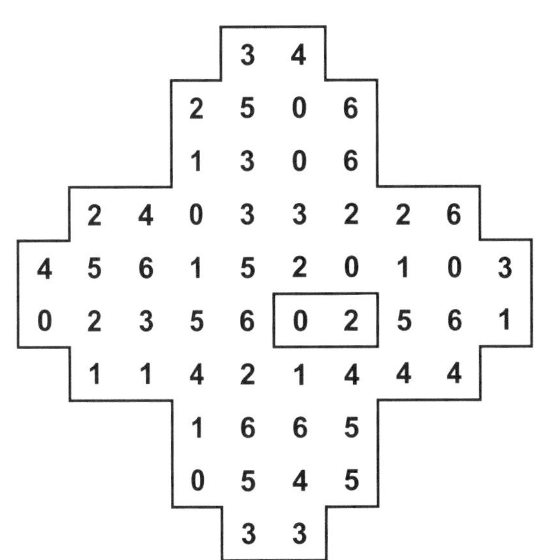

LEVEL 1

43

Draw a single continuous loop, by connecting the dots. No line may cross the path of another.

The figure inside each set of any four surrounding dots indicates the total number of surrounding lines.

			3	1		2	1	2	
1	0					2	0		1
		2					1		
1		0		1					3
		0		1		1		1	
	3				1				3
		2	3		1		1		
			2			1		2	0
2	0	0	2		2	1			2
1			3	1	1			1	
	3	2				1	1	0	1
3	2			2	1				

44

Place the eight tiles into the puzzle grid so that all adjacent numbers on each tile match up.

Tiles may be rotated through 360 degrees, but none may be flipped over.

1	2
3	2

3	4
1	4

3	1
3	4

3	3
1	2

3	1
4	3

3	4
2	2

4	4
1	1

4	3
3	2

		3	2		
		2	1		

LEVEL 1

45 Which of the four lettered alternatives (A, B, C, or D) fits most logically into the empty square?

96	56	152
144	8	40
32	64	72

96	144	24
60	12	156
36	168	72

45	126	63
144	9	27
81	243	18

?

100	39	48
74	13	87
125	52	26

A

14	56	35
91	7	63
21	42	84

B

14	56	124
48	4	16
112	24	64

C

144	102	36
96	6	90
84	42	121

D

46 Which four pieces can be fitted together to form an exact copy of this shape?

LEVEL 1

47 Twelve L-shapes need to be inserted in the grid, and each L has one hole in it.

There are three pieces of each of the four kinds shown here, and any piece may be turned or flipped over before being put in the grid. No pieces of the same kind touch, even at a corner.

The pieces fit together so well that you cannot see any spaces between them; only the holes show.

Can you tell where the Ls are?

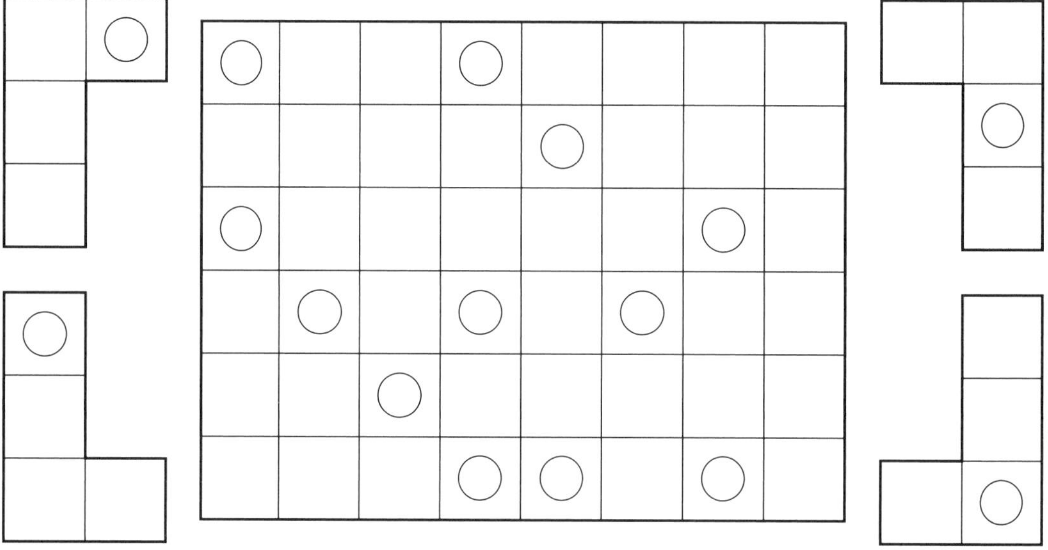

48 Each symbol stands for a different number. In order to reach the correct total at the end of each row and column, what is the value of the circle, cross, pentagon, square and star?

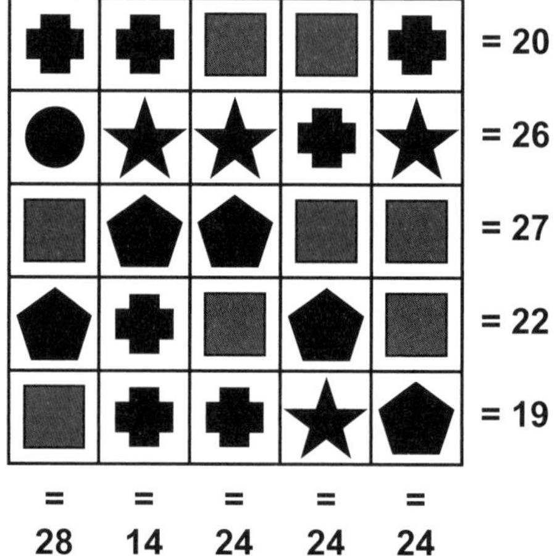

LEVEL 1

49 Each of the small squares in the grid below contains either A, B, or C. Each row, column, and diagonal line of six squares has exactly two of each letter. Can you tell the letter in each square?

Across
- **1** No two letters the same are directly next to each other
- **2** The As are next to each other
- **3** The Bs are further right than the As
- **4** The Bs are further right than the As
- **5** The Cs are further right than the As
- **6** The Cs are between the As

Down
- **1** The As are next to each other
- **2** No two letters the same are directly next to each other
- **3** The Cs are lower than the As
- **4** No two letters the same are directly next to each other
- **5** The Cs are next to each other
- **6** The Bs are between the Cs

	1	2	3	4	5	6
1						
2						
3						
4						
5						
6						

50 Which is the odd one out?

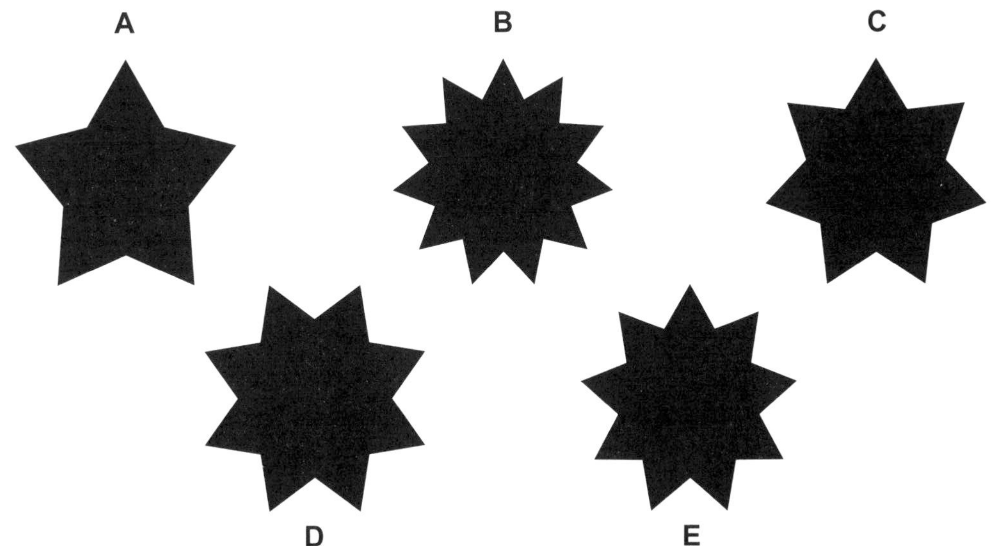

LEVEL 1

51 The chart gives directions to a hidden treasure behind the central black square in the grid. Move the indicated number of spaces north, south, east, and west (eg 4N means move four squares north) stopping at every square once only to arrive there. At which square should you start?

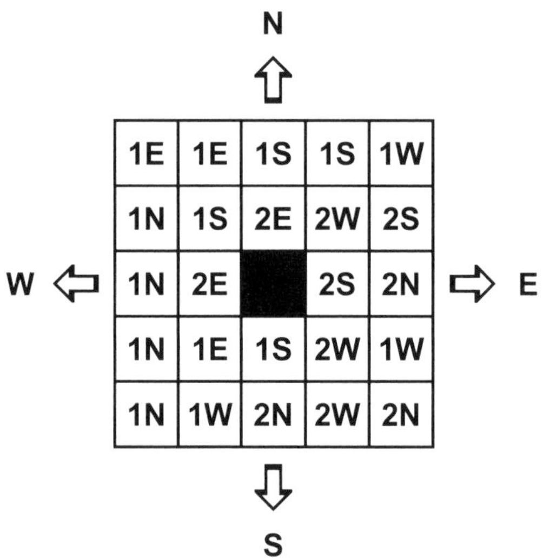

52 What letter should replace the question mark?

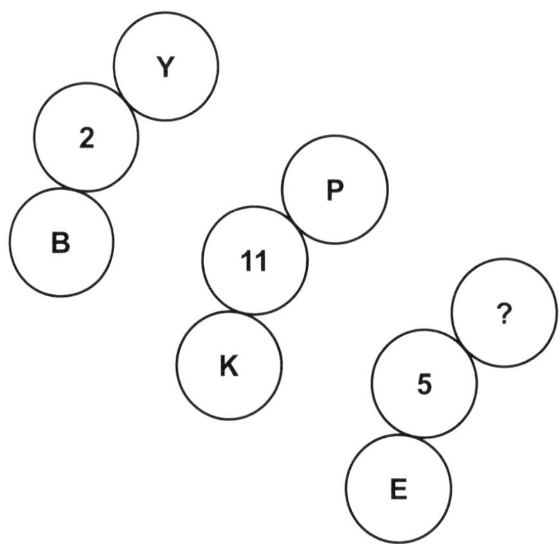

LEVEL 1

53 In the grid below, what number should replace the question mark?

14	20	3	15	12	9	16
29	1	34	20	11	6	18
7	13	7	8	17	22	3
11	21	2	18	29	21	1
6	17	15	22	17	21	27
15	5	8	17	5	4	38
2	13	27	2	17	31	?

54 The blank squares below should be filled with whole numbers between 1 and 30 inclusive, any of which may occur more than once, or not at all.

The numbers in every horizontal row add up to the totals on the right, as do the two long diagonal lines; while those in every vertical column add up to the totals along the bottom.

							132
		16	11	8	20	9	99
12	17	29		6		23	116
24	30	3		26	2		125
1		15	27		7	25	93
	20	28	10	3		17	109
5			23	20	16	8	89
	4		29		15	16	109
85	118	111	136	81	92	117	95

55

Can you place the hexagons into the grid, so that where any hexagon touches another along a straight line, the number in both triangles is the same? No rotation of any hexagon is allowed!

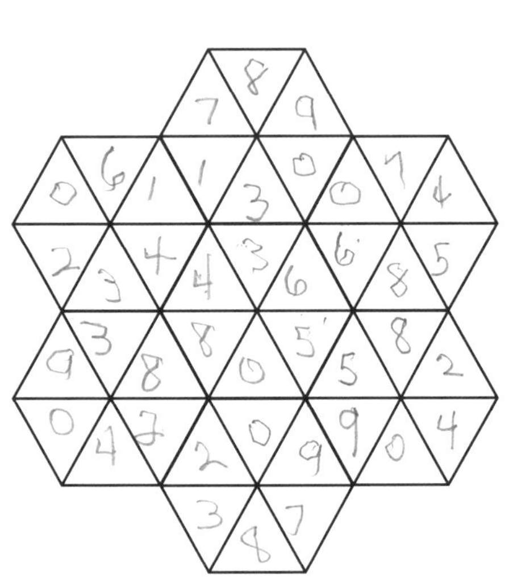

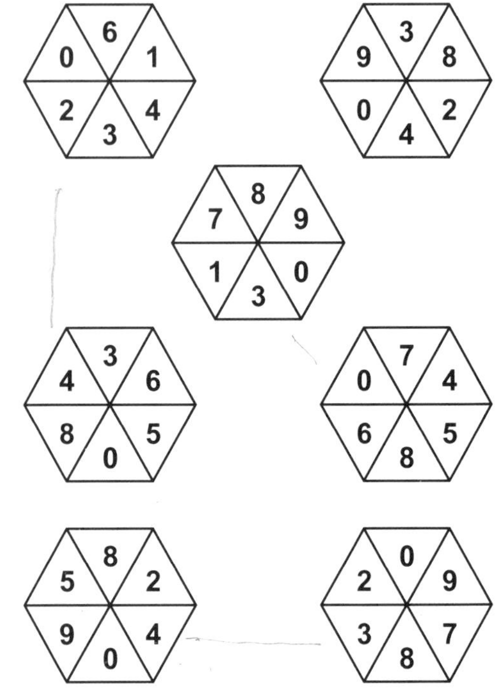

56

Can you place the vessels into the diagram? Some parts of vessels or sea squares have already been filled in. A number to the right or below a row or column refers to the number of occupied squares in that row or column.

Any vessel may be positioned horizontally or vertically, but no part of a vessel touches part of any other vessel, either horizontally, vertically, or diagonally.

Empty Area of Sea: ≈

Aircraft Carrier: ◀■■▶

Battleships: ◀■▶ ◀■▶

Cruisers: ◀▶ ◀▶ ◀▶

Submarines: ● ● ● ●

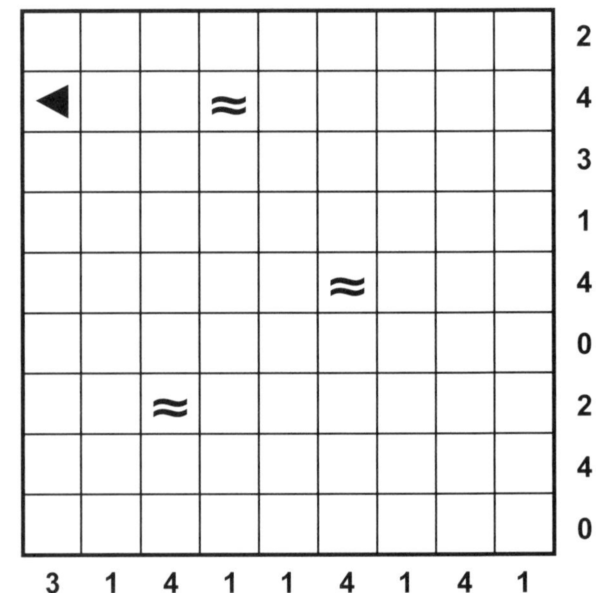

57 Each horizontal row and vertical column should contain different shapes and different numbers.

Every square will contain one number and one shape, and no combination may be repeated anywhere else in the puzzle.

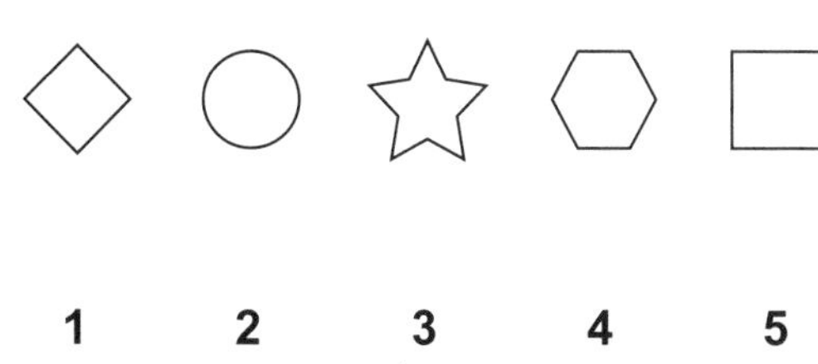

58 In the diagram below, what number should replace the question mark?

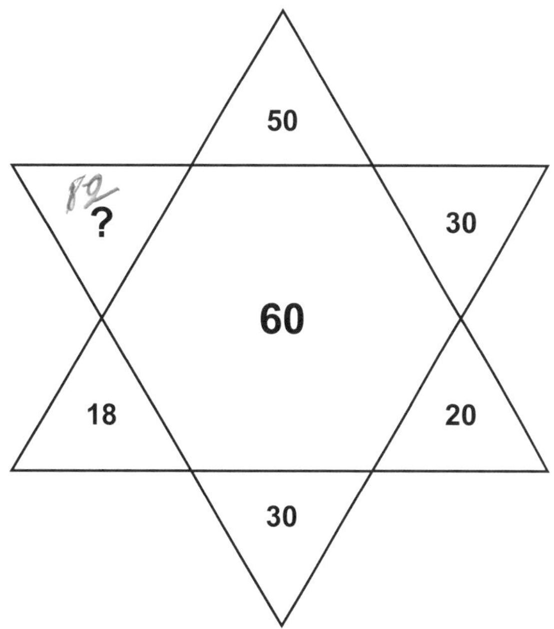

LEVEL 1

59

Every brick in this pyramid contains a number which is the sum of the two numbers below it, so that F=A+B, etc.

Just work out the missing numbers!

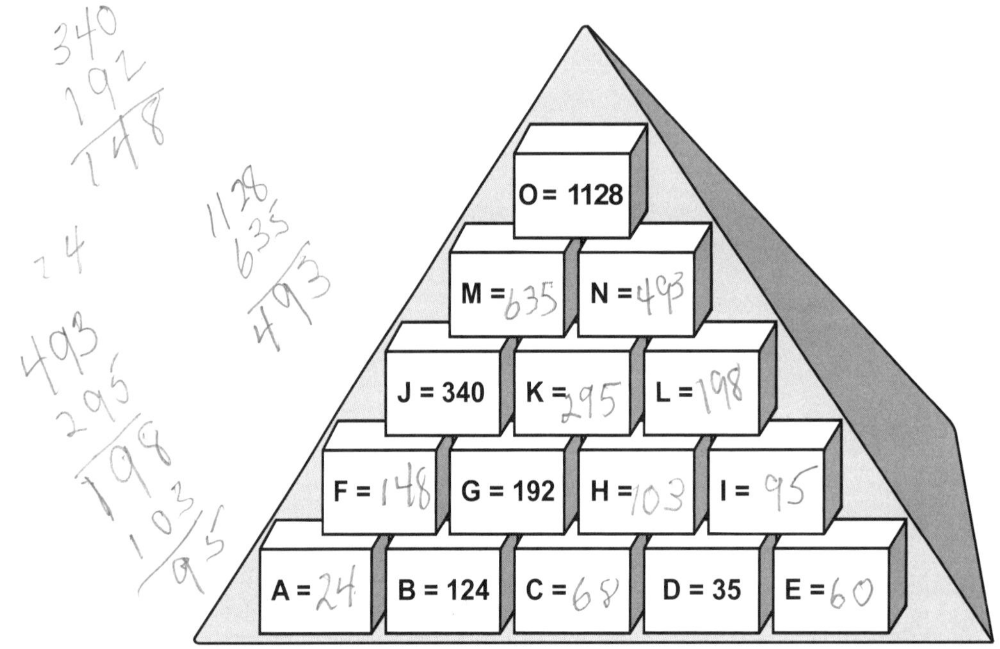

60

In this puzzle, an amateur coin collector has been out with his metal detector, searching for booty. He didn't have time to dig up all the coins he found, so has made a grid map, showing their locations, in the hope that if he loses the map, at least no-one else will understand it…

Those squares containing numbers are empty, but where a number appears in a square, it indicates how many coins are located in the squares (up to a maximum of eight) surrounding the numbered one, touching it at any corner or side. There is only one coin in any individual square.

Place a circle into every square containing a coin.

	1	0				3			
					4		4		2
1					2				2
		1		1	1			3	
0			3						
	0				1			1	1
	2			2					2
	3		3			3		3	
	4		3				4		2
		2			3				

LEVEL 1

61

Given that the letters are valued 1-26 according to their places in the alphabet, can you crack the mystery code to reveal the missing letter?

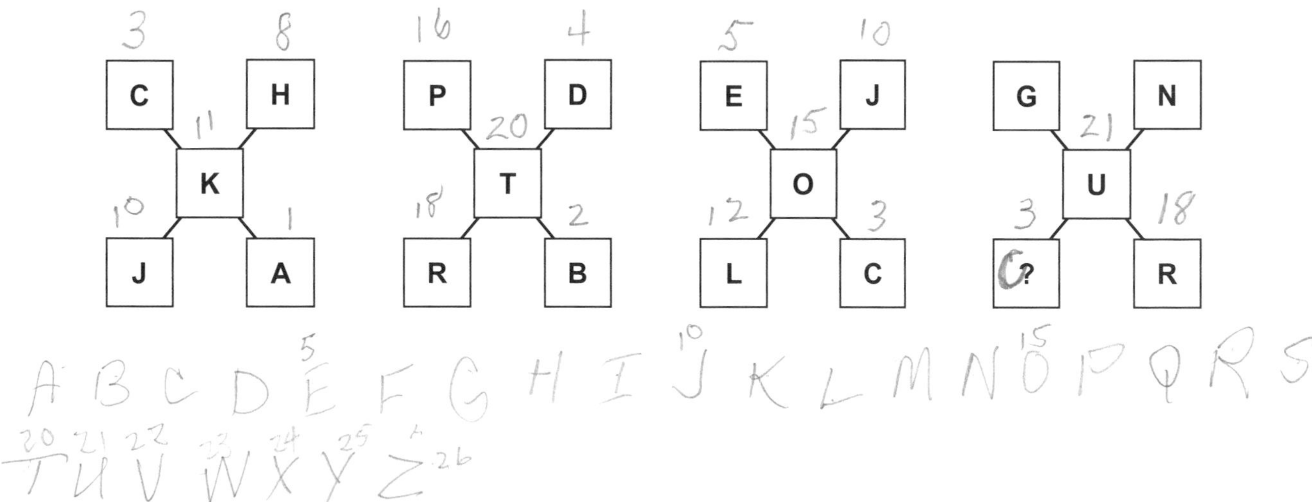

62

Place all twelve of the pieces into the grid. Any may be rotated or flipped over, but none may touch another, not even diagonally. The numbers outside the grid refer to the number of consecutive black squares; and each block is separated from the others by at least one white square. For instance, "3 2" could refer to a row with none, one or more white squares, then three black squares, then at least one white square, then two more black squares, followed by any number of white squares.

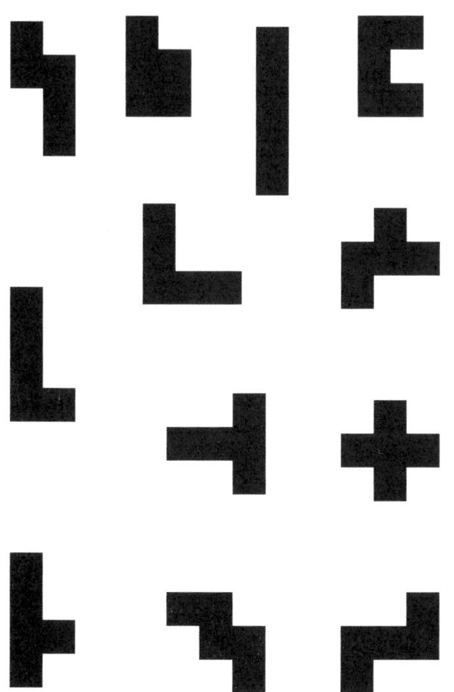

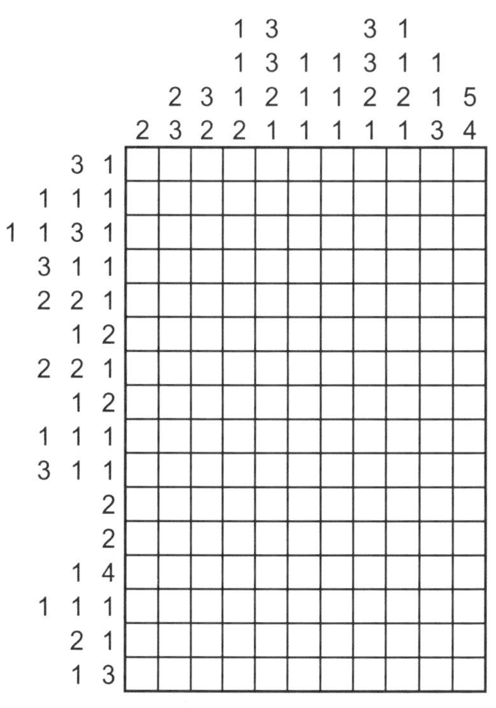

LEVEL 1

63 Each of the eight segments of the spider's web should be filled with a different number from 1 to 8, in such a way that every ring also contains a different number from 1 to 8.

The segments run from the outside of the spider's web to the middle, and the rings run all the way around.

Some numbers are already in place. Can you fill in the rest?

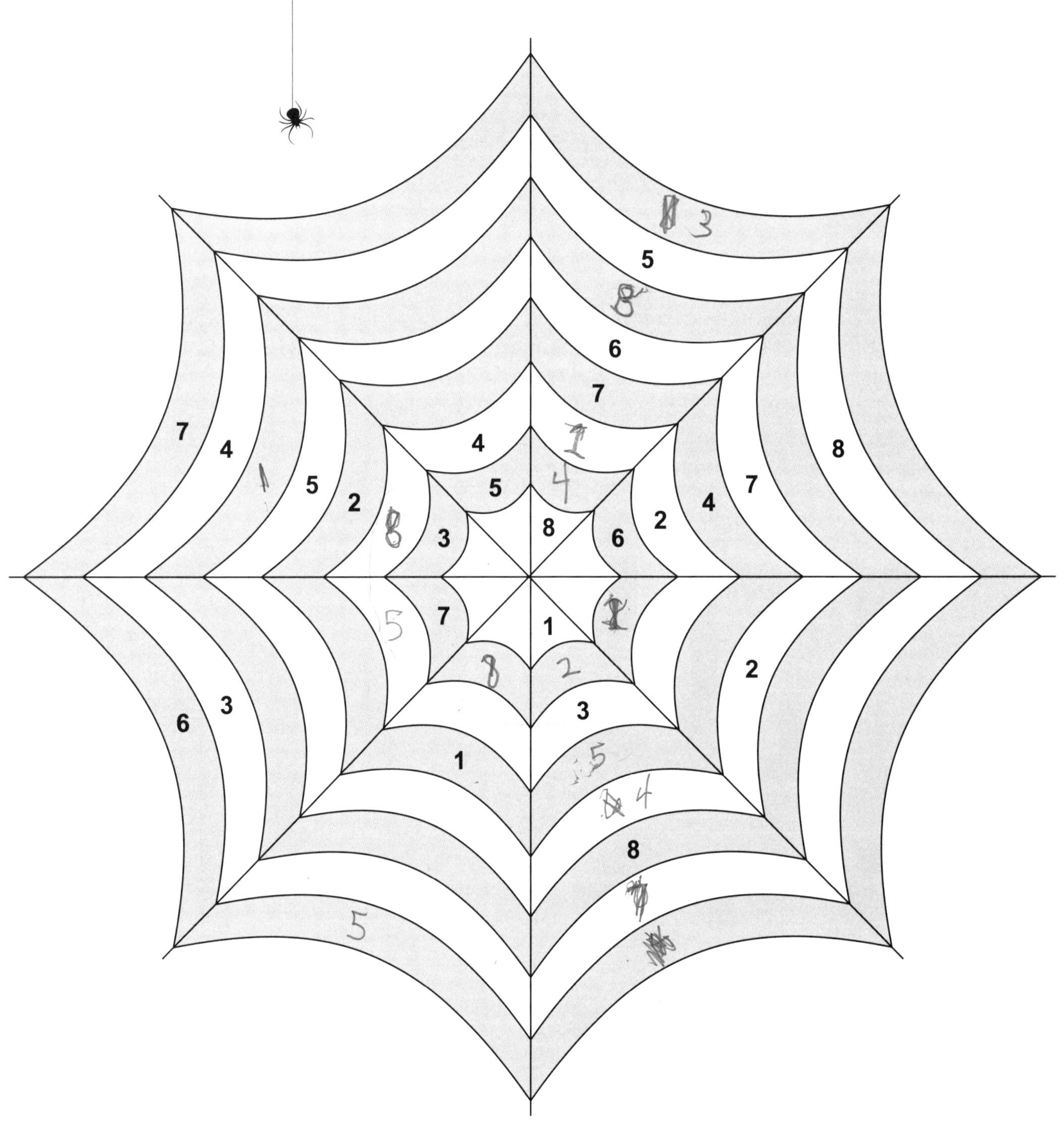

64 Every row and column in this grid originally contained one heart, one club, one diamond, one spade, and two blank squares, although not necessarily in that order.

Every symbol with a black arrow refers to the first of the four symbols encountered in the direction of the arrow. Every symbol with a white arrow refers to the second of the four symbols encountered in the direction of the arrow.

Can you complete the original grid?

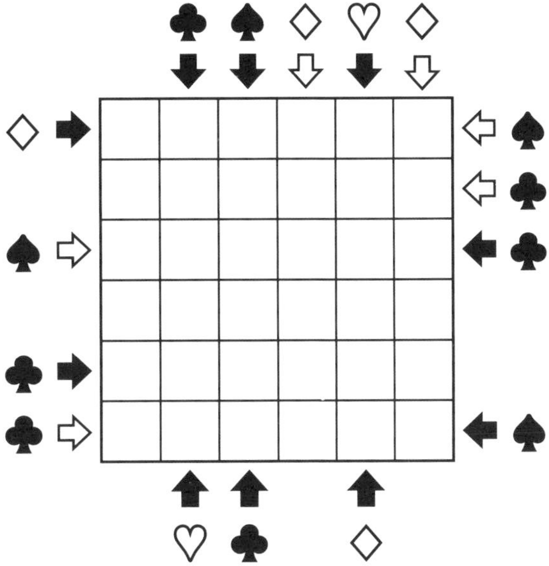

65 Fill the grid so that every horizontal row and vertical column contains the numbers 1-5. Any arrows in the grid always point toward a square that contains a lower number.

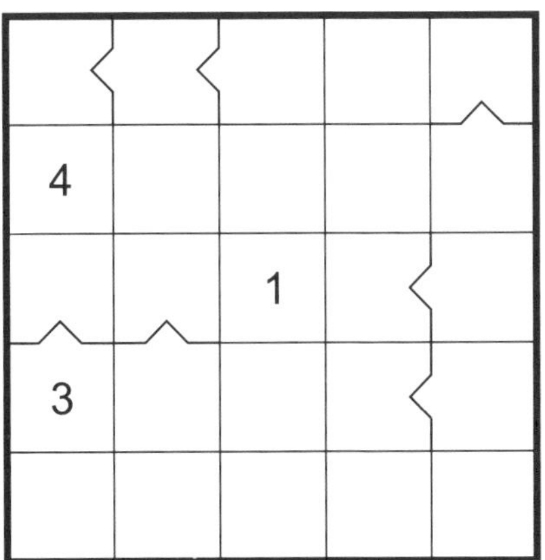

LEVEL 1

66

With the starters already given, can you fit all of the remaining listed numbers into this grid? Take care, this puzzle may not be as easy as it looks!

12	482	905	18827	66820
40	487	975	20616	67156
41	500	1895	23638	67326
57	589	2278	30742	70119
60	672	2412	31104	86257
66	700	6010	32135	90661
71	718	8104	33162	94408
81	812	8492	41555	96255
243	821	12188	47294	308028
280	841	13471	49158	313783
361	876	13566	51158 ✓	562247
459	878	16168	57738	850716

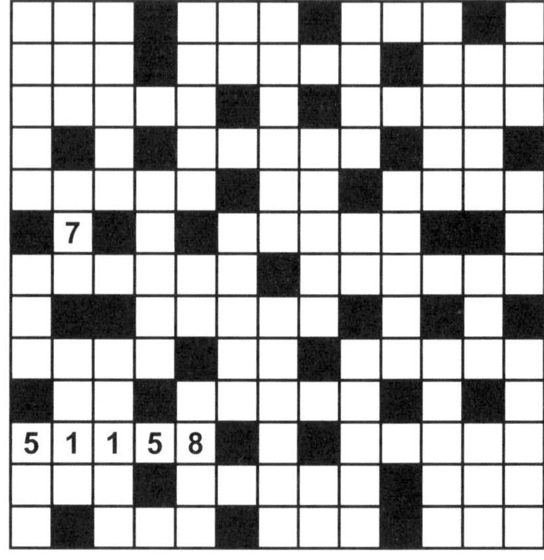

67

The grid should be filled with numbers from 1 to 6, so that each number appears just once in every row and column.

The clues refer to the digit totals in the squares, e.g. A 1 2 3 = 6 means that the numbers in squares A1, A2 and A3 add up to 6.

1 A B 3 = 3
2 C D E 4 = 9
3 E F 5 = 3
4 A B 6 = 10
5 A 1 2 = 8
6 B 1 2 = 4
7 C 5 6 = 5
8 D 2 3 = 10
9 E 1 2 = 10
10 F 1 2 3 = 11
11 C D 1 = 3

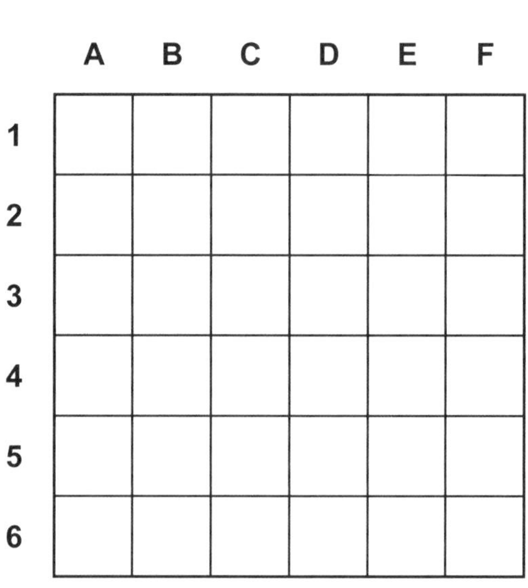

68

The object of this puzzle is to trace a single path from the top left corner to the bottom right corner of the grid, moving through all of the cells in either a horizontal, vertical, or diagonal direction.

Every cell must be entered once only, and your path should take you through the numbers in the sequence 1-2-3-4-5-6-1-2-3-4-5-6, etc.

Can you find the way?

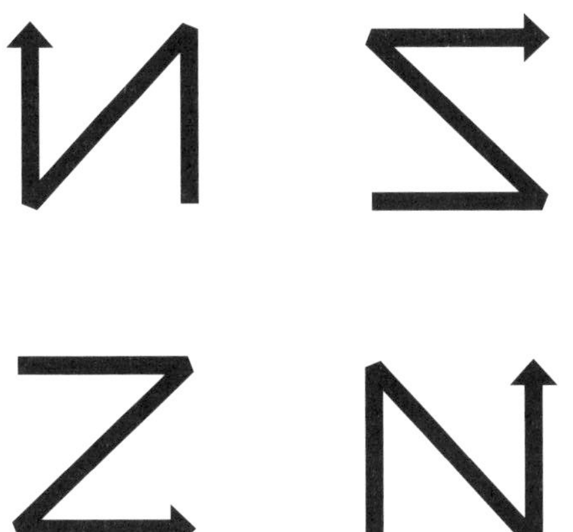

1	2	3	4	5	1
6	4	3	3	2	6
1	5	5	2	4	5
2	4	1	6	1	6
3	6	1	2	2	5
5	4	3	3	4	6

69

A standard set of 28 dominoes has been laid out as shown. Can you draw in the edges of them all?

The check-box is provided as an aid and the domino already placed will help.

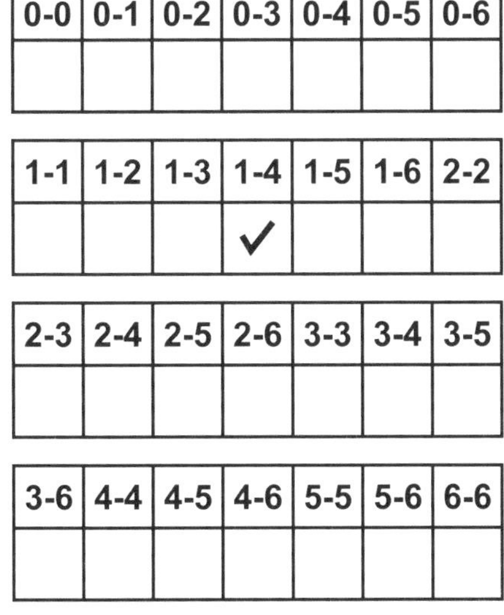

0-0	0-1	0-2	0-3	0-4	0-5	0-6

1-1	1-2	1-3	1-4	1-5	1-6	2-2
			✓			

2-3	2-4	2-5	2-6	3-3	3-4	3-5

3-6	4-4	4-5	4-6	5-5	5-6	6-6

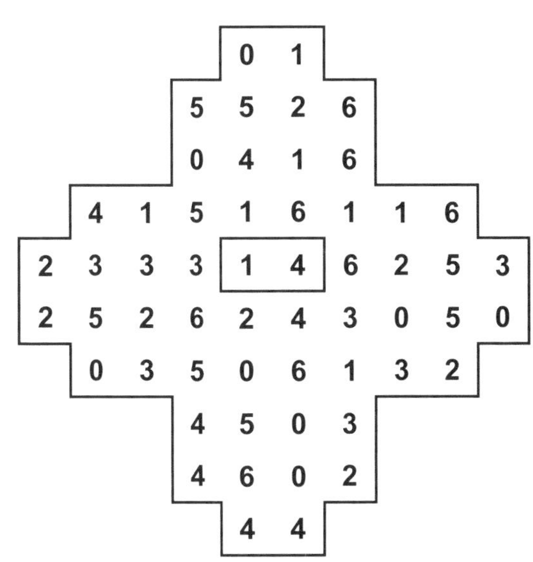

LEVEL 1

70

Draw a single continuous loop, by connecting the dots. No line may cross the path of another.

The figure inside each set of any four surrounding dots indicates the total number of surrounding lines.

	1	3		2	1		1		
	1	3		2		1		0	2
	2	2	1			1			
1			3		1	1	3	1	2
			1	0		1			
2	0				0	1			2
			1	3				2	
3	1	2					3		
2									
			2	2	3	2	1		1
	0		3				2		1
	3			1	3			1	

71

Place the eight tiles into the puzzle grid so that all adjacent numbers on each tile match up.

Tiles may be rotated through 360 degrees, but none may be flipped over.

1	1
4	2

3	3
1	2

1	1
1	4

3	2
2	1

4	3
1	1

2	3
1	4

2	2
4	1

4	4
1	4

				3	3
				4	2

LEVEL 1

72

Every oval shape in this diagram contains a different letter of the alphabet from A to K inclusive.

Use the clues to determine their locations. Reference in the clues to "due" means in any location along the same horizontal or vertical line.

1 The B is next to the A, which is due west of the G, which is due north of the I.

2 The C is next to and east of the D, which is due north of (but not next to) the H.

3 The D is due east of the K, which is due north of the E.

4 The F is next to and west of the A, which is due north of the J.

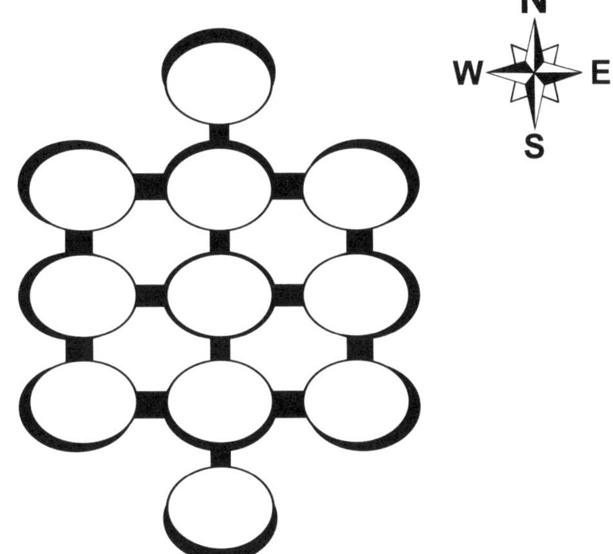

73

Draw walls to partition the grid into areas (some walls are already drawn in for you).

Each area must contain two circles, area sizes must match those numbers shown next to the grid, and each "+" must be linked to at least two walls.

3, 4, 5, 6, 7

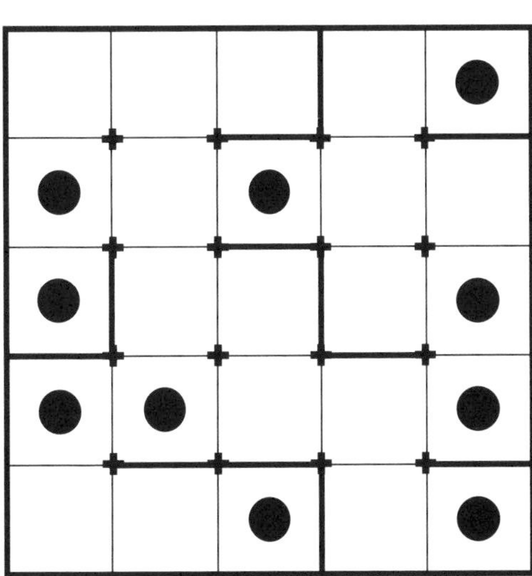

74 Twelve L-shapes need to be inserted in the grid, and each L has one hole in it.

There are three pieces of each of the four kinds shown here, and any piece may be turned or flipped over before being put in the grid. No pieces of the same kind touch, even at a corner.

The pieces fit together so well that you cannot see any spaces between them; only the holes show.

Can you tell where the Ls are?

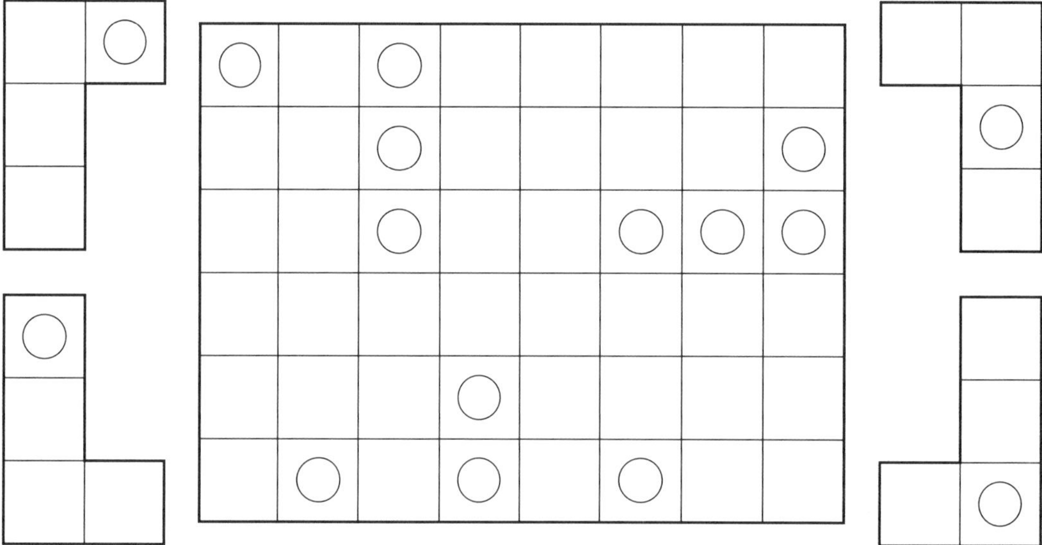

75 Fill the three empty circles with the symbols +, –, and x in some order, to make a sum that totals the central number. Each symbol must be used once, and calculations are made in the direction of travel (clockwise).

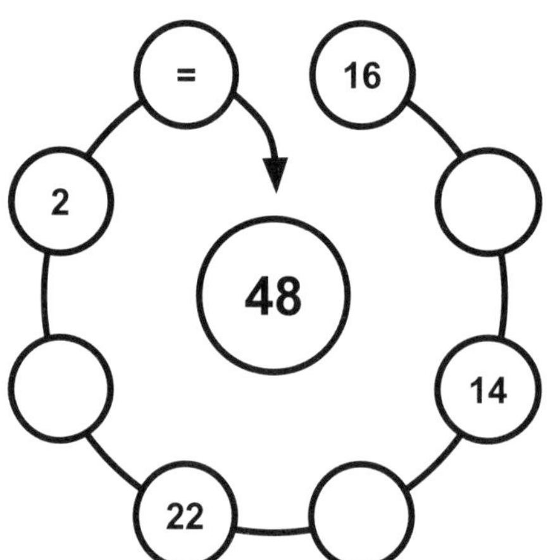

LEVEL 1

76 Each of the small squares in the grid below contains either A, B, or C. Each row, column, and diagonal line of six squares has exactly two of each letter. Can you tell the letter in each square?

Across

1 The Bs are next to each other
2 The Cs are next to each other
3 The As are further right than the Bs
4 Each A is directly next to and right of a C
5 The Bs are next to each other
6 The Bs are further right than the Cs

Down

1 No two letters the same are directly next to each other
2 The As are lower than the Bs
3 The Bs are next to each other and lower than the As
4 Each B is directly next to and below a C
5 The As are next to each other
6 Each B is directly next to and below a C

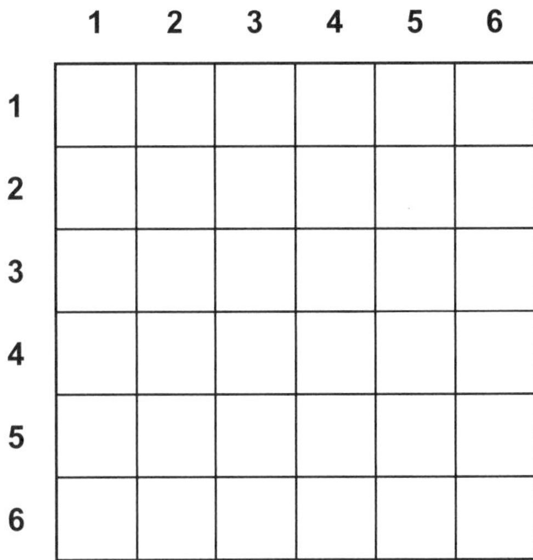

77 Using the numbers below, complete these six equations (three reading across and three reading downwards).

Every number is used once.

1 2 3 4 5
6 7 8 9

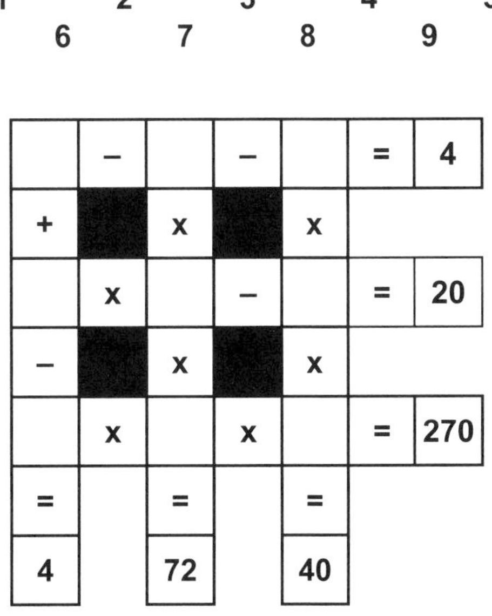

78 The chart gives directions to a hidden treasure behind the central black square in the grid. Move the indicated number of spaces north, south, east, and west (eg 4N means move four squares north) stopping at every square once only to arrive there. At which square should you start?

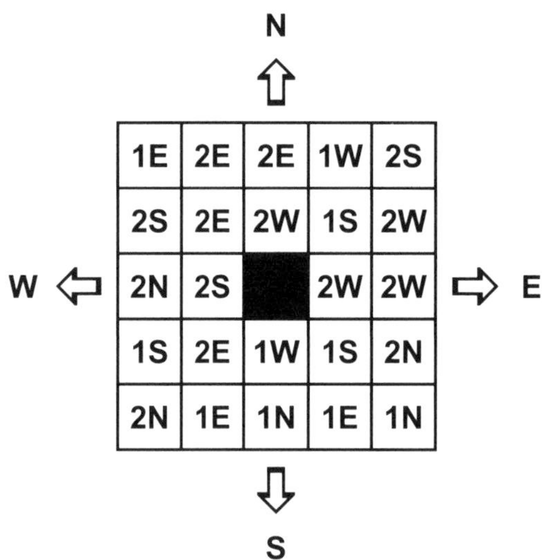

79 The numbers at the top and on the left side show the quantity of single-digit numbers (1-9) used in that row and column. The numbers at the bottom and on the right show the sum of the digits. A number may appear more than once in a row or column, but no numbers are in squares that touch, even at a corner.

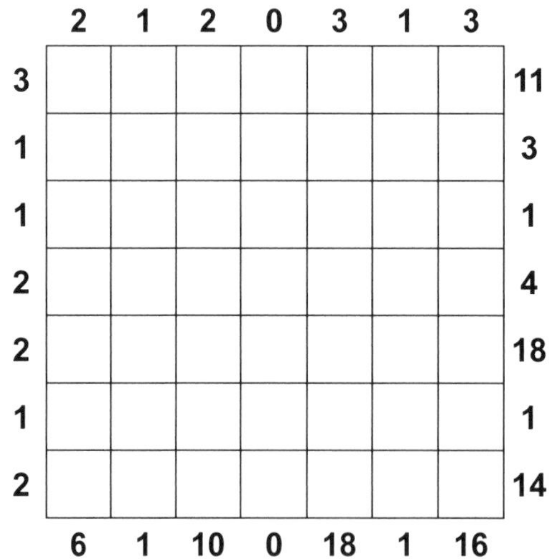

LEVEL 1

80

In the square below, change the positions of six numbers, one per horizontal row, vertical column, and long diagonal line of six smaller squares, in such a way that the numbers in each row, column, and long diagonal line total exactly 171. Any number may appear more than once in a row, column or line.

44	17	24	30	38	15
32	28	31	18	31	26
45	40	28	50	15	23
35	38	31	6	15	39
26	22	19	42	23	31
19	19	31	20	41	34

81

The blank squares below should be filled with whole numbers between 1 and 30 inclusive, any of which may occur more than once, or not at all.

The numbers in every horizontal row add up to the totals on the right, as do the two long diagonal lines; while those in every vertical column add up to the totals along the bottom.

							103
21		14		4	17	5	116
11	13	6	20			9	91
19		12	1	3	27	7	93
	14	29	22	15			130
18	5		13		8		108
	6	21	18	15		19	92
20	10			9	4	11	83
104	100	112	117	72	118	90	109

LEVEL 2

1 Can you place the hexagons into the grid, so that where any hexagon touches another along a straight line, the number in both triangles is the same? No rotation of any hexagon is allowed!

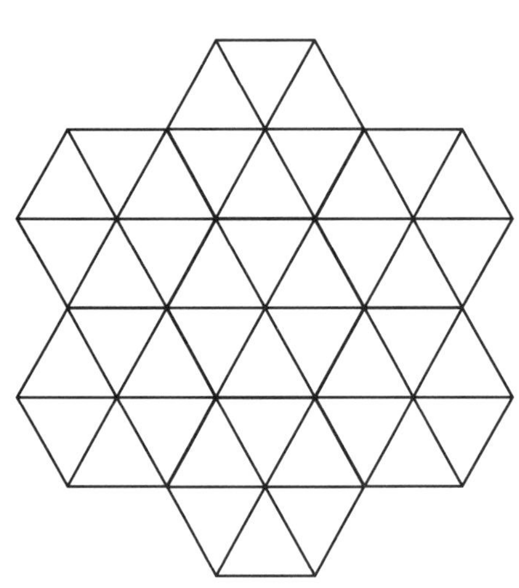

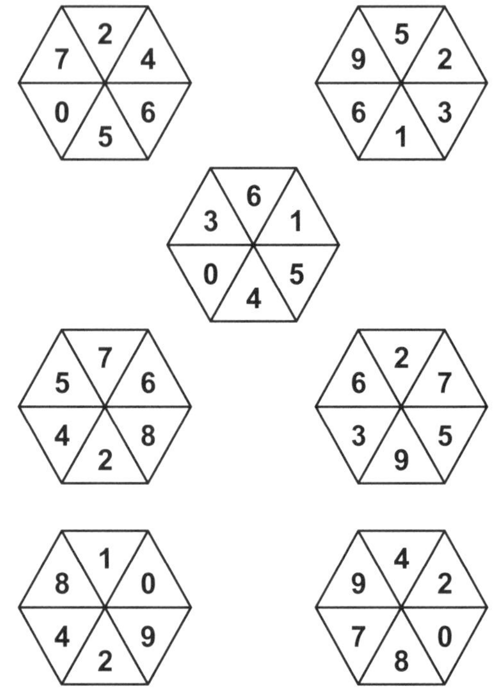

2 Can you place the vessels into the diagram? Some parts of vessels or sea squares have already been filled in. A number to the right or below a row or column refers to the number of occupied squares in that row or column.

Any vessel may be positioned horizontally or vertically, but no part of a vessel touches part of any other vessel, either horizontally, vertically, or diagonally.

Empty Area of Sea: ≈

Aircraft Carrier:

Battleships:

Cruisers:

Submarines:

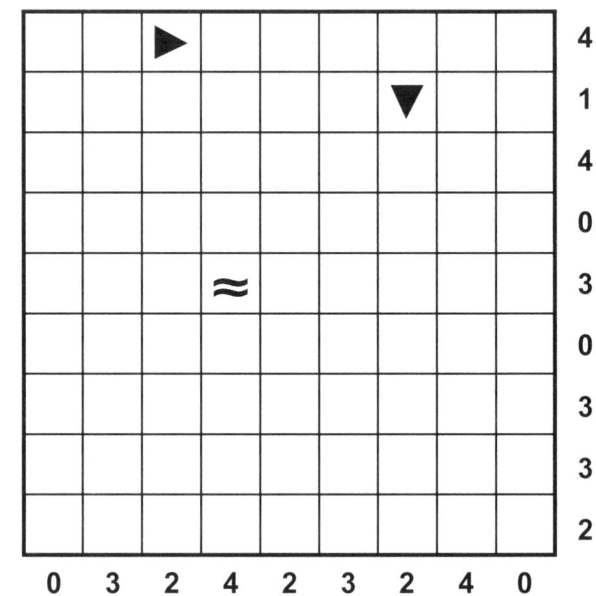

LEVEL 2

3

Each horizontal row and vertical column should contain different shapes and different numbers.

Every square will contain one number and one shape, and no combination may be repeated anywhere else in the puzzle.

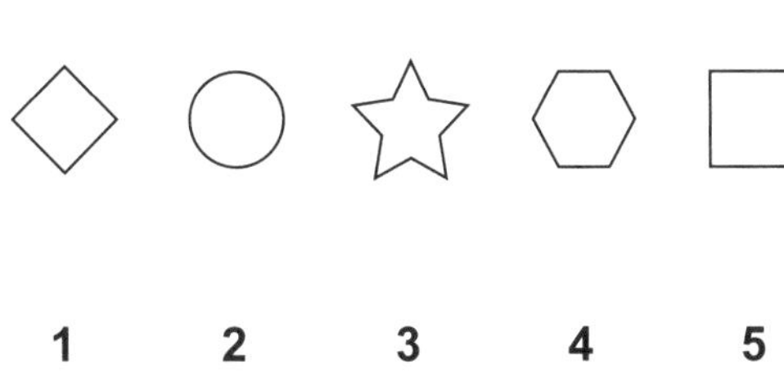

3			4	
			1	
				4
	4		5	
			2	5

4

In the diagram below, what letter should replace the question mark?

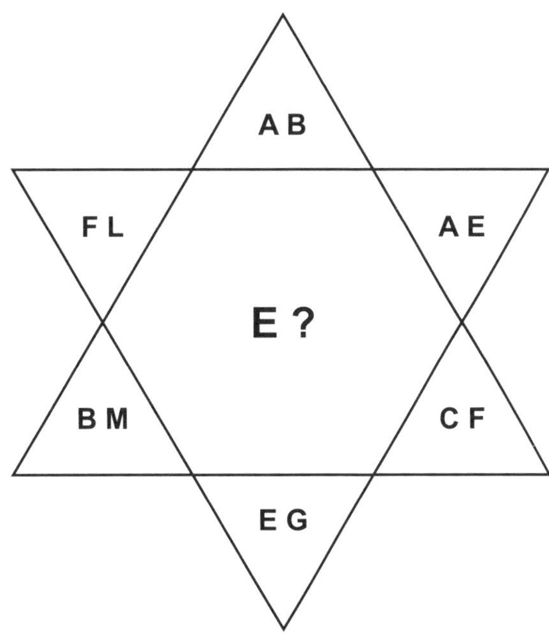

LEVEL 2

5 Every brick in this pyramid contains a number which is the sum of the two numbers below it, so that F=A+B, etc.

Just work out the missing numbers!

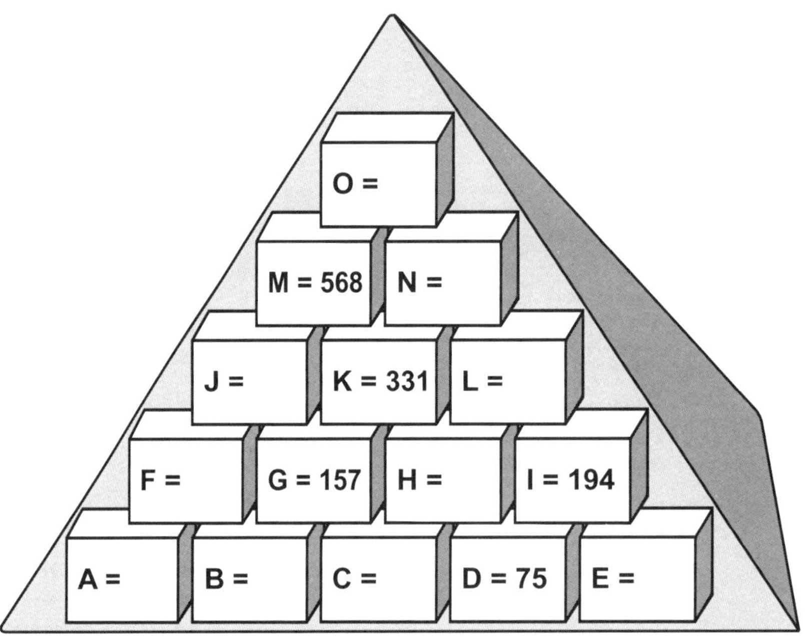

6 In this puzzle, an amateur coin collector has been out with his metal detector, searching for booty. He didn't have time to dig up all the coins he found, so has made a grid map, showing their locations, in the hope that if he loses the map, at least no-one else will understand it…

Those squares containing numbers are empty, but where a number appears in a square, it indicates how many coins are located in the squares (up to a maximum of eight) surrounding the numbered one, touching it at any corner or side. There is only one coin in any individual square.

Place a circle into every square containing a coin.

	1	2		2				1	
1							3		2
	3	4			1				
					1		5		
	3	3			1				1
	2	1		2		2	2		
0								2	
0					1	2			
2			3	1		3			0
			2	1					

LEVEL 2

7 Given that the letters are valued 1-26 according to their places in the alphabet, can you crack the mystery code to reveal the missing letter?

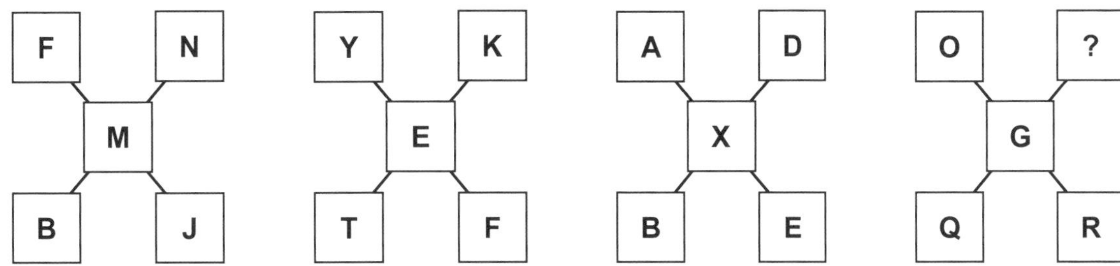

8 Place all twelve of the pieces into the grid. Any may be rotated or flipped over, but none may touch another, not even diagonally. The numbers outside the grid refer to the number of consecutive black squares; and each block is separated from the others by at least one white square. For instance, "3 2" could refer to a row with none, one or more white squares, then three black squares, then at least one white square, then two more black squares, followed by any number of white squares.

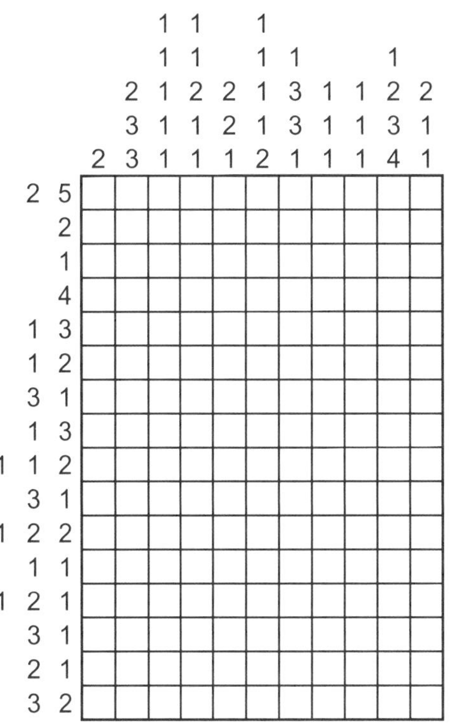

LEVEL 2

9 Each of the eight segments of the spider's web should be filled with a different number from 1 to 8, in such a way that every ring also contains a different number from 1 to 8.

The segments run from the outside of the spider's web to the middle, and the rings run all the way around.

Some numbers are already in place. Can you fill in the rest?

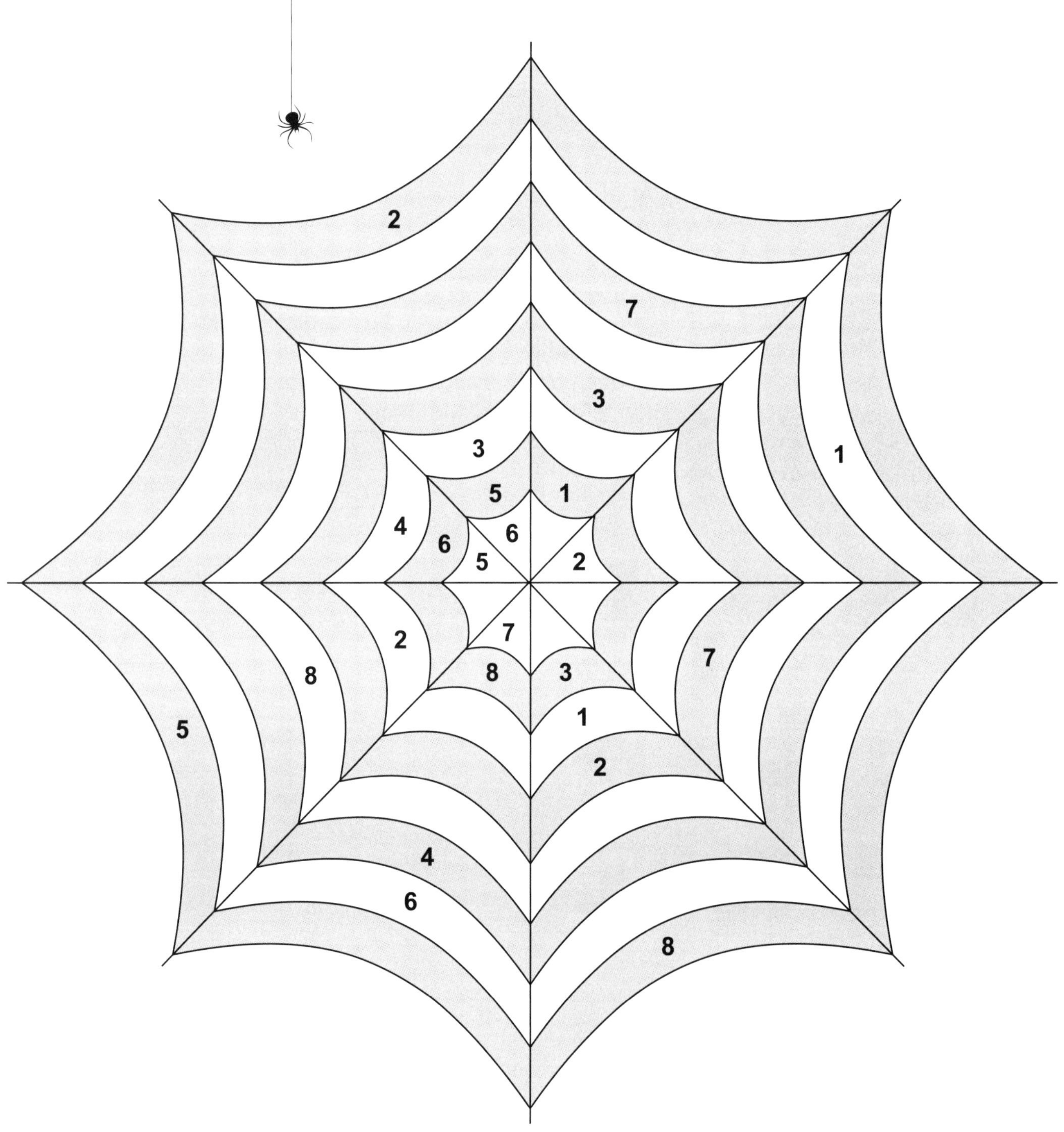

LEVEL 2

10 Every row and column in this grid originally contained one heart, one club, one diamond, one spade, and two blank squares, although not necessarily in that order.

Every symbol with a black arrow refers to the first of the four symbols encountered in the direction of the arrow. Every symbol with a white arrow refers to the second of the four symbols encountered in the direction of the arrow.

Can you complete the original grid?

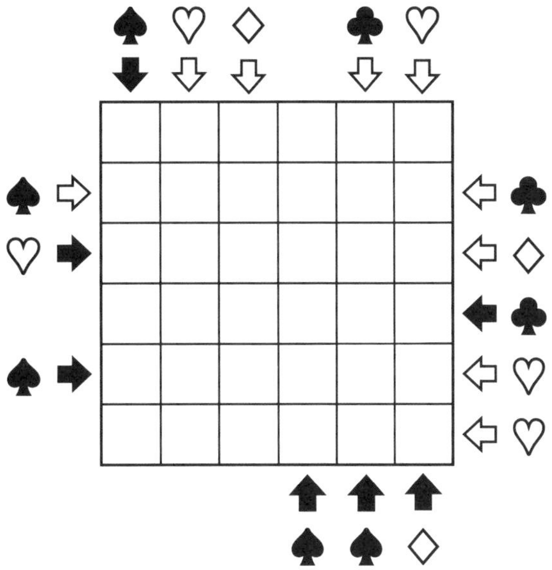

11 Fill the grid so that every horizontal row and vertical column contains the numbers 1-5. Any arrows in the grid always point toward a square that contains a lower number.

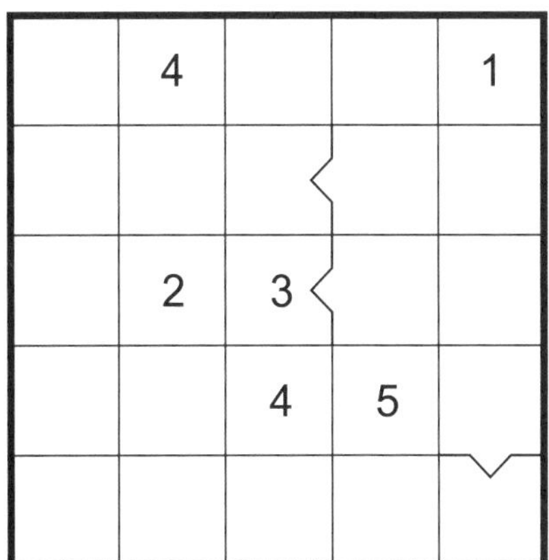

LEVEL 2

12

With the starter already given, can you fit all of the remaining listed numbers into this grid? Take care, this puzzle may not be as easy as it looks!

23	344	693	4412	28039
29	400	749	4767	29107
35	403	756	5633	30756
45	424	829	5650	36044
69	484	895	6719	38537
78	496	937	7085	45235
175	509	1477	17527	79496
199	571	1878	18013	85567
280	603	2576	18430	108361
300	629	2999	19468 ✓	398759
313	677	4020	23550	451380
324	678	4133	27068	946099

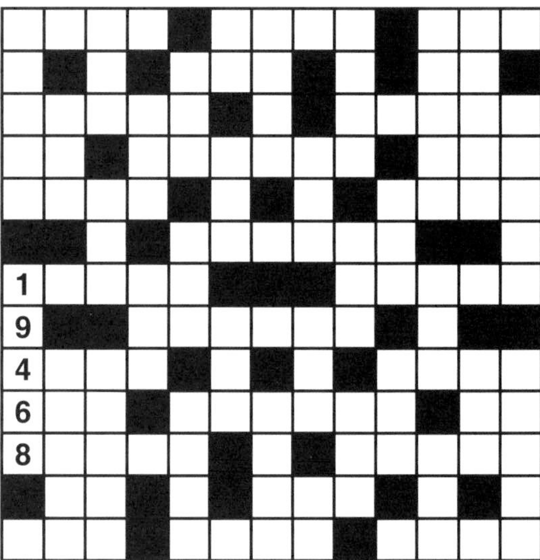

13

The grid should be filled with numbers from 1 to 6, so that each number appears just once in every row and column.

The clues refer to the digit totals in the squares, e.g. A 1 2 3 = 6 means that the numbers in squares A1, A2 and A3 add up to 6.

1. D 2 3 4 = 15
2. E 3 4 = 6
3. F 4 5 = 9
4. B C D 1 = 9
5. E F 2 = 3
6. A B 3 = 6
7. B C 4 = 8
8. C D 5 = 8
9. C D 6 = 8
10. A 4 5 = 8
11. B 5 6 = 5

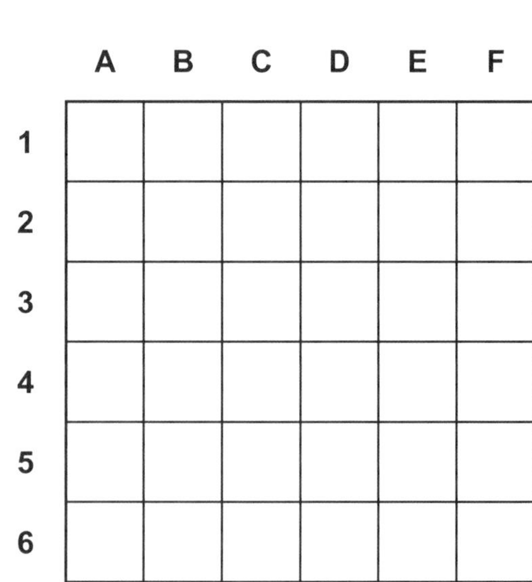

LEVEL 2

14 The object of this puzzle is to trace a single path from the top left corner to the bottom right corner of the grid, moving through all of the cells in either a horizontal, vertical, or diagonal direction.

Every cell must be entered once only, and your path should take you through the numbers in the sequence 1-2-3-4-5-6-1-2-3-4-5-6, etc.

Can you find the way?

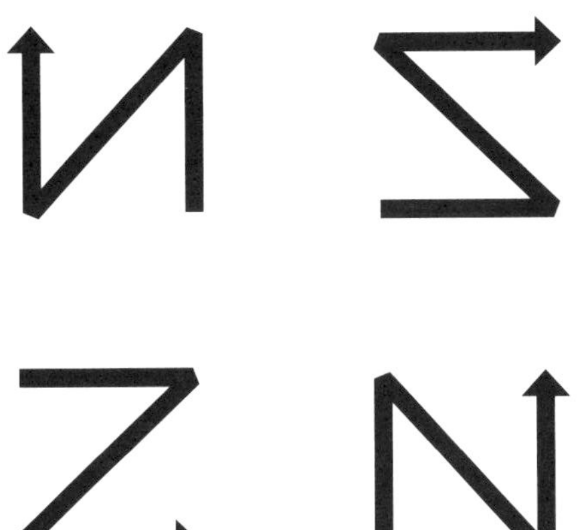

1	3	2	3	4	6
4	2	1	5	5	1
6	5	6	6	4	2
5	1	3	1	3	4
2	4	2	6	3	5
3	4	5	1	2	6

15 A standard set of 28 dominoes has been laid out as shown. Can you draw in the edges of them all?

The check-box is provided as an aid and the domino already placed will help.

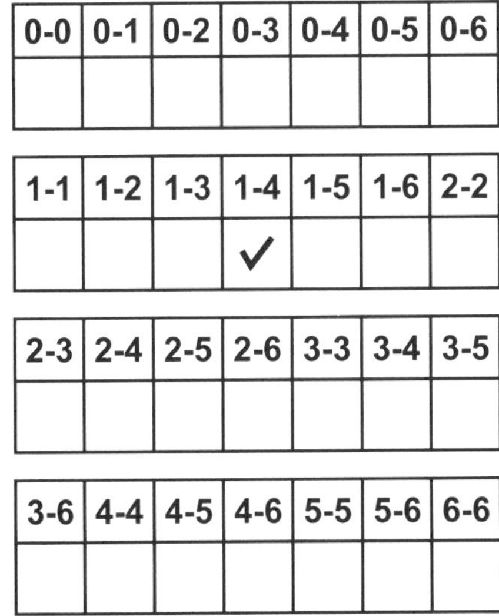

0-0	0-1	0-2	0-3	0-4	0-5	0-6

1-1	1-2	1-3	1-4	1-5	1-6	2-2
			✓			

2-3	2-4	2-5	2-6	3-3	3-4	3-5

3-6	4-4	4-5	4-6	5-5	5-6	6-6

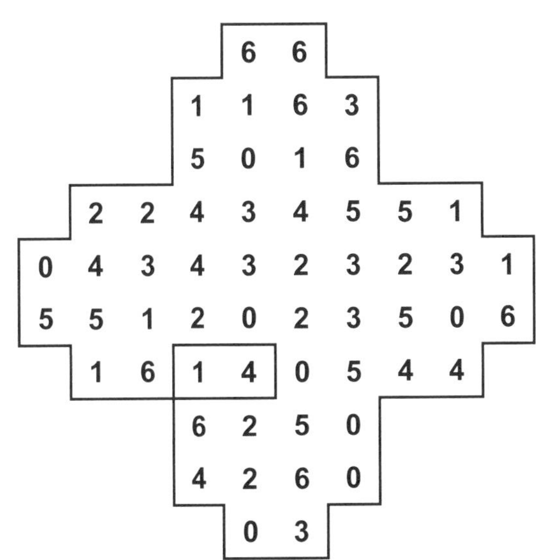

LEVEL 2

16

Draw a single continuous loop, by connecting the dots. No line may cross the path of another.

The figure inside each set of any four surrounding dots indicates the total number of surrounding lines.

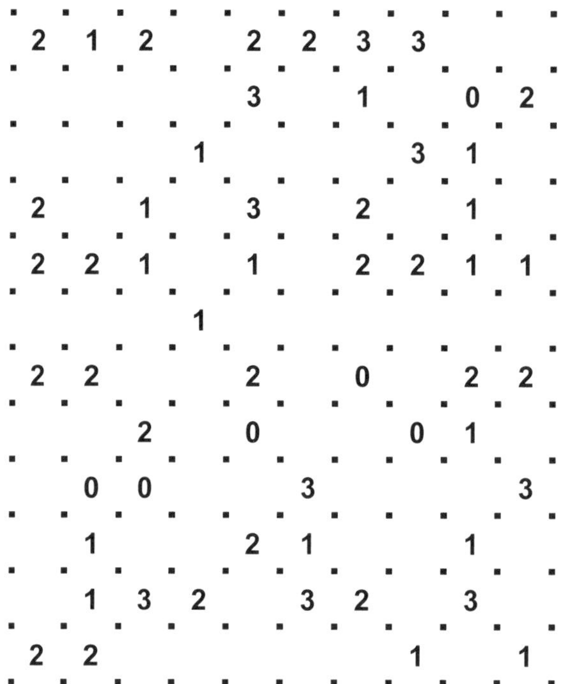

17

Place the eight tiles into the puzzle grid so that all adjacent numbers on each tile match up.

Tiles may be rotated through 360 degrees, but none may be flipped over.

4	1
1	3

4	2
4	3

1	4
2	3

2	3
3	2

3	1
4	3

3	4
4	1

4	4
3	1

2	4
2	3

1	3				
2	2				

LEVEL 2

18 Every oval shape in this diagram contains a different letter of the alphabet from A to K inclusive.

Use the clues to determine their locations. Reference in the clues to "due" means in any location along the same horizontal or vertical line.

1. The C is further south than the I, which is further west than the B.
2. The D is due north of the B, which is next to and east of the H.
3. The E is next to and south of the J, which is due east of the C.
4. The G is next to and south of the A, which is due west of the K.
5. The H is next to and north of the F, which is further west than the D, which is further east than the J.

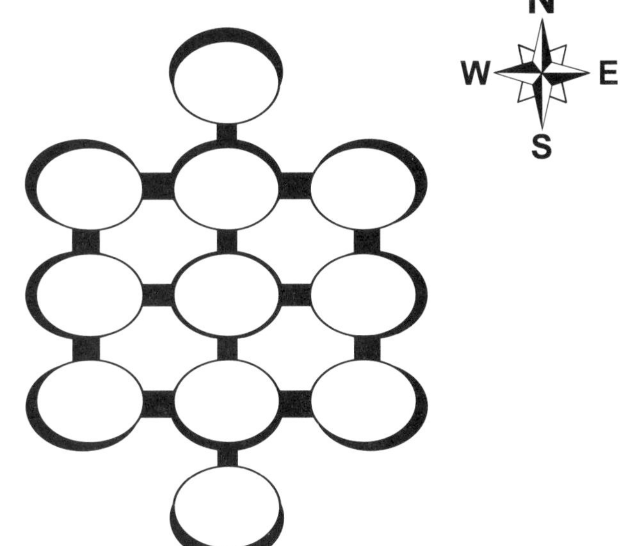

19 Draw walls to partition the grid into areas (some walls are already drawn in for you).

Each area must contain two circles, area sizes must match those numbers shown next to the grid, and each "+" must be linked to at least two walls.

4, 5, 5, 5, 6

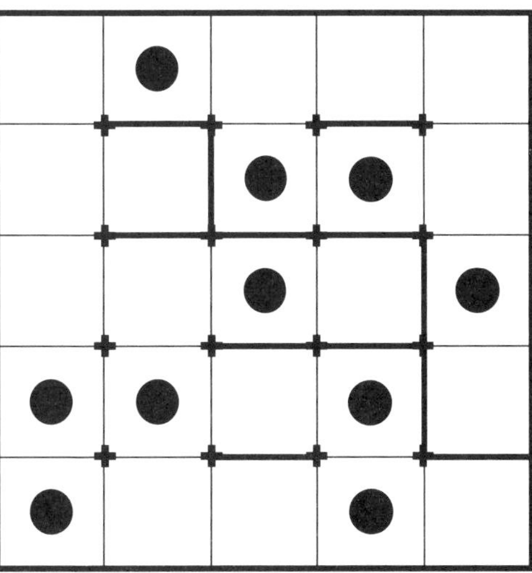

LEVEL 2

20 Twelve L-shapes need to be inserted in the grid, and each L has one hole in it.

There are three pieces of each of the four kinds shown here, and any piece may be turned or flipped over before being put in the grid. No pieces of the same kind touch, even at a corner.

The pieces fit together so well that you cannot see any spaces between them; only the holes show.

Can you tell where the Ls are? One piece is already in place.

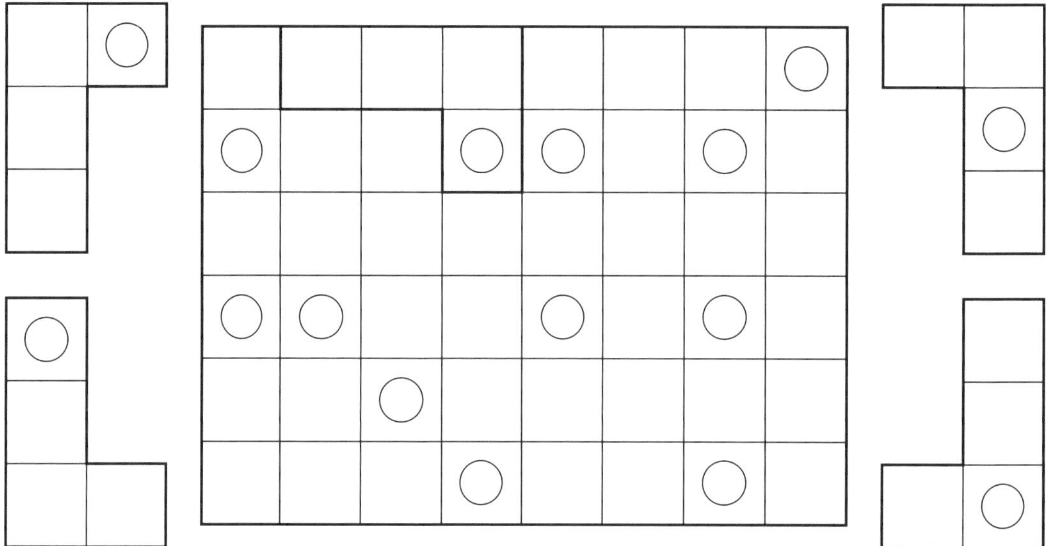

21 Fill the three empty circles with the symbols +, –, and x in some order, to make a sum that totals the central number. Each symbol must be used once, and calculations are made in the direction of travel (clockwise).

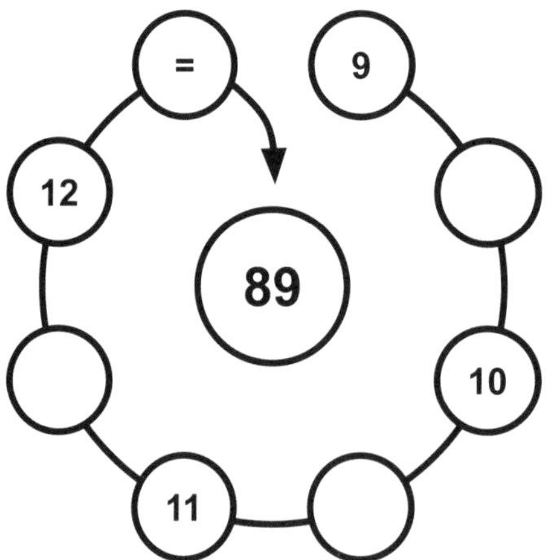

LEVEL 2

22

Each of the small squares in the grid below contains either A, B, or C. Each row, column, and diagonal line of six squares has exactly two of each letter. Can you tell the letter in each square?

Across

1 The Cs are between the Bs
2 The Bs are between the As
3 No two letters the same are directly next to each other
4 No two letters the same are directly next to each other
5 The Cs are between the As
6 The Bs are between the Cs

Down

1 Each C is directly next to and below a B
2 No two letters the same are directly next to each other
3 The Cs are lower than the Bs
4 The Bs are lower than the Cs
5 Each C is directly next to and below a B
6 No two letters the same are directly next to each other

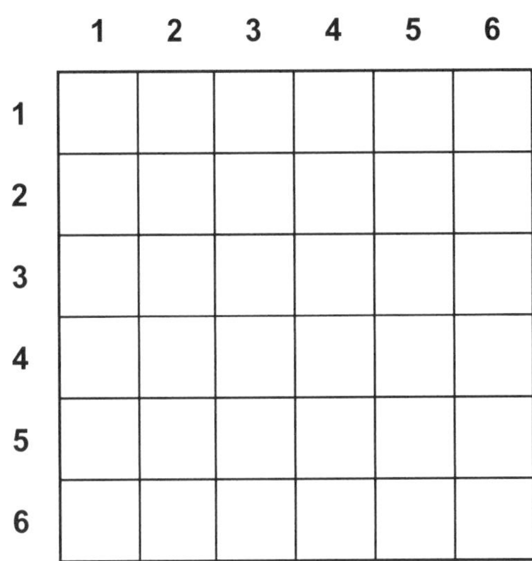

23

Using the numbers below, complete these six equations (three reading across and three reading downwards).

Every number is used once.

1 2 3 4 5
6 7 8 9

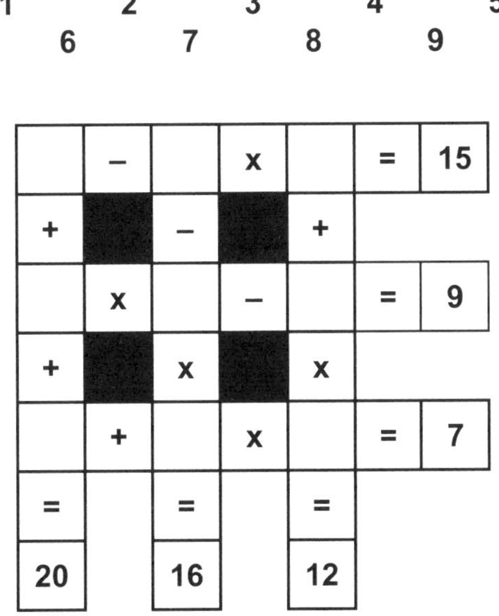

LEVEL 2

24 The chart gives directions to a hidden treasure behind the central black square in the grid. Move the indicated number of spaces north, south, east, and west (eg 4N means move four squares north) stopping at every square once only to arrive there. At which square should you start?

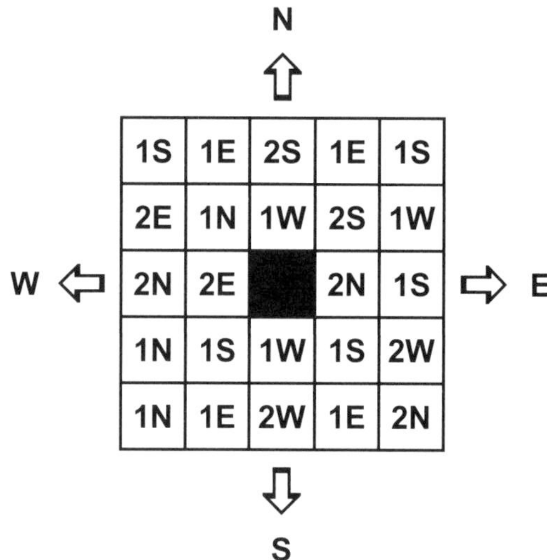

25 The numbers at the top and on the left side show the quantity of single-digit numbers (1-9) used in that row and column. The numbers at the bottom and on the right show the sum of the digits. A number may appear more than once in a row or column, but no numbers are in squares that touch, even at a corner.

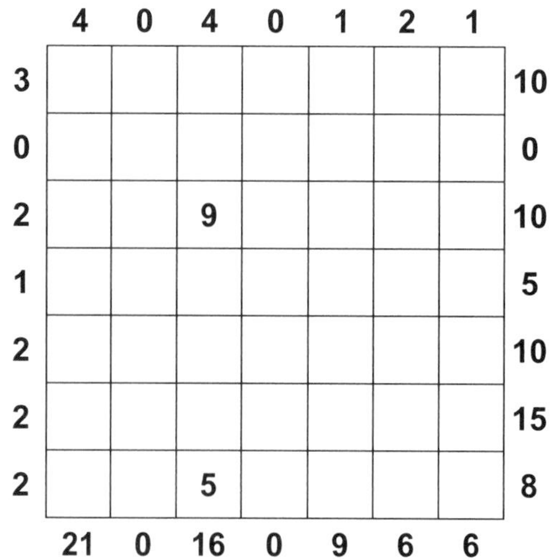

LEVEL 2

26 In the square below, change the positions of six numbers, one per horizontal row, vertical column, and long diagonal line of six smaller squares, in such a way that the numbers in each row, column, and long diagonal line total exactly 137. Any number may appear more than once in a row, column or line.

16	16	13	30	34	30
31	22	24	14	27	24
26	35	22	18	20	5
23	33	27	26	10	23
18	22	29	31	29	20
25	21	9	23	22	24

27 The blank squares below should be filled with whole numbers between 1 and 30 inclusive, any of which may occur more than once, or not at all.

The numbers in every horizontal row add up to the totals on the right, as do the two long diagonal lines; while those in every vertical column add up to the totals along the bottom.

							121
	14		27	29	16		108
18		4		15	17		86
		19	24	30	16	12	140
4	7	20	29			2	87
	25	18		27	21	5	110
14	17		16	12		22	109
1	18	4	10		23	28	104
81	114	87	113	145	115	89	142

LEVEL 2

28 Can you place the hexagons into the grid, so that where any hexagon touches another along a straight line, the number in both triangles is the same? No rotation of any hexagon is allowed!

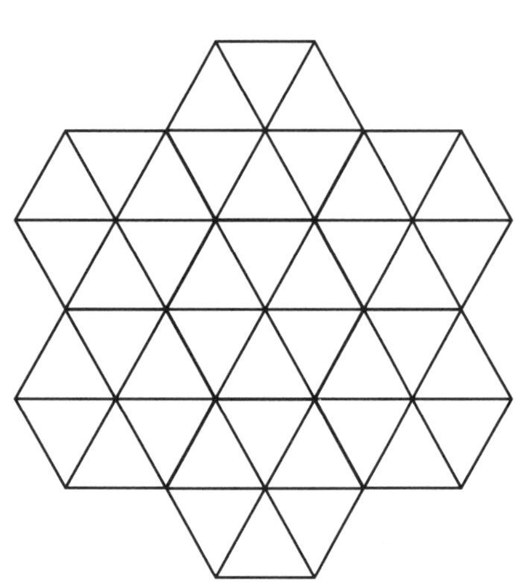

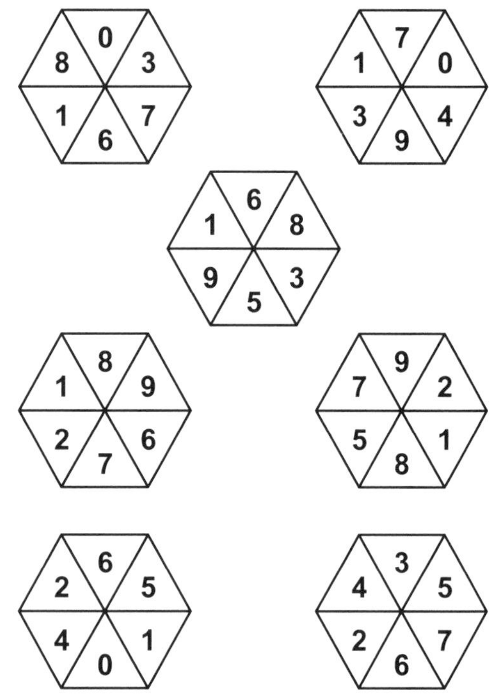

29 Can you place the vessels into the diagram? Some parts of vessels or sea squares have already been filled in. A number to the right or below a row or column refers to the number of occupied squares in that row or column.

Any vessel may be positioned horizontally or vertically, but no part of a vessel touches part of any other vessel, either horizontally, vertically, or diagonally.

Empty Area of Sea: ≈

Aircraft Carrier: ◀■■▶

Battleships: ◀■▶ ◀■▶

Cruisers: ◀▶ ◀▶ ◀▶

Submarines: ● ● ● ●

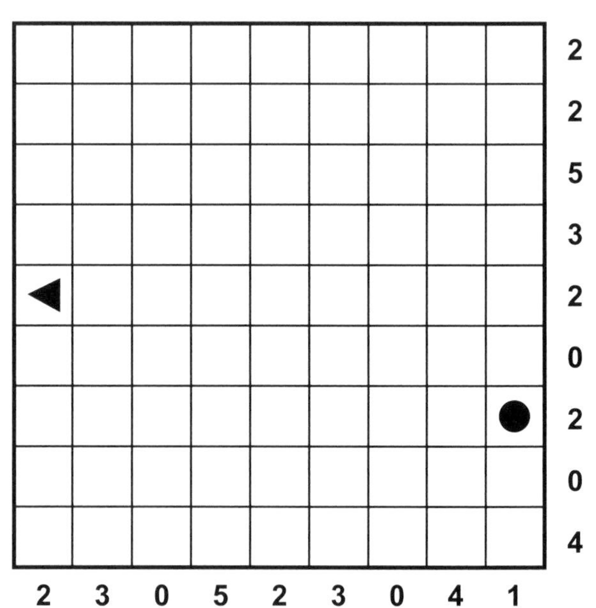

LEVEL 2

30 Each horizontal row and vertical column should contain different shapes and different numbers.

Every square will contain one number and one shape, and no combination may be repeated anywhere else in the puzzle.

1	2	3	4	5

		1		2
			4	
4				
3				1

31 In the diagram below, what number should replace the question mark?

26	12	6
11	9	20
9	15	12

15	9	20
8	17	15
13	20	3

16	14	14
7	21	12
5	22	9

?

17	15	12
8	17	16
15	8	11

A

16	16	8
12	9	18
7	15	17

B

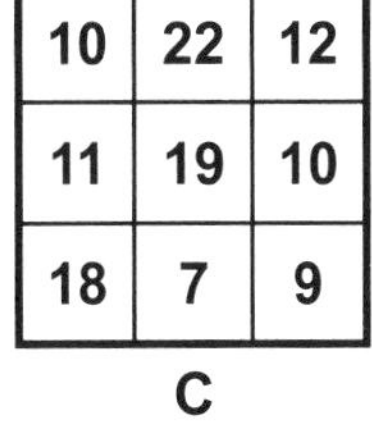

10	22	12
11	19	10
18	7	9

C

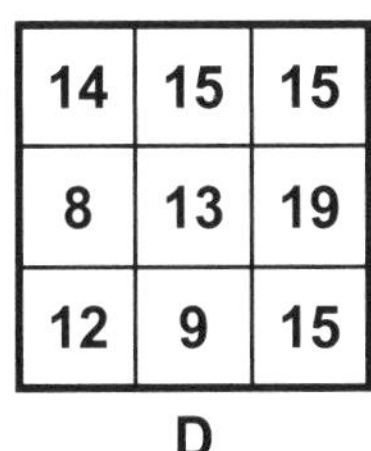

14	15	15
8	13	19
12	9	15

D

LEVEL 2

32 Every brick in this pyramid contains a number which is the sum of the two numbers below it, so that F=A+B, etc.

Just work out the missing numbers!

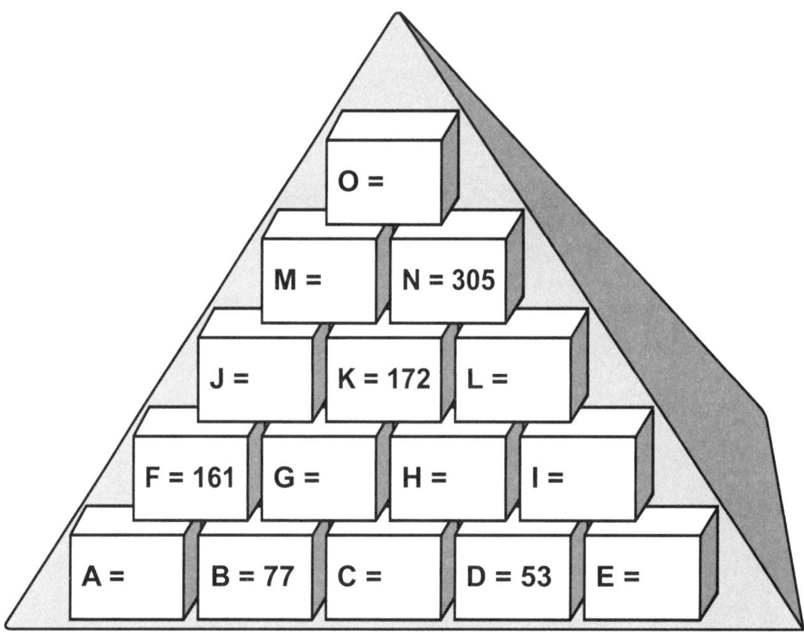

33 In this puzzle, an amateur coin collector has been out with his metal detector, searching for booty. He didn't have time to dig up all the coins he found, so has made a grid map, showing their locations, in the hope that if he loses the map, at least no-one else will understand it…

Those squares containing numbers are empty, but where a number appears in a square, it indicates how many coins are located in the squares (up to a maximum of eight) surrounding the numbered one, touching it at any corner or side. There is only one coin in any individual square.

Place a circle into every square containing a coin.

			0						1
	1	1			5		4	3	
				1			4		
1				3					
		2			2		2	2	2
	0						0		
	1		2	2				3	
3					3				
			4				1		0
2			3	2					

LEVEL 2

34 Given that the letters are valued 1-26 according to their places in the alphabet, can you crack the mystery code to reveal the missing letter?

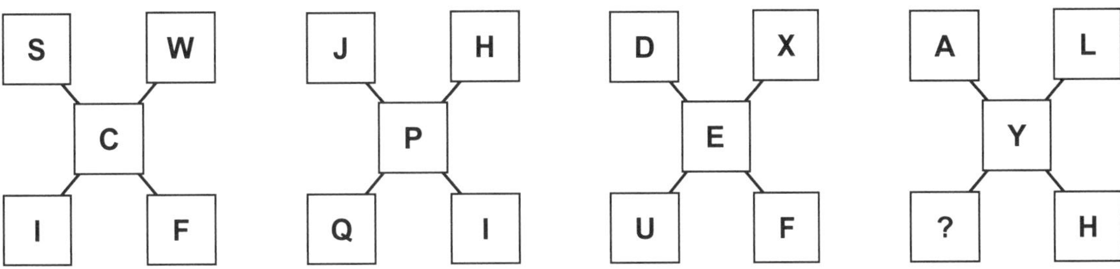

35 Place all twelve of the pieces into the grid. Any may be rotated or flipped over, but none may touch another, not even diagonally. The numbers outside the grid refer to the number of consecutive black squares; and each block is separated from the others by at least one white square. For instance, “3 2” could refer to a row with none, one or more white squares, then three black squares, then at least one white square, then two more black squares, followed by any number of white squares.

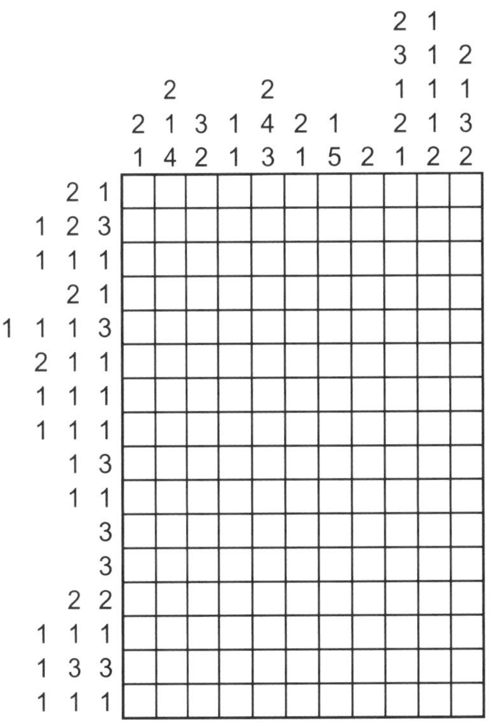

36

Each of the eight segments of the spider's web should be filled with a different number from 1 to 8, in such a way that every ring also contains a different number from 1 to 8.

The segments run from the outside of the spider's web to the middle, and the rings run all the way around.

Some numbers are already in place. Can you fill in the rest?

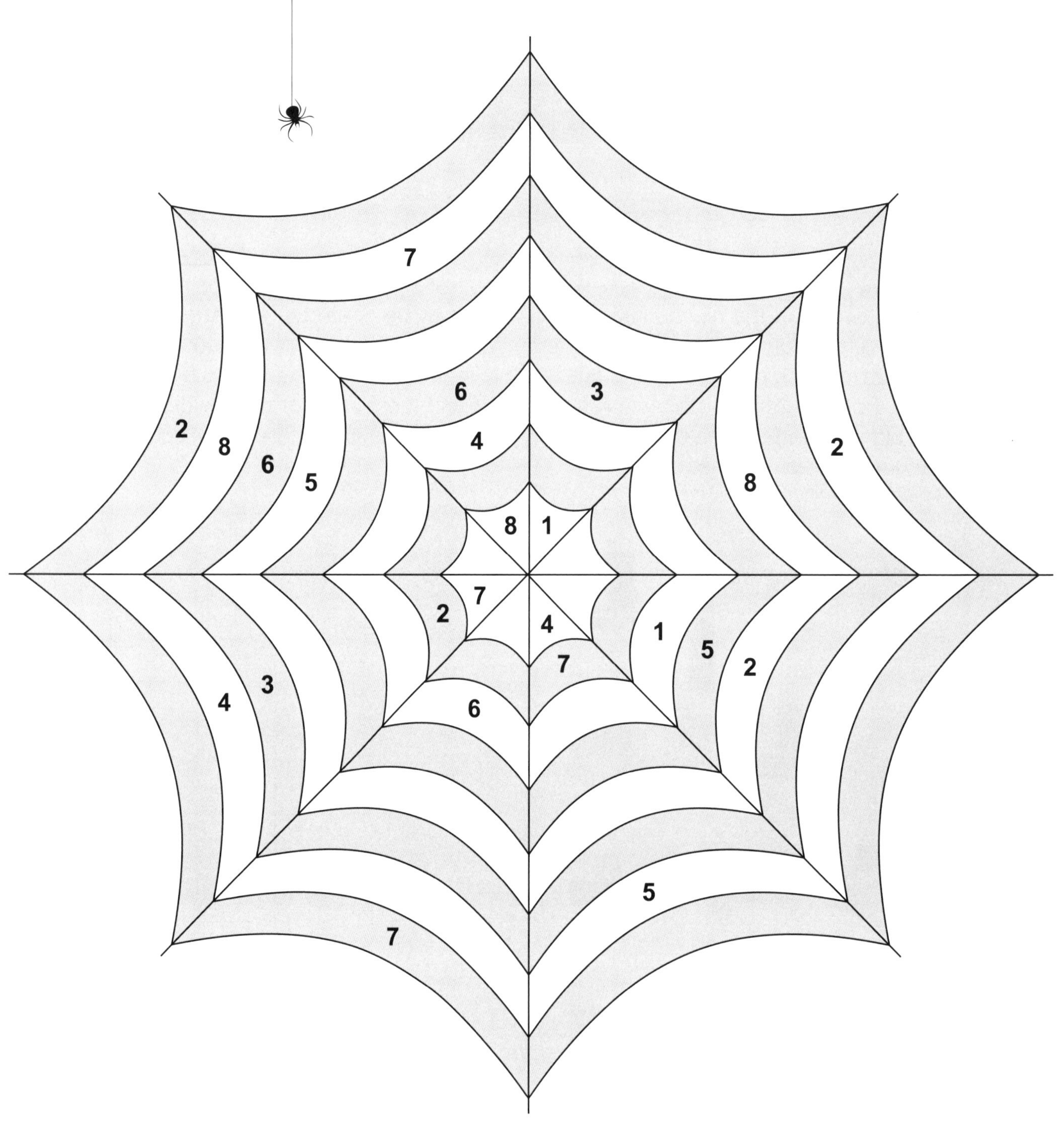

37 Every row and column in this grid originally contained one heart, one club, one diamond, one spade, and two blank squares, although not necessarily in that order.

Every symbol with a black arrow refers to the first of the four symbols encountered in the direction of the arrow. Every symbol with a white arrow refers to the second of the four symbols encountered in the direction of the arrow.

Can you complete the original grid?

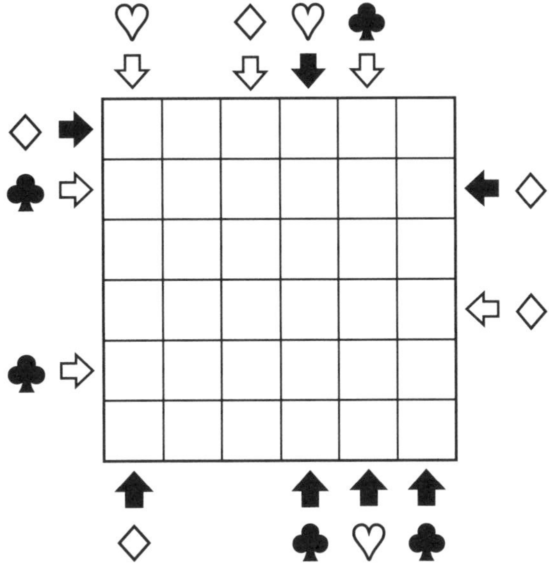

38 Fill the grid so that every horizontal row and vertical column contains the numbers 1-5. Any arrows in the grid always point toward a square that contains a lower number.

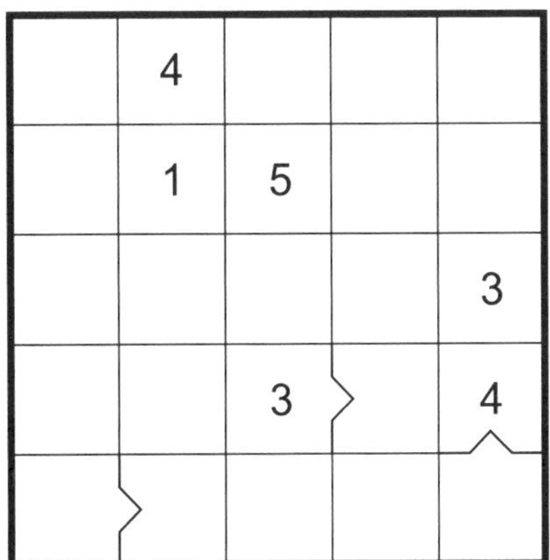

39

With the starter already given, can you fit all of the remaining listed numbers into this grid? Take care, this puzzle may not be as easy as it looks!

15	470	2408	33029	85340
33	474	2901	36993	86935
55	620	3534	39535 ✓	145707
65	660	5343	45559	155977
67	755	6769	49537	366449
73	780	7034	49843	473497
76	883	8431	49930	576028
89	927	8552	50429	586962
91	1183	24637	57030	630000
97	1597	25534	60006	840447
156	1605	29953	63801	2456053
220	2380	30574	74905	3036389

40

The grid should be filled with numbers from 1 to 6, so that each number appears just once in every row and column.

The clues refer to the digit totals in the squares, e.g. A 1 2 3 = 6 means that the numbers in squares A1, A2 and A3 add up to 6.

1 E F 4 = 3
2 D E 5 = 3
3 E F 6 = 6
4 A 4 5 6 = 13
5 B 2 3 4 = 10
6 C 4 5 = 9
7 D 3 4 = 4
8 E 1 2 = 11
9 F 2 3 = 8
10 A B 1 = 3
11 C D 2 = 6

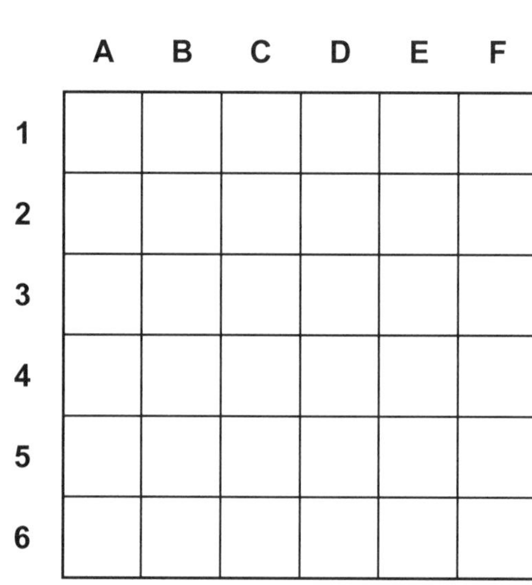

LEVEL 2

41 The object of this puzzle is to trace a single path from the top left corner to the bottom right corner of the grid, moving through all of the cells in either a horizontal, vertical, or diagonal direction.

Every cell must be entered once only, and your path should take you through the numbers in the sequence 1-2-3-4-5-6-1-2-3-4-5-6, etc.

Can you find the way?

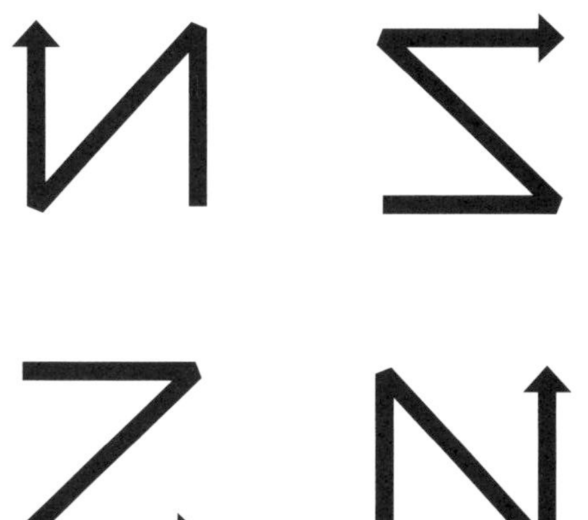

1	2	6	5	3	2
3	3	1	4	6	1
4	2	4	5	1	3
5	5	1	6	4	2
6	6	4	2	5	5
1	2	3	3	4	6

42 A standard set of 28 dominoes has been laid out as shown. Can you draw in the edges of them all?

The check-box is provided as an aid and the domino already placed will help.

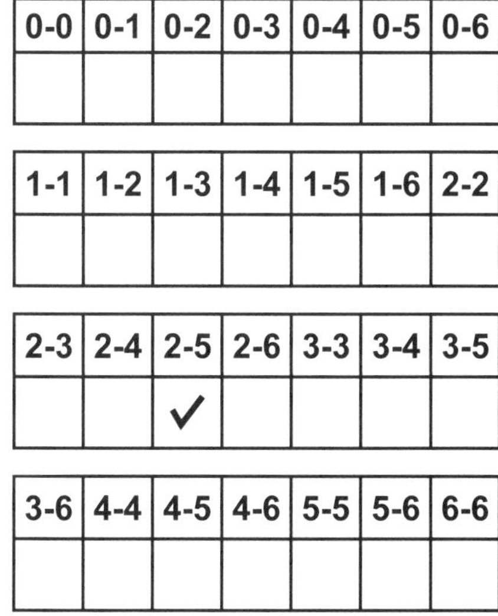

0-0	0-1	0-2	0-3	0-4	0-5	0-6

1-1	1-2	1-3	1-4	1-5	1-6	2-2

2-3	2-4	2-5	2-6	3-3	3-4	3-5
		✓				

3-6	4-4	4-5	4-6	5-5	5-6	6-6

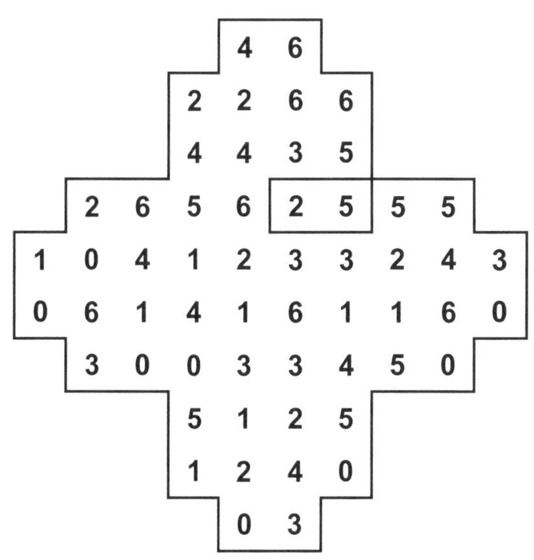

43

Draw a single continuous loop, by connecting the dots. No line may cross the path of another.

The figure inside each set of any four surrounding dots indicates the total number of surrounding lines.

2			2	1	1	2	3	1	
2			1				2		
	0	1			1	2	3	1	1
	0	1	0						2
2	2		1	1					
			1		1		3	1	
3	3		2				2		1
1	1				1				1
			0	1	0				
	1		2				1		
				1		2	0		2
3	1	3		2			2	2	2

44

Place the eight tiles into the puzzle grid so that all adjacent numbers on each tile match up.

Tiles may be rotated through 360 degrees, but none may be flipped over.

1	4
3	3

1	4
3	2

1	2
4	4

2	4
4	1

4	1
2	3

1	3
1	2

4	1
4	1

4	2
3	4

4	2				
1	1				

LEVEL 2

45 Which of the four lettered alternatives (A, B, C, or D) fits most logically into the empty square?

14	7	18
11	16	9
13	17	3

12	9	16
13	14	11
15	19	5

10	11	14
15	12	13
17	21	7

?

9	10	13
15	12	11
19	21	7

A

8	13	15
12	10	13
17	23	7

B

8	13	12
17	10	15
19	23	9

C

8	17	16
13	10	15
19	25	9

D

46 Which four pieces can be fitted together to form an exact copy of this shape?

A

B
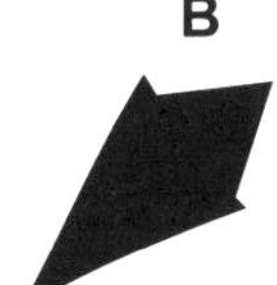

C

D

E

F

G

H
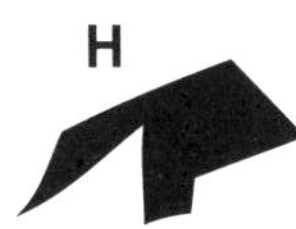

I

J

47 Twelve L-shapes need to be inserted in the grid, and each L has one hole in it.

There are three pieces of each of the four kinds shown here, and any piece may be turned or flipped over before being put in the grid. No pieces of the same kind touch, even at a corner.

The pieces fit together so well that you cannot see any spaces between them; only the holes show.

Can you tell where the Ls are?

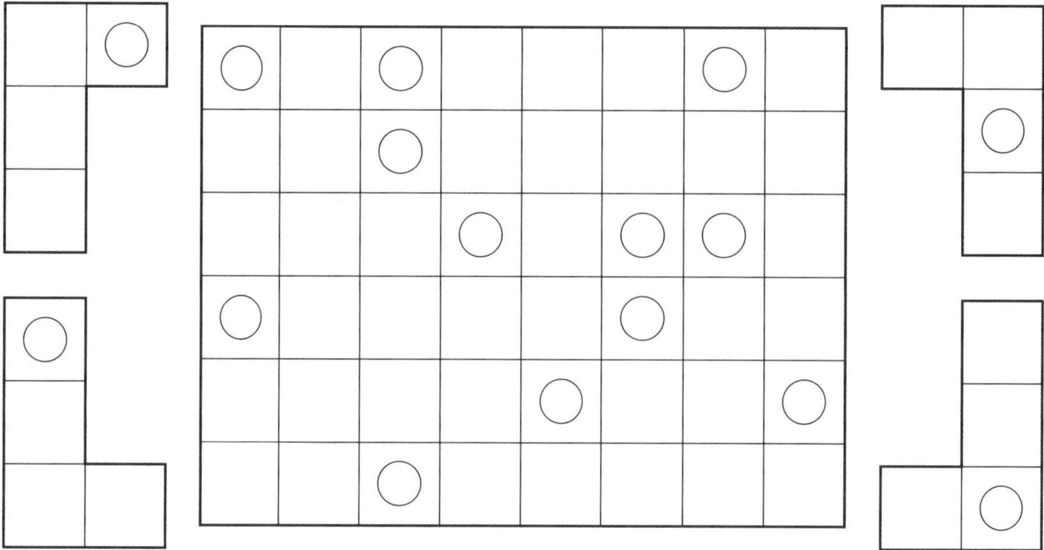

48 Each symbol stands for a different number. In order to reach the correct total at the end of each row and column, what is the value of the circle, cross, pentagon, square and star?

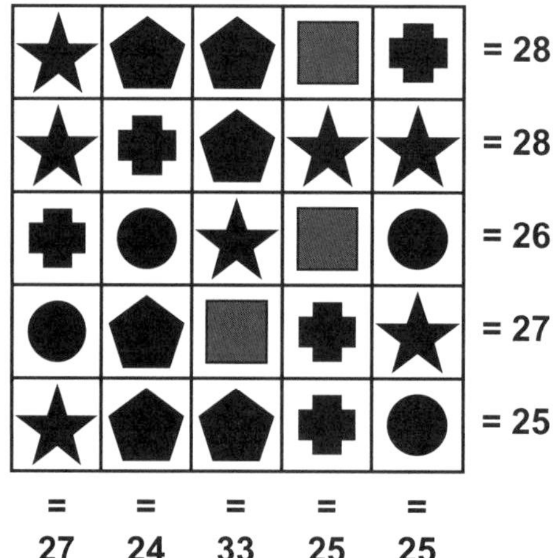

49 Each of the small squares in the grid below contains either A, B, or C. Each row, column, and diagonal line of six squares has exactly two of each letter. Can you tell the letter in each square?

Across
1 The Bs are between the Cs
2 The As are between the Bs
3 The Cs are next to each other
4 Each B is directly next to and right of an A
5 The Bs are further right than the As
6 The As are next to each other

Down
1 The As are next to each other
2 The As are next to each other
3 Each C is directly next to and below a B
4 The As are lower than the Bs
5 The As are between the Cs
6 The Cs are lower than the As

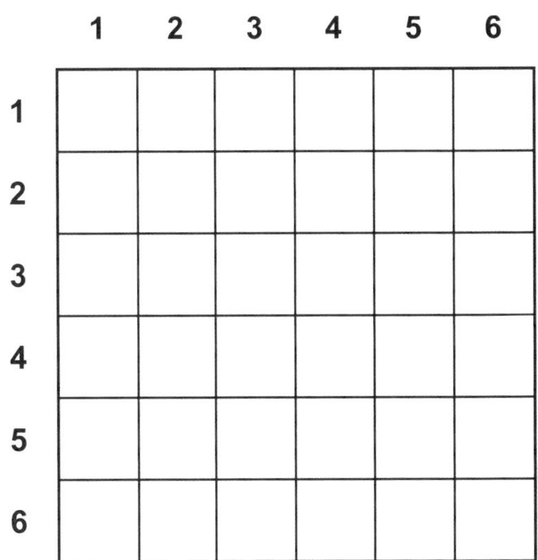

50 Which of the alternatives (A, B, C, or D) comes next in this sequence?

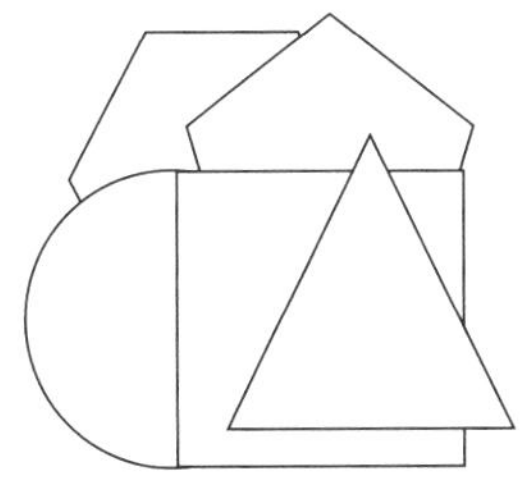
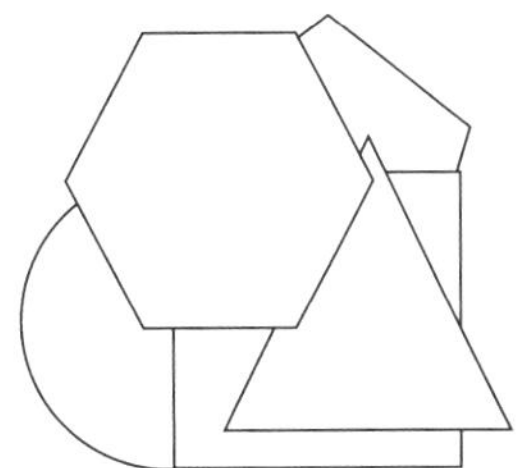
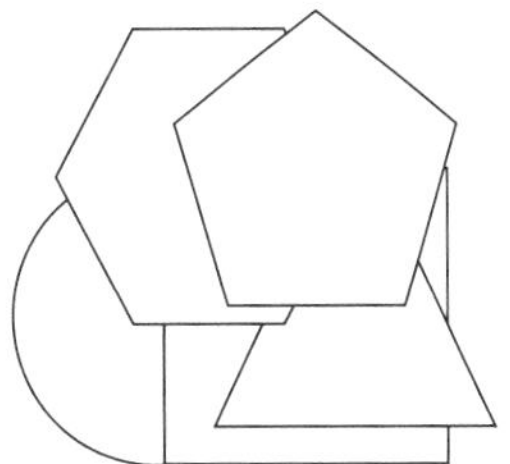
?

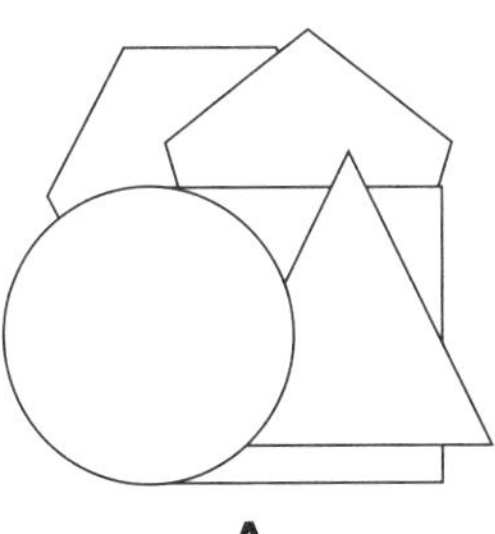
A

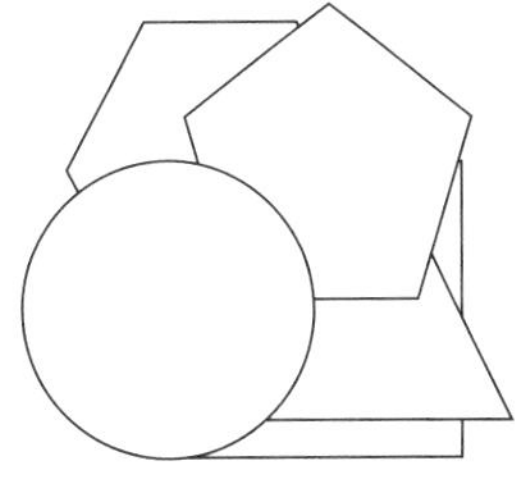
B

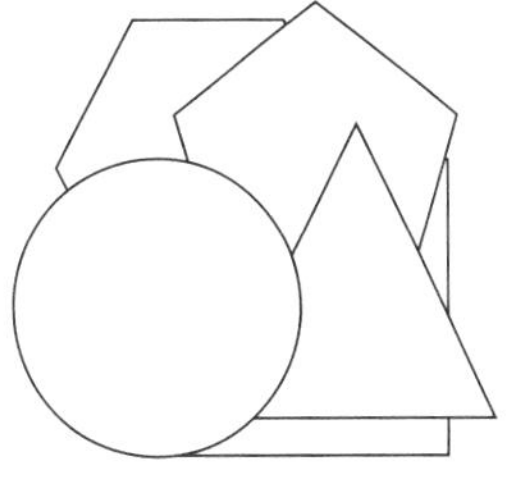
C

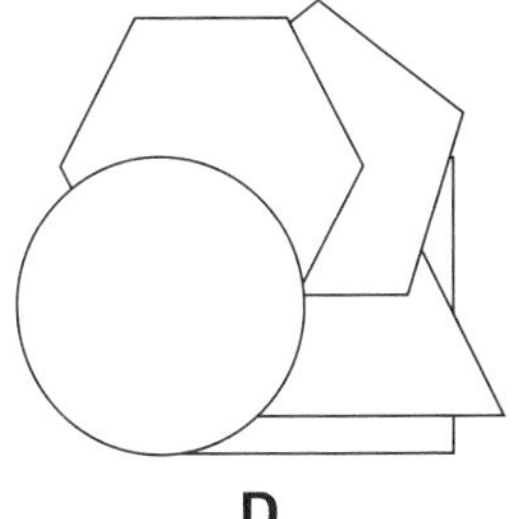
D

51 The chart gives directions to a hidden treasure behind the central black square in the grid. Move the indicated number of spaces north, south, east, and west (eg 4N means move four squares north) stopping at every square once only to arrive there. At which square should you start?

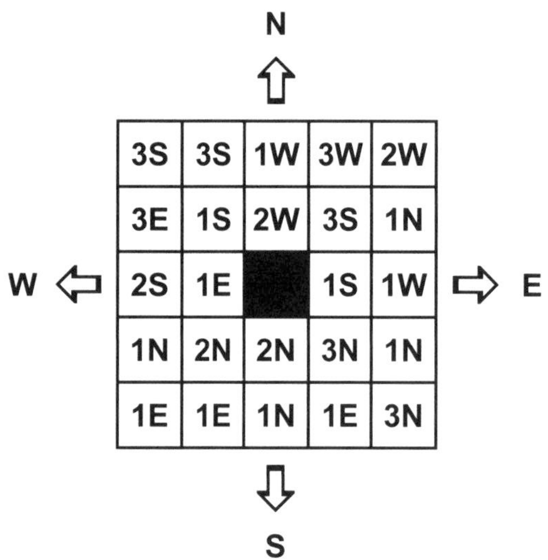

52 What number should replace the question mark?

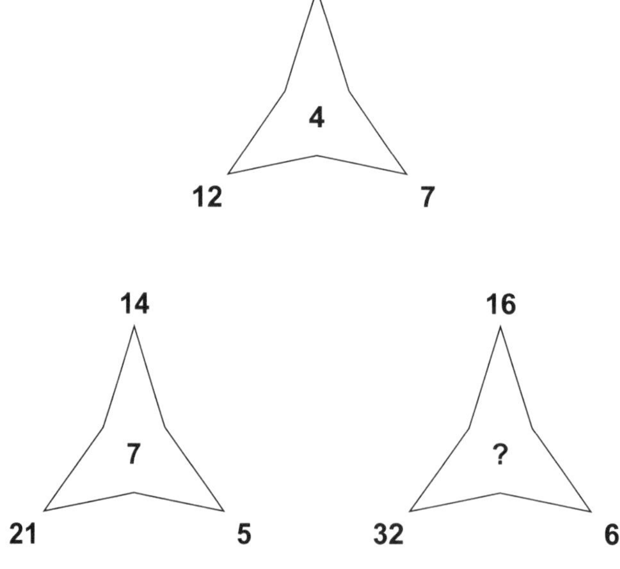

LEVEL 2

53 In the grid below, what number should replace the question mark?

12	15	21	13	16	14	19
15	18	24	16	19	17	22
20	23	29	21	24	22	27
27	30	36	?	31	29	34
35	38	44	36	39	37	42
41	44	50	42	45	43	48
45	48	54	46	49	47	52

54 The blank squares below should be filled with whole numbers between 1 and 30 inclusive, any of which may occur more than once, or not at all.

The numbers in every horizontal row add up to the totals on the right, as do the two long diagonal lines; while those in every vertical column add up to the totals along the bottom.

							125
16	27		9	4		14	100
7		15			30		115
	14	8	29	21	13	11	97
5		12		10	6	25	81
	23	4	19	28		13	119
2	16		11	17	22		110
20	17	4	5		14		91
69	111	68	117	124	116	108	118

55

Can you place the hexagons into the grid, so that where any hexagon touches another along a straight line, the number in both triangles is the same? No rotation of any hexagon is allowed!

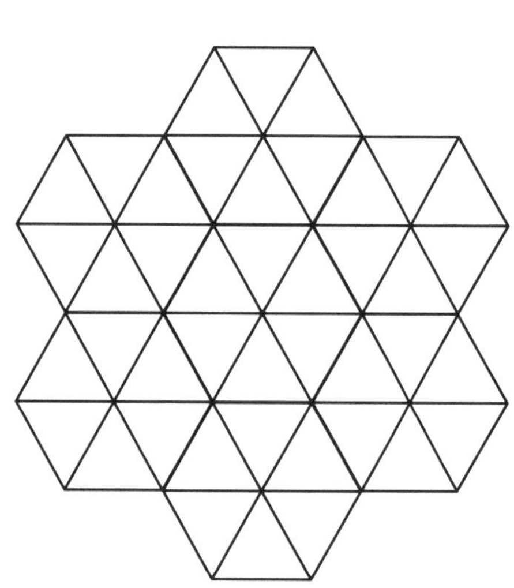

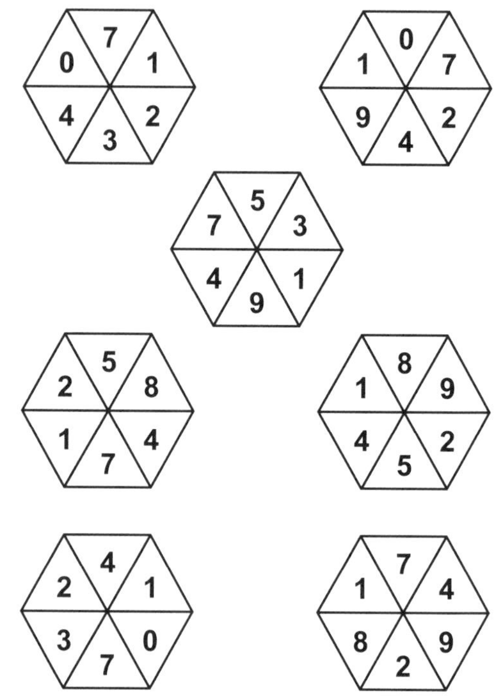

56

Can you place the vessels into the diagram? Some parts of vessels or sea squares have already been filled in. A number to the right or below a row or column refers to the number of occupied squares in that row or column.

Any vessel may be positioned horizontally or vertically, but no part of a vessel touches part of any other vessel, either horizontally, vertically, or diagonally.

Empty Area of Sea: ≈

Aircraft Carrier: ◀■■▶

Battleships: ◀■▶ ◀■▶

Cruisers: ◀▶ ◀▶ ◀▶

Submarines: ● ● ● ●

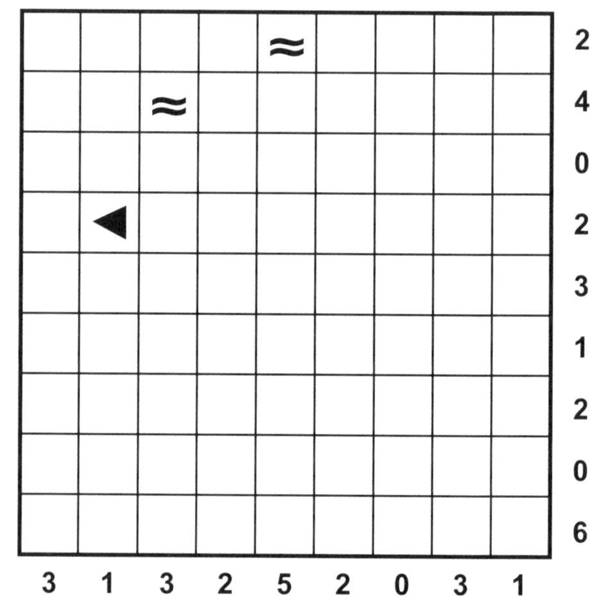

LEVEL 2

57 Each horizontal row and vertical column should contain different shapes and different numbers.

Every square will contain one number and one shape, and no combination may be repeated anywhere else in the puzzle.

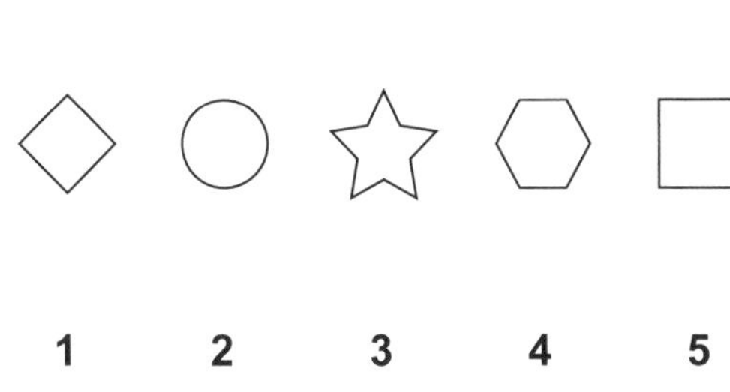

			5	
		5		
	4	1		
				2

58 In the diagram below, what number should replace the question mark?

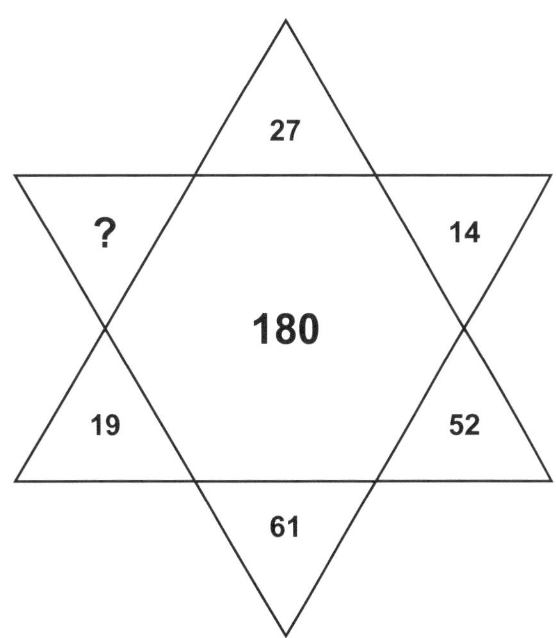

LEVEL 2

59

Every brick in this pyramid contains a number which is the sum of the two numbers below it, so that F=A+B, etc.

Just work out the missing numbers!

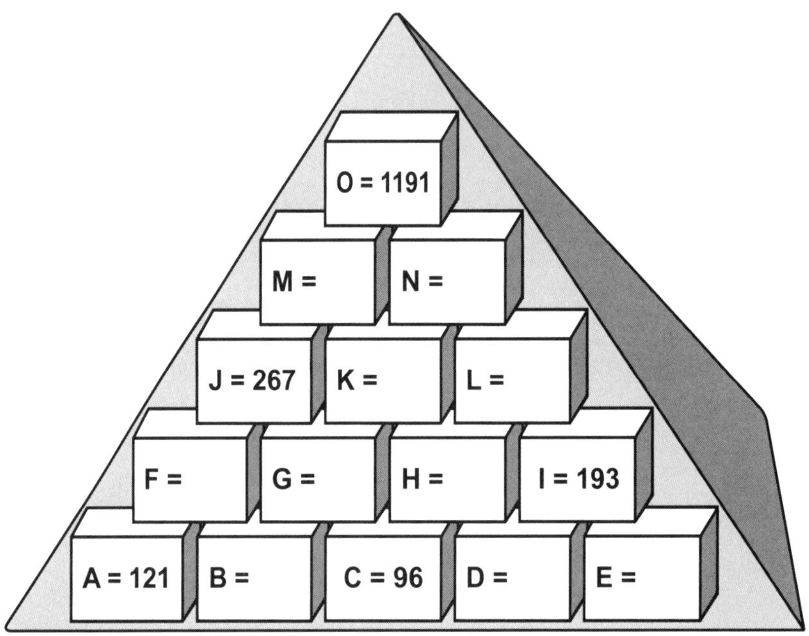

60

In this puzzle, an amateur coin collector has been out with his metal detector, searching for booty. He didn't have time to dig up all the coins he found, so has made a grid map, showing their locations, in the hope that if he loses the map, at least no-one else will understand it…

Those squares containing numbers are empty, but where a number appears in a square, it indicates how many coins are located in the squares (up to a maximum of eight) surrounding the numbered one, touching it at any corner or side. There is only one coin in any individual square.

Place a circle into every square containing a coin.

				2		2	2	2	
1	3	2							
			4			4		1	
1		3							
	3			1					1
2					0		2		1
						2			3
0		0	1		2		4		
1		2		2			3		
						1		1	

LEVEL 2

61 Given that the letters are valued 1-26 according to their places in the alphabet, can you crack the mystery code to reveal the missing letter?

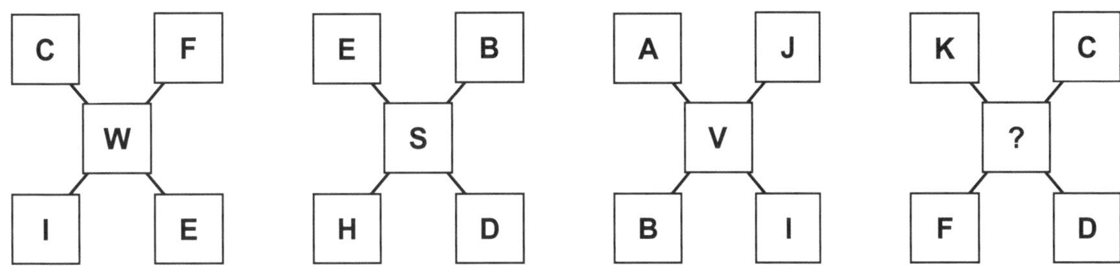

62 Place all twelve of the pieces into the grid. Any may be rotated or flipped over, but none may touch another, not even diagonally. The numbers outside the grid refer to the number of consecutive black squares; and each block is separated from the others by at least one white square. For instance, "3 2" could refer to a row with none, one or more white squares, then three black squares, then at least one white square, then two more black squares, followed by any number of white squares.

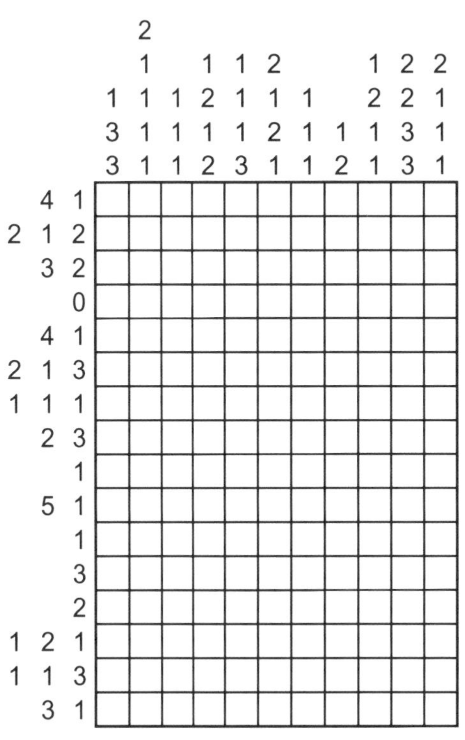

LEVEL 2

63 Each of the eight segments of the spider's web should be filled with a different number from 1 to 8, in such a way that every ring also contains a different number from 1 to 8.

The segments run from the outside of the spider's web to the middle, and the rings run all the way around.

Some numbers are already in place. Can you fill in the rest?

64 Every row and column in this grid originally contained one heart, one club, one diamond, one spade, and two blank squares, although not necessarily in that order.

Every symbol with a black arrow refers to the first of the four symbols encountered in the direction of the arrow. Every symbol with a white arrow refers to the second of the four symbols encountered in the direction of the arrow.

Can you complete the original grid?

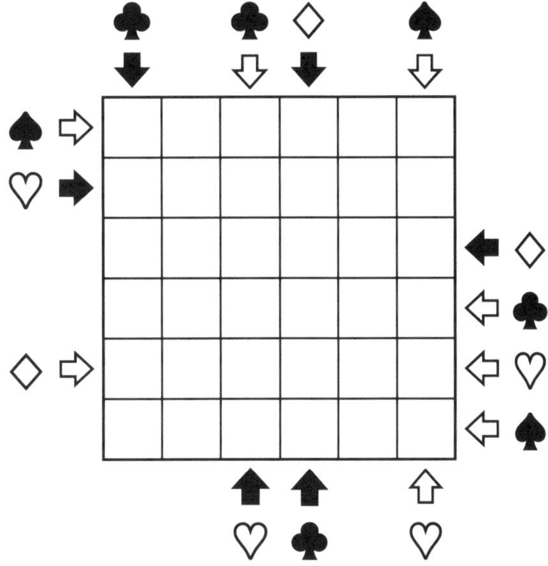

65 Fill the grid so that every horizontal row and vertical column contains the numbers 1-5. Any arrows in the grid always point toward a square that contains a lower number.

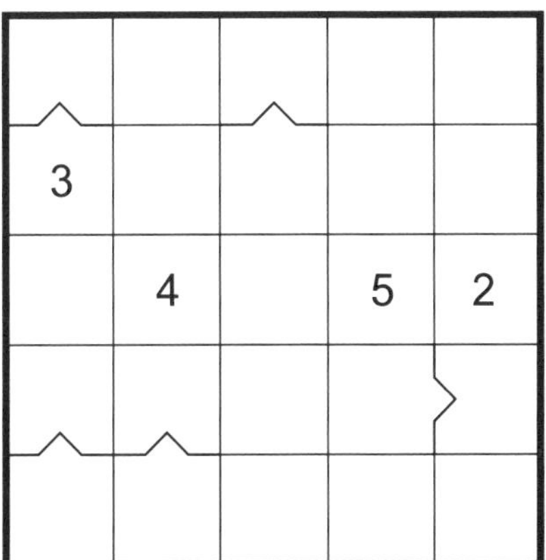

LEVEL 2

66

With the starter already given, can you fit all of the remaining listed numbers into this grid? Take care, this puzzle may not be as easy as it looks!

12	338 ✓	723	7315	224291
21	370	741	8004	234109
25	394	755	9983	239477
41	417	782	23179	384109
49	418	869	25713	443318
50	425	887	29430	472509
74	488	980	39904	544419
92	493	999	54355	605504
129	555	2057	55528	1403331
147	601	3223	105002	2330210
266	670	4868	115105	6048589
304	693	6024	189088	9050118
		7254	189937	

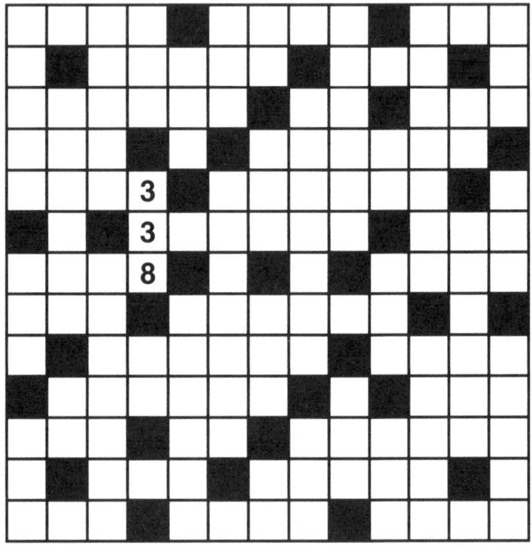

67

The grid should be filled with numbers from 1 to 6, so that each number appears just once in every row and column.

The clues refer to the digit totals in the squares, e.g. A 1 2 3 = 6 means that the numbers in squares A1, A2 and A3 add up to 6.

1 C D E 4 = 8
2 D E F 5 = 13
3 B C 6 = 4
4 A 3 4 = 8
5 B 3 4 = 9
6 C 2 3 = 3
7 D 1 2 = 5
8 E 2 3 = 8
9 F 1 2 = 3
10 A B 1 = 9
11 A B 2 = 8

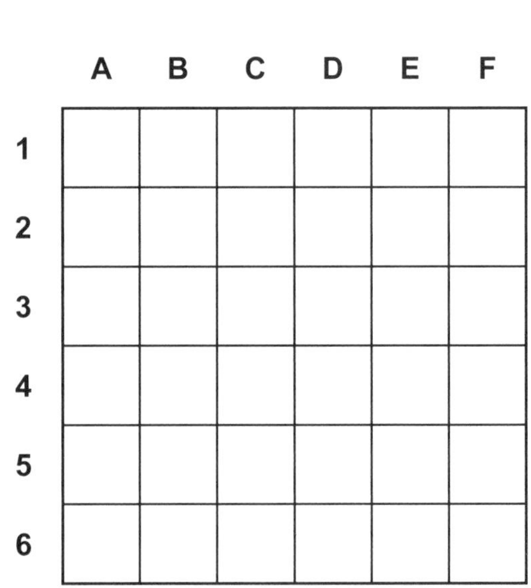

LEVEL 2

68 The object of this puzzle is to trace a single path from the top left corner to the bottom right corner of the grid, moving through all of the cells in either a horizontal, vertical, or diagonal direction.

Every cell must be entered once only, and your path should take you through the numbers in the sequence 1-2-3-4-5-6-1-2-3-4-5-6, etc.

Can you find the way?

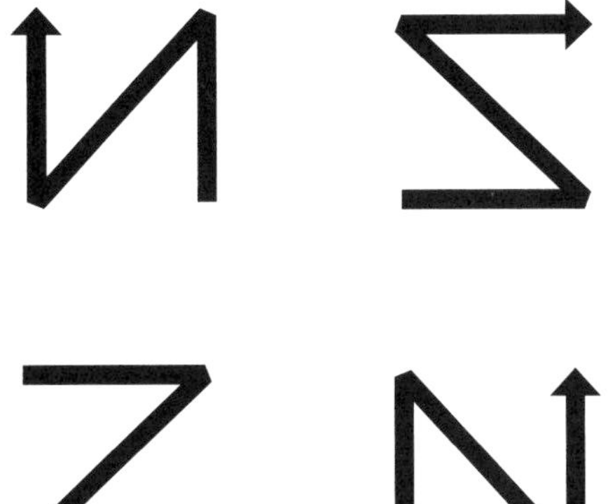

1	5	6	1	6	1
2	3	4	2	5	2
2	1	4	3	4	3
3	5	6	3	2	4
4	5	2	3	5	1
6	1	4	5	6	6

69 A standard set of 28 dominoes has been laid out as shown. Can you draw in the edges of them all?

The check-box is provided as an aid and the domino already placed will help.

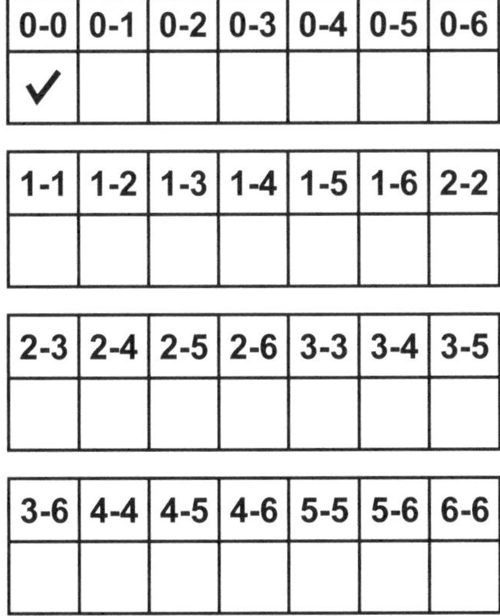

0-0	0-1	0-2	0-3	0-4	0-5	0-6
✓						

1-1	1-2	1-3	1-4	1-5	1-6	2-2

2-3	2-4	2-5	2-6	3-3	3-4	3-5

3-6	4-4	4-5	4-6	5-5	5-6	6-6

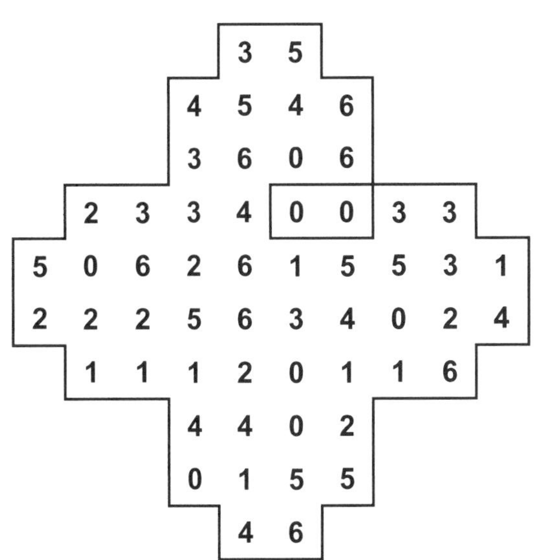

LEVEL 2

70

Draw a single continuous loop, by connecting the dots. No line may cross the path of another.

The figure inside each set of any four surrounding dots indicates the total number of surrounding lines.

1		2	3			1		2	
		0	1	0	2			1	
2							0		1
1			0				2	0	
			1	3	3				
	0				1	1	2	1	3
2			1	3	2				3
0		3						2	
			2		2	2	2		3
	2		2				2	1	2
2		3		1	1	1			
2	1			2					

71

Place the eight tiles into the puzzle grid so that all adjacent numbers on each tile match up.

Tiles may be rotated through 360 degrees, but none may be flipped over.

3	1
3	2

2	2
2	2

2	1
1	3

1	2
1	3

1	4
2	2

3	3
4	2

4	1
3	2

1	3
2	2

				4	1
				3	1

LEVEL 2

72

Every oval shape in this diagram contains a different letter of the alphabet from A to K inclusive.

Use the clues to determine their locations. Reference in the clues to "due" means in any location along the same horizontal or vertical line.

1 The A is next to and east of the I, which is further south than the K, which is further east than the H.

2 The B is next to and south of the E, which is next to and east of the C.

3 The D is due north of the H, which is due west of the F, which is further south than the C.

4 The E is due west of the J, which is further south than the A.

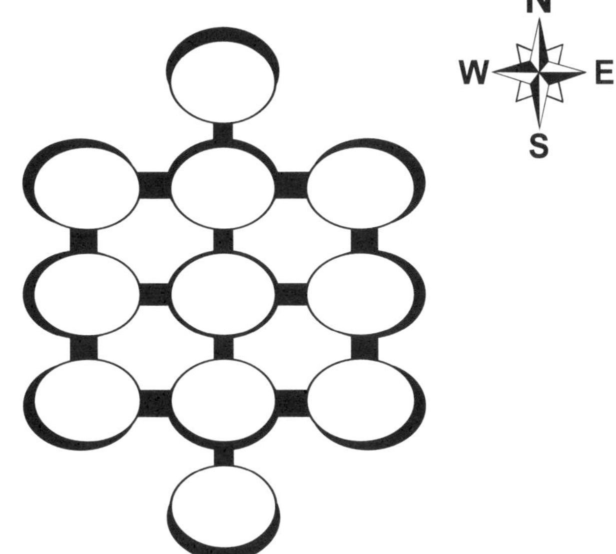

73

Draw walls to partition the grid into areas (some walls are already drawn in for you).

Each area must contain two circles, area sizes must match those numbers shown next to the grid, and each "+" must be linked to at least two walls.

2, 4, 4, 4, 5, 6

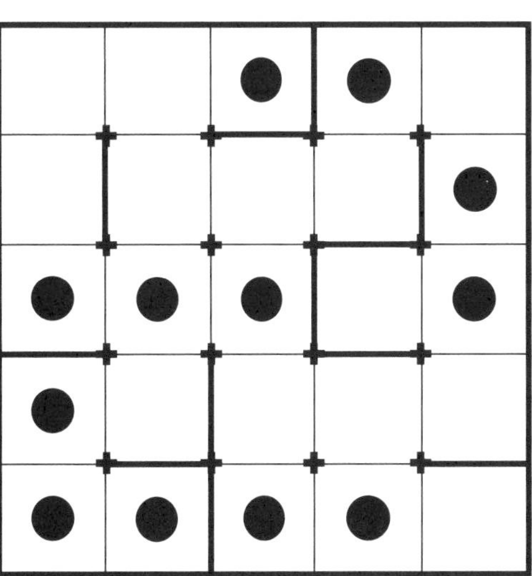

74 Twelve L-shapes need to be inserted in the grid, and each L has one hole in it.

There are three pieces of each of the four kinds shown here, and any piece may be turned or flipped over before being put in the grid. No pieces of the same kind touch, even at a corner.

The pieces fit together so well that you cannot see any spaces between them; only the holes show.

Can you tell where the Ls are? One piece is already in place.

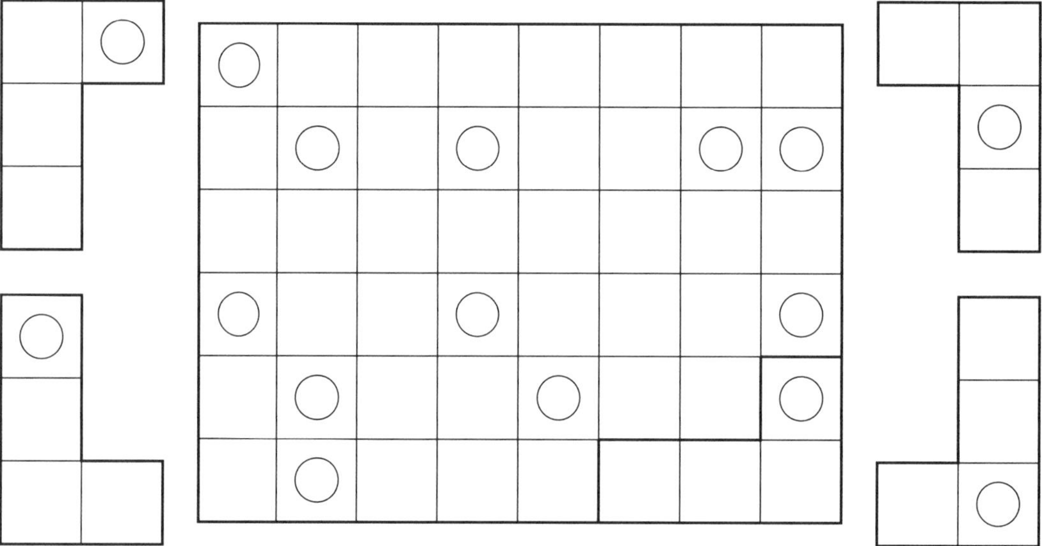

75 Fill the three empty circles with the symbols +, –, and x in some order, to make a sum that totals the central number. Each symbol must be used once, and calculations are made in the direction of travel (clockwise).

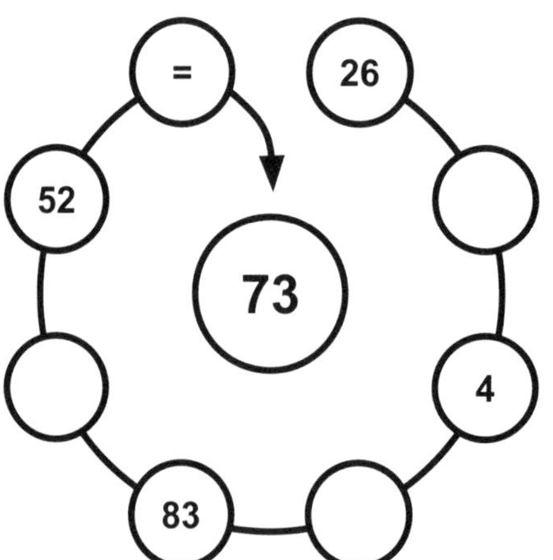

LEVEL 2

76

Each of the small squares in the grid below contains either A, B, or C. Each row, column, and diagonal line of six squares has exactly two of each letter. Can you tell the letter in each square?

Across

1 Each C is directly next to and right of an A
2 The As are between the Bs
3 The Cs are next to each other
4 The Bs are next to each other
5 The Bs are between the As
6 Each C is directly next to and right of a B

Down

1 No two letters the same are directly next to each other
2 The As are between the Cs
3 No two letters the same are directly next to each other
4 The Cs are between the Bs
5 The Bs are lower than the Cs
6 The As are between the Cs

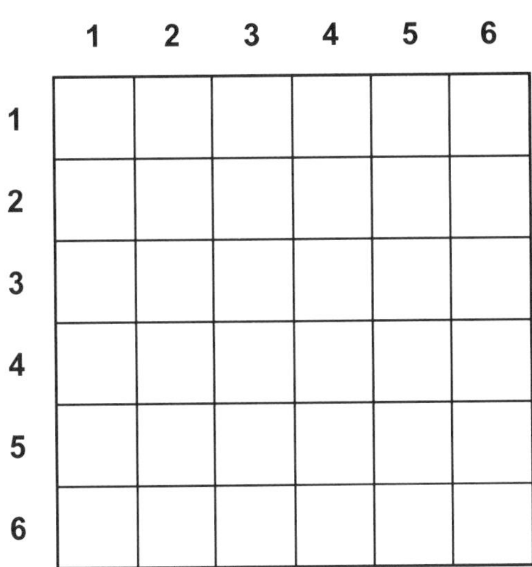

77

Using the numbers below, complete these six equations (three reading across and three reading downwards).

Every number is used once.

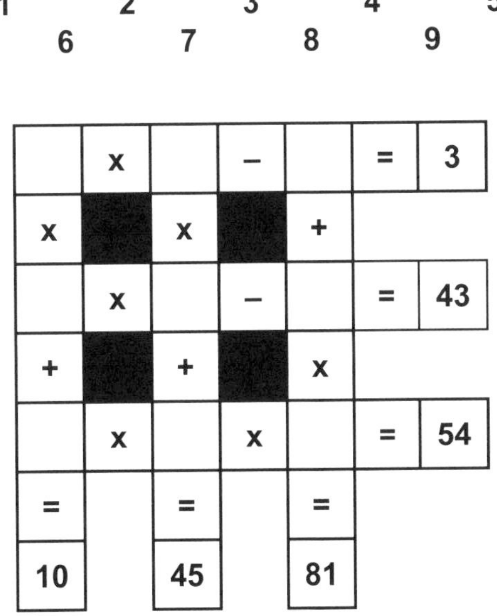

LEVEL 2

78 The chart gives directions to a hidden treasure behind the central black square in the grid. Move the indicated number of spaces north, south, east, and west (eg 4N means move four squares north) stopping at every square once only to arrive there. At which square should you start?

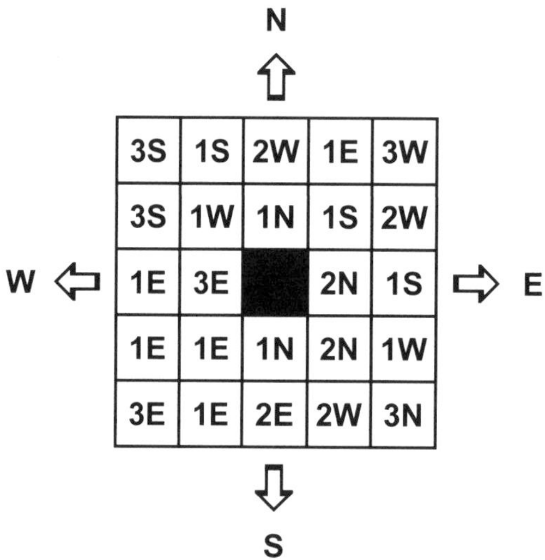

79 The numbers at the top and on the left side show the quantity of single-digit numbers (1-9) used in that row and column. The numbers at the bottom and on the right show the sum of the digits. A number may appear more than once in a row or column, but no numbers are in squares that touch, even at a corner.

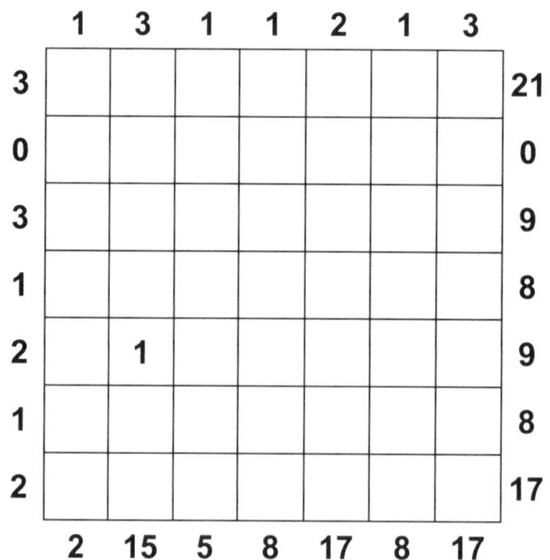

80

In the square below, change the positions of six numbers, one per horizontal row, vertical column, and long diagonal line of six smaller squares, in such a way that the numbers in each row, column, and long diagonal line total exactly 219. Any number may appear more than once in a row, column or line.

54	8	20	20	59	36
38	36	29	38	39	47
32	65	36	34	33	32
30	45	39	38	17	47
29	24	45	43	31	33
33	27	28	54	53	42

81

The blank squares below should be filled with whole numbers between 1 and 30 inclusive, any of which may occur more than once, or not at all.

The numbers in every horizontal row add up to the totals on the right, as do the two long diagonal lines; while those in every vertical column add up to the totals along the bottom.

							82
11	27			30	4		131
17	29	14		7	18		105
12				6	1	3	88
		28	26	14	17	8	117
2	9	12	11		19	21	84
	2	14	25	20		15	129
2	6	29	16			6	91
80	105	141	127	111	97	84	137

LEVEL 3

1 Can you place the hexagons into the grid, so that where any hexagon touches another along a straight line, the number in both triangles is the same? No rotation of any hexagon is allowed!

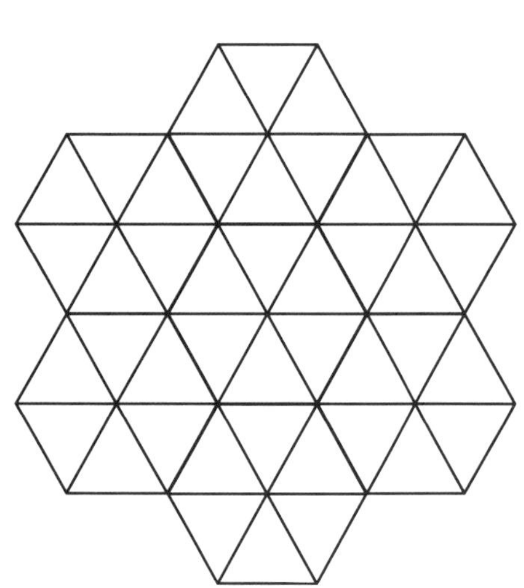

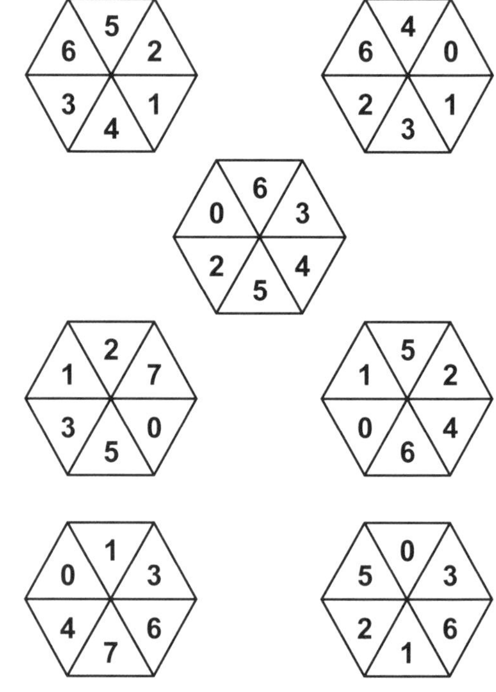

2 Can you place the vessels into the diagram? Some parts of vessels or sea squares have already been filled in. A number to the right or below a row or column refers to the number of occupied squares in that row or column.

Any vessel may be positioned horizontally or vertically, but no part of a vessel touches part of any other vessel, either horizontally, vertically, or diagonally.

Empty Area of Sea: ≈

Aircraft Carrier: ◀■■▶

Battleships: ◀■▶ ◀■▶

Cruisers: ◀▶ ◀▶ ◀▶

Submarines: ● ● ● ●

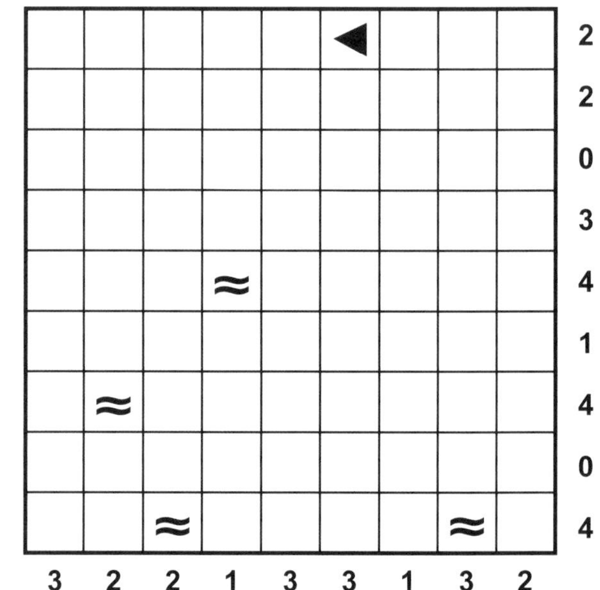

LEVEL 3

3 Each horizontal row and vertical column should contain different shapes and different numbers.

Every square will contain one number and one shape, and no combination may be repeated anywhere else in the puzzle.

◇	○	☆	⬡	□
1	2	3	4	5

○	4			⬡
4	□	⬡		
			○	
☆	5		□	
	1			2

4 In the diagram below, what letter should replace the question mark?

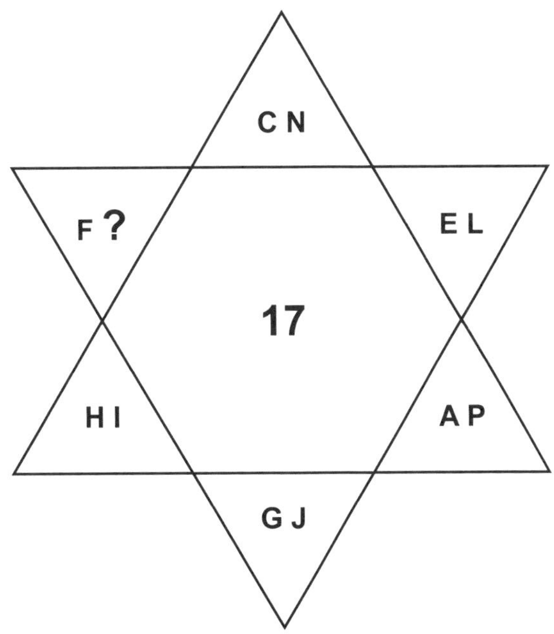

LEVEL 3

5 Every brick in this pyramid contains a number which is the sum of the two numbers below it, so that F=A+B, etc.

Just work out the missing numbers!

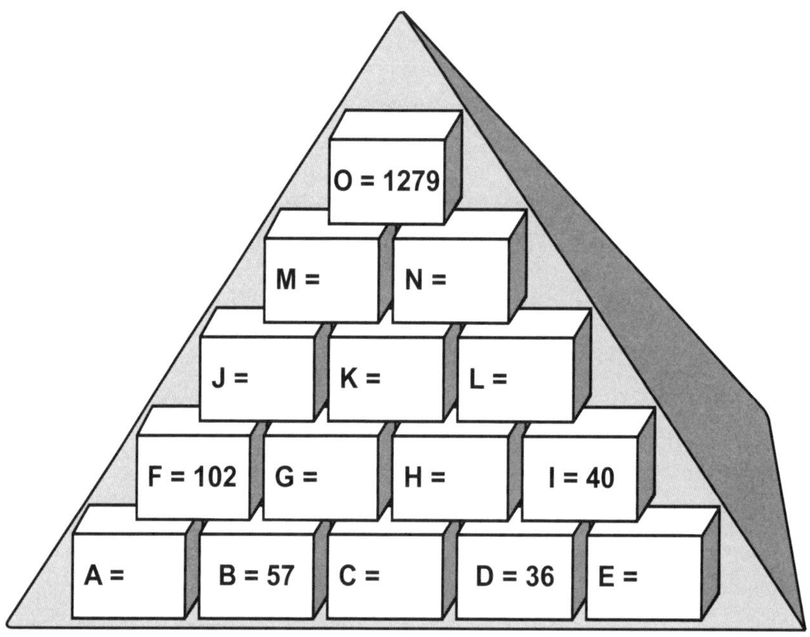

6 In this puzzle, an amateur coin collector has been out with his metal detector, searching for booty. He didn't have time to dig up all the coins he found, so has made a grid map, showing their locations, in the hope that if he loses the map, at least no-one else will understand it…

Those squares containing numbers are empty, but where a number appears in a square, it indicates how many coins are located in the squares (up to a maximum of eight) surrounding the numbered one, touching it at any corner or side. There is only one coin in any individual square.

Place a circle into every square containing a coin.

3		4		2			2		0
						4			
			4		2	3			
	1				1			1	
		3		1					1
0							2		1
		3				2		2	
			3	1		2		3	
	2			4			3		
									2

LEVEL 3

7 Given that the letters are valued 1-26 according to their places in the alphabet, can you crack the mystery code to reveal the missing letter?

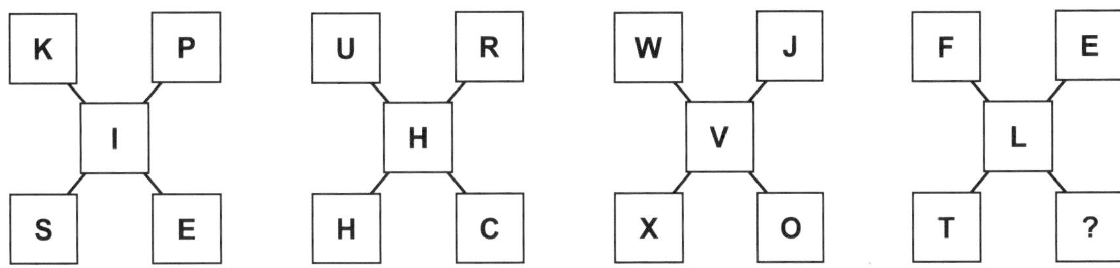

8 Place all twelve of the pieces into the grid. Any may be rotated or flipped over, but none may touch another, not even diagonally. The numbers outside the grid refer to the number of consecutive black squares; and each block is separated from the others by at least one white square. For instance, "3 2" could refer to a row with none, one or more white squares, then three black squares, then at least one white square, then two more black squares, followed by any number of white squares.

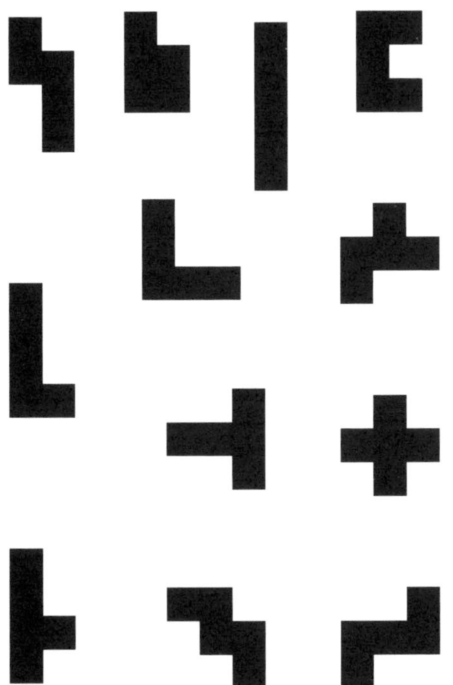

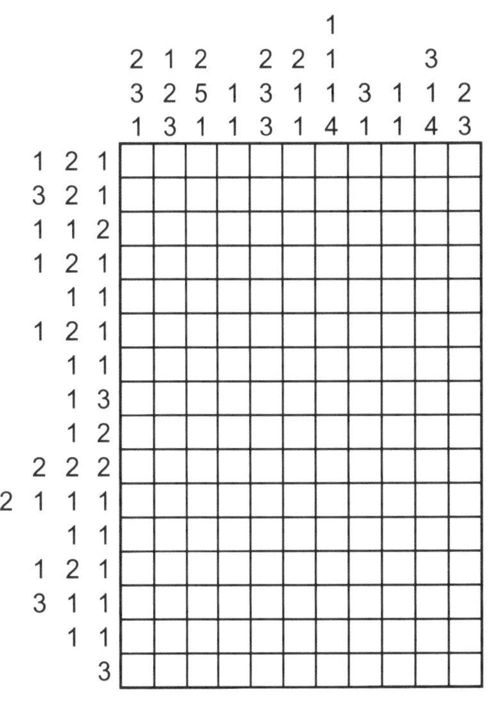

LEVEL 3

9 Each of the eight segments of the spider's web should be filled with a different number from 1 to 8, in such a way that every ring also contains a different number from 1 to 8.

The segments run from the outside of the spider's web to the middle, and the rings run all the way around.

Some numbers are already in place. Can you fill in the rest?

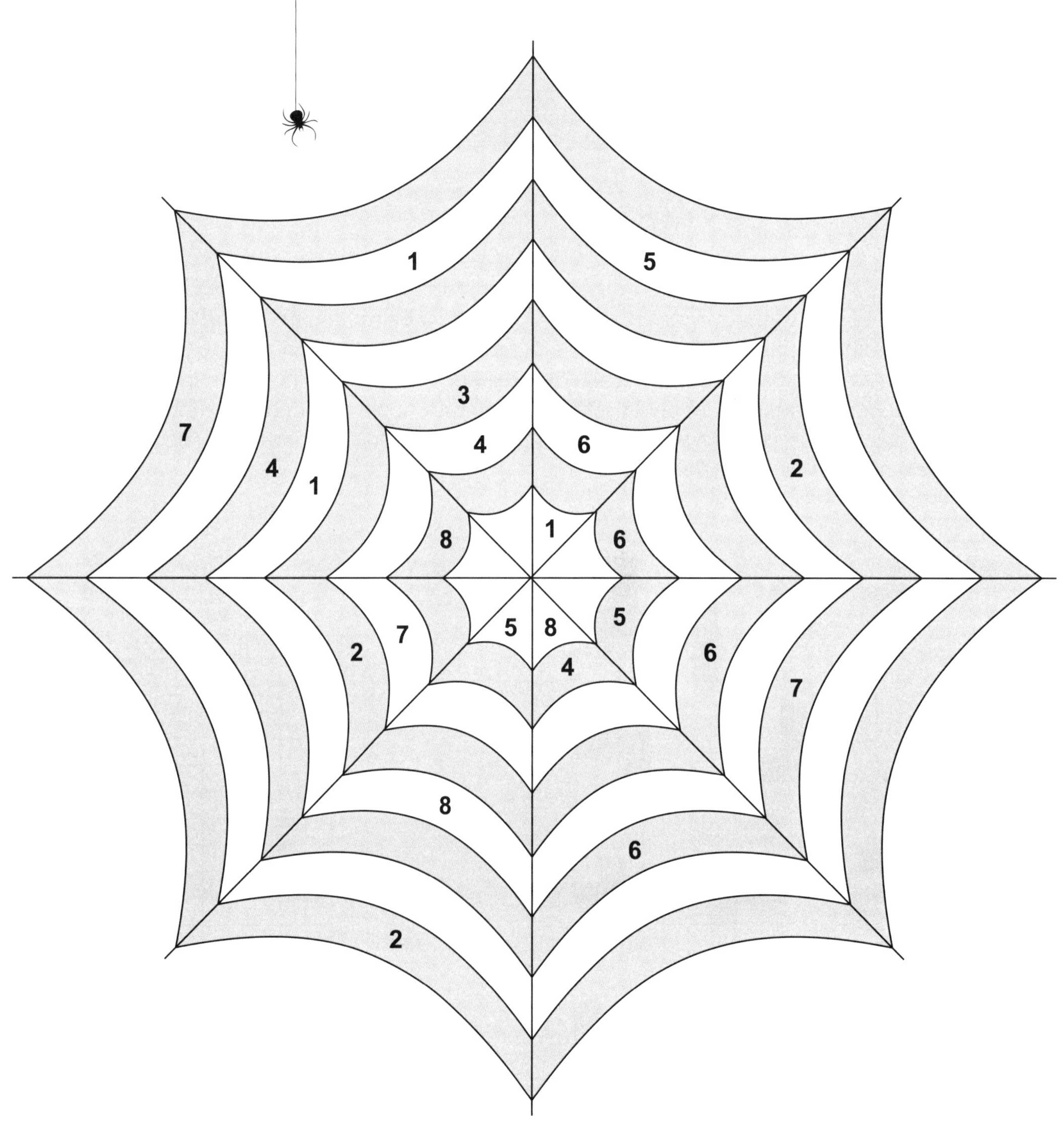

10 Every row and column in this grid originally contained one heart, one club, one diamond, one spade, and two blank squares, although not necessarily in that order.

Every symbol with a black arrow refers to the first of the four symbols encountered in the direction of the arrow. Every symbol with a white arrow refers to the second of the four symbols encountered in the direction of the arrow.

Can you complete the original grid?

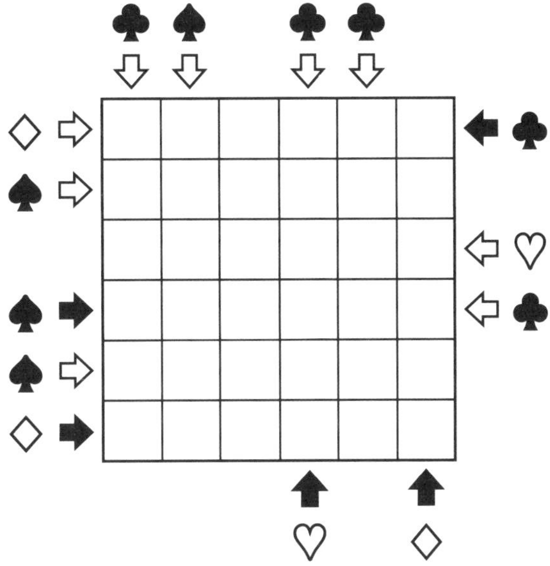

11 Fill the grid so that every horizontal row and vertical column contains the numbers 1-5. Any arrows in the grid always point toward a square that contains a lower number.

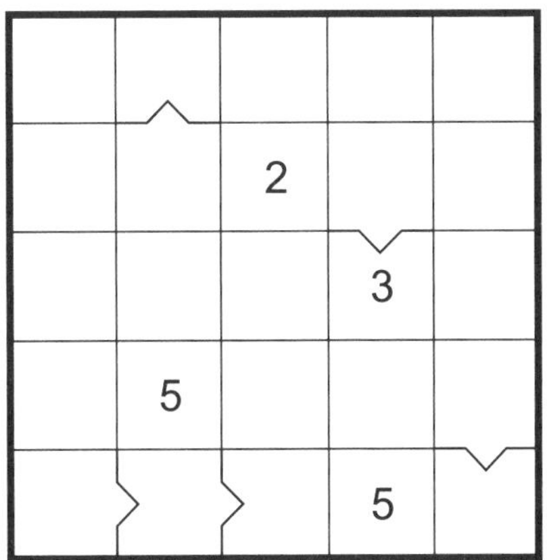

LEVEL 3

12

With the starters already given, can you fit all of the remaining listed numbers into this grid? Take care, this puzzle may not be as easy as it looks!

15	596	1580	5096	67775
21	670	2098	5218	90614
32	719	2643	5524	109025
44	720	2842	6028	200093
51	742	3116	6335	223250
52	760	3389	7921	260594
84	764 ✓	3592	8288	332274
94	779	3680	9111	453186
150	938	3883	9635	474511
170	958	3939	9720	511719
199	1088	4835	36072	673784
266	1400	4991	39291	786499

13

The grid should be filled with numbers from 1 to 6, so that each number appears just once in every row and column.

The clues refer to the digit totals in the squares, e.g. A 1 2 3 = 6 means that the numbers in squares A1, A2 and A3 add up to 6.

1 B C 1 = 7
2 B C D 2 = 8
3 D E F 3 = 14
4 E F 4 = 8
5 E F 5 = 5
6 B C 6 = 10
7 A 2 3 = 8
8 B 4 5 = 11
9 C 3 4 = 7
10 D 5 6 = 7
11 E 1 2 = 9

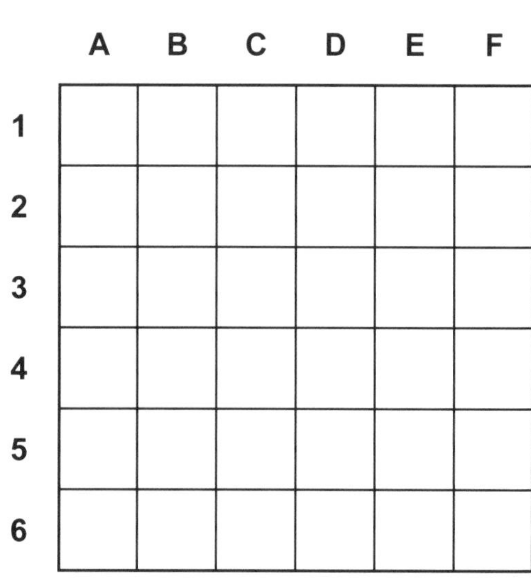

LEVEL 3

14 The object of this puzzle is to trace a single path from the top left corner to the bottom right corner of the grid, moving through all of the cells in either a horizontal, vertical, or diagonal direction.

Every cell must be entered once only, and your path should take you through the numbers in the sequence 1-2-3-4-1-2-3-4, etc.

Can you find the way?

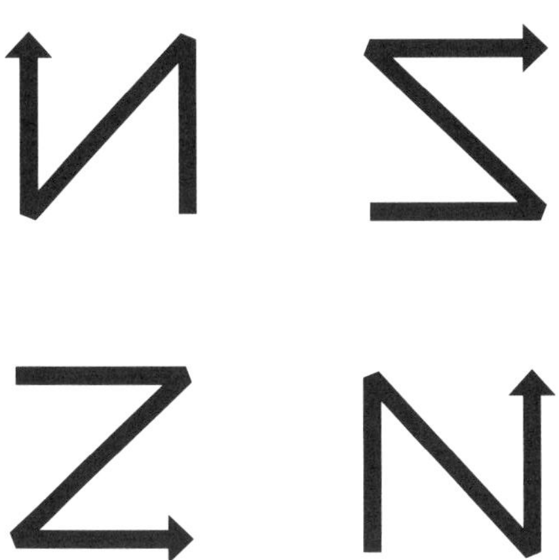

1	4	3	2	4	2	4	3
2	4	1	1	3	1	2	4
3	1	1	2	2	3	3	1
2	4	3	2	1	2	4	1
1	3	1	3	4	4	1	2
4	2	2	4	1	3	3	4
3	4	4	3	2	2	2	3
1	2	3	1	4	1	3	4

15 A standard set of 28 dominoes has been laid out as shown. Can you draw in the edges of them all?

The check-box is provided as an aid and the domino already placed will help.

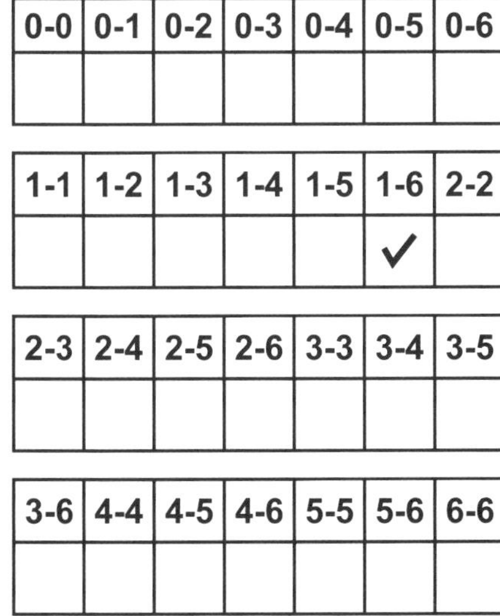

0-0	0-1	0-2	0-3	0-4	0-5	0-6

1-1	1-2	1-3	1-4	1-5	1-6	2-2
					✓	

2-3	2-4	2-5	2-6	3-3	3-4	3-5

3-6	4-4	4-5	4-6	5-5	5-6	6-6

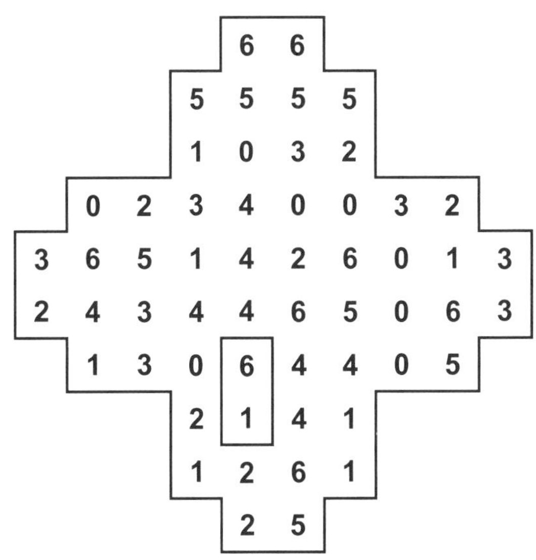

LEVEL 3

16

Draw a single continuous loop, by connecting the dots. No line may cross the path of another.

The figure inside each set of any four surrounding dots indicates the total number of surrounding lines.

	2	1	1	1				3	
	3				0	3	2	1	
	1	0						1	
		2	2	3				0	
3		1			1			1	
1		2		1	1	2		2	
2		1	1				1	2	
2				2	2				2
	2	1		0		3		1	
		2			3		0		
		1		2			2		
	3	2			3		3		3

17

Place the eight tiles into the puzzle grid so that all adjacent numbers on each tile match up.

Tiles may be rotated through 360 degrees, but none may be flipped over.

4	1
2	3

4	1
3	3

1	1
3	1

1	4
3	4

1	4
2	2

3	3
1	2

4	2
4	2

1	4
2	1

2	1				
3	1				

LEVEL 3

18

Every oval shape in this diagram contains a different letter of the alphabet from A to K inclusive.

Use the clues to determine their locations. Reference in the clues to "due" means in any location along the same horizontal or vertical line.

1. The A is due north of the C, which is next to and west of the J, which is next to and south of the D.
2. The B is next to and west of the F, which is due south of the G.
3. The E is further south than the K, which is further south than the B.
4. The I is due east of the H, which is next to and north of the B.

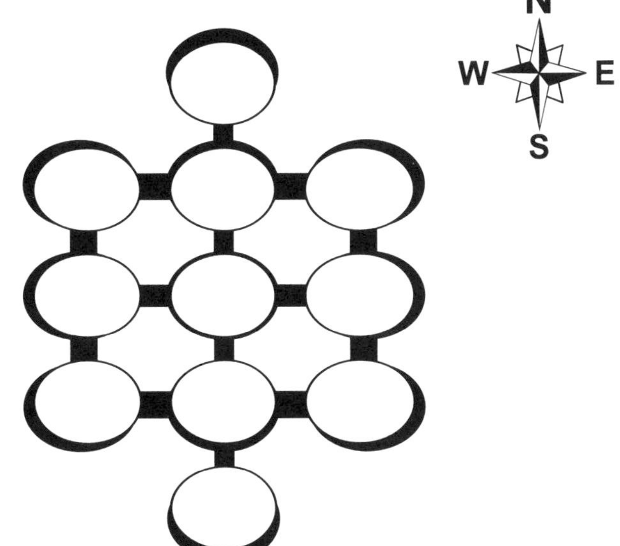

19

Draw walls to partition the grid into areas (some walls are already drawn in for you).

Each area must contain two circles, area sizes must match those numbers shown next to the grid, and each "+" must be linked to at least two walls.

2, 3, 6, 7, 7

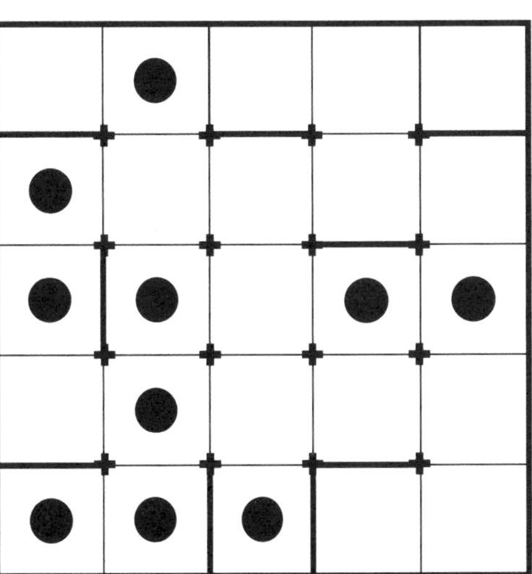

LEVEL 3

20 Twelve L-shapes need to be inserted in the grid, and each L has one hole in it.

There are three pieces of each of the four kinds shown here, and any piece may be turned or flipped over before being put in the grid. No pieces of the same kind touch, even at a corner.

The pieces fit together so well that you cannot see any spaces between them; only the holes show.

Can you tell where the Ls are?

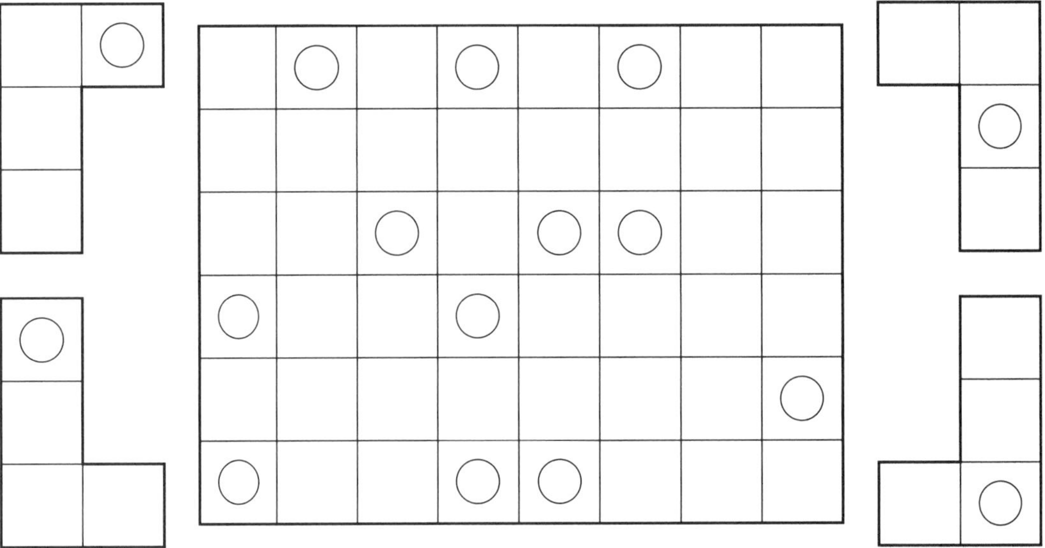

21 Fill the three empty circles with the symbols +, –, and x in some order, to make a sum that totals the central number. Each symbol must be used once, and calculations are made in the direction of travel (clockwise).

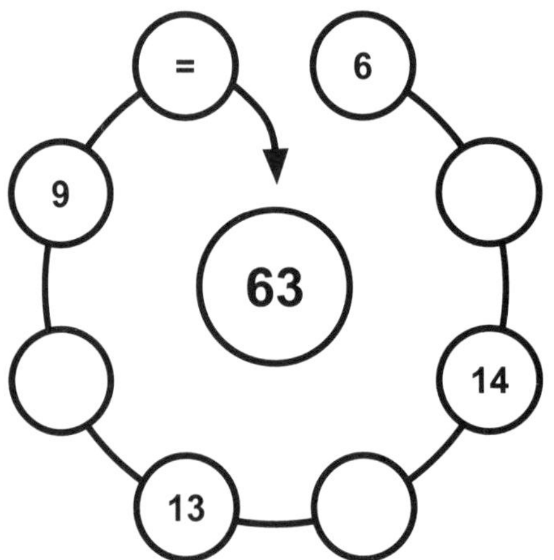

LEVEL 3

22

Each of the small squares in the grid below contains either A, B, or C. Each row, column, and diagonal line of six squares has exactly two of each letter. Can you tell the letter in each square?

Across

3 The Bs are between the Cs

5 Each B is directly next to and right of an A

Down

2 The Cs are between the As

3 The Bs are between the As

4 Each B is directly next to and below a C

5 The Bs are next to each other

6 The As are next to each other

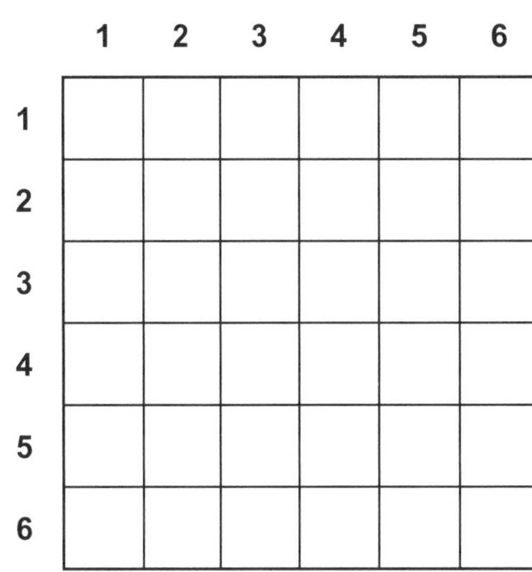

23

Using the numbers below, complete these six equations (three reading across and three reading downwards).

Every number is used once.

LEVEL 3

24 The chart gives directions to a hidden treasure behind the central black square in the grid. Move the indicated number of spaces north, south, east, and west (eg 4N means move four squares north) stopping at every square once only to arrive there. At which square should you start?

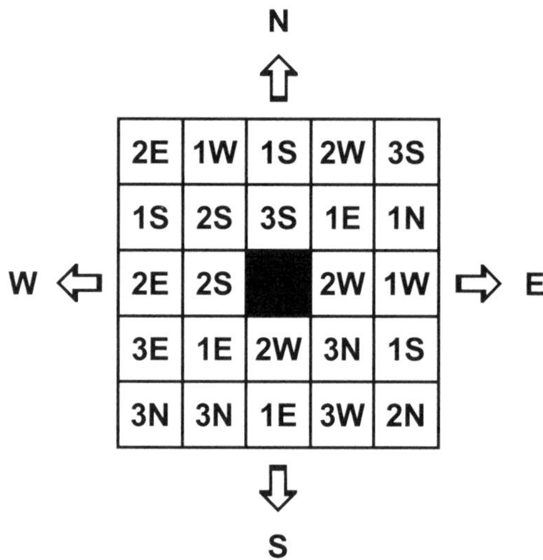

25 The numbers at the top and on the left side show the quantity of single-digit numbers (1-9) used in that row and column. The numbers at the bottom and on the right show the sum of the digits. A number may appear more than once in a row or column, but no numbers are in squares that touch, even at a corner.

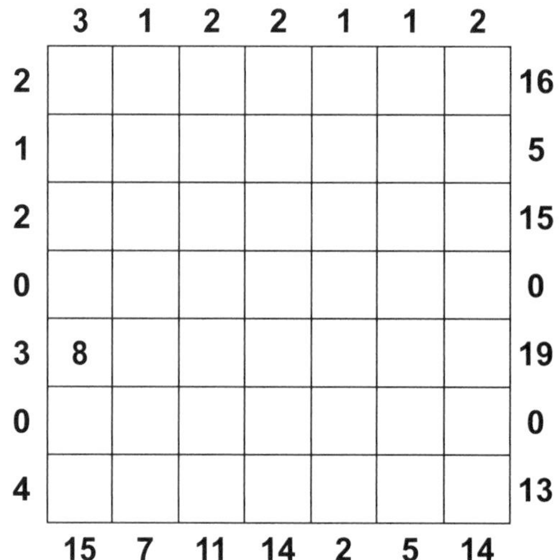

LEVEL 3

26 In the square below, change the positions of six numbers, one per horizontal row, vertical column, and long diagonal line of six smaller squares, in such a way that the numbers in each row, column, and long diagonal line total exactly 144. Any number may appear more than once in a row, column or line.

25	45	12	38	15	25
36	44	24	26	40	6
4	21	8	38	19	21
12	8	44	8	54	22
9	4	16	32	38	37
25	38	29	6	10	25

27 The blank squares below should be filled with whole numbers between 1 and 30 inclusive, any of which may occur more than once, or not at all.

The numbers in every horizontal row add up to the totals on the right, as do the two long diagonal lines; while those in every vertical column add up to the totals along the bottom.

							113
	4	10	12	27		2	100
14	24		5	17	18		107
3	6	11				19	93
1		21	26	15	13		96
	10	14			9	14	106
28	16		5	8	6	15	91
		30	25	23	2	7	108
109	76	103	108	117	98	90	97

LEVEL 3

28

Can you place the hexagons into the grid, so that where any hexagon touches another along a straight line, the number in both triangles is the same? No rotation of any hexagon is allowed!

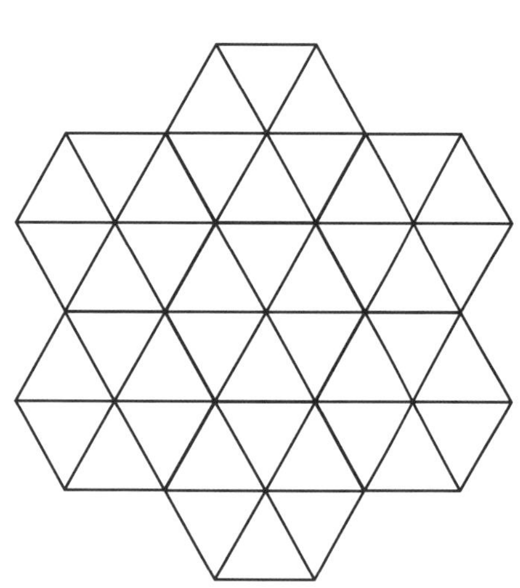

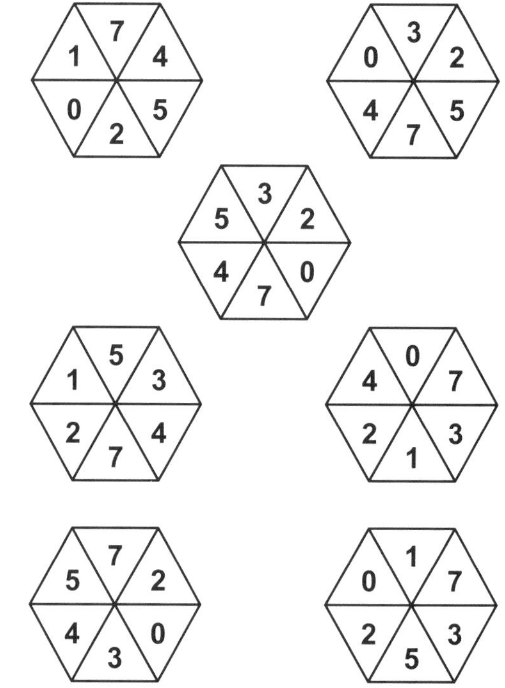

29

Can you place the vessels into the diagram? Some parts of vessels or sea squares have already been filled in. A number to the right or below a row or column refers to the number of occupied squares in that row or column.

Any vessel may be positioned horizontally or vertically, but no part of a vessel touches part of any other vessel, either horizontally, vertically, or diagonally.

Empty Area of Sea: ≈

Aircraft Carrier: ◀■■▶

Battleships: ◀■▶ ◀■▶

Cruisers: ◀▶ ◀▶ ◀▶

Submarines: ● ● ● ●

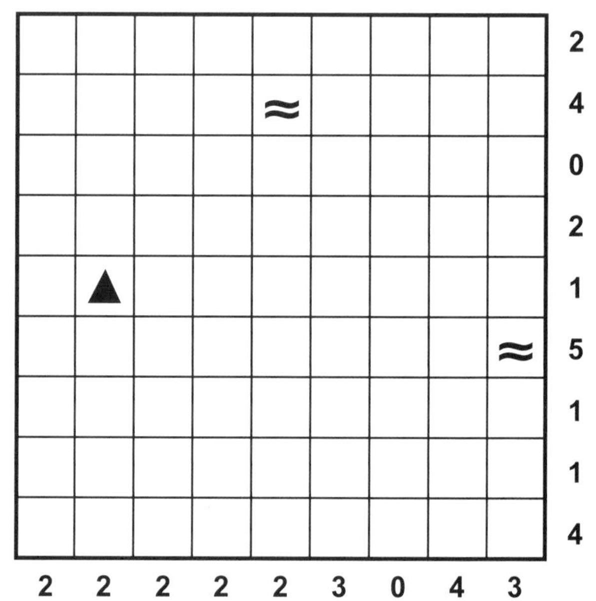

LEVEL 3

30 Each horizontal row and vertical column should contain different shapes and different numbers.

Every square will contain one number and one shape, and no combination may be repeated anywhere else in the puzzle.

1 2 3 4 5

			5	
	2	1	3	
			1	
				1

31 In the diagram below, what number should replace the question mark?

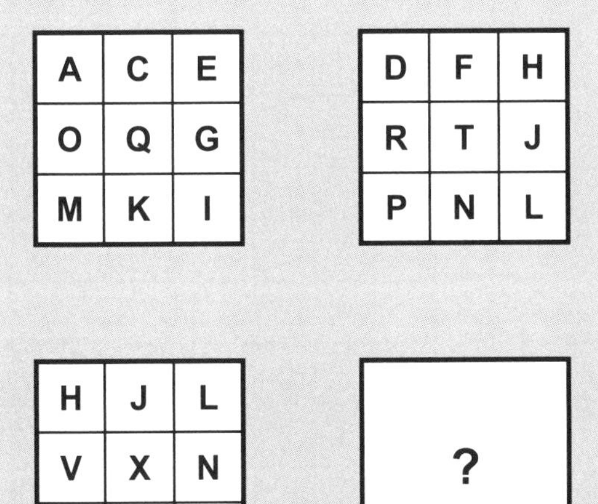

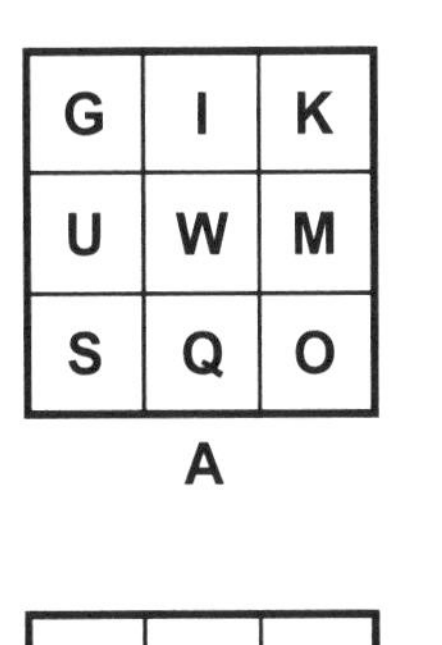

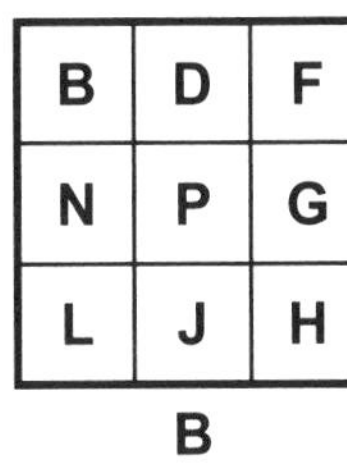

G	I	J
T	V	L
R	P	N

D

LEVEL 3

32 Every brick in this pyramid contains a number which is the sum of the two numbers below it, so that F=A+B, etc.

Just work out the missing numbers!

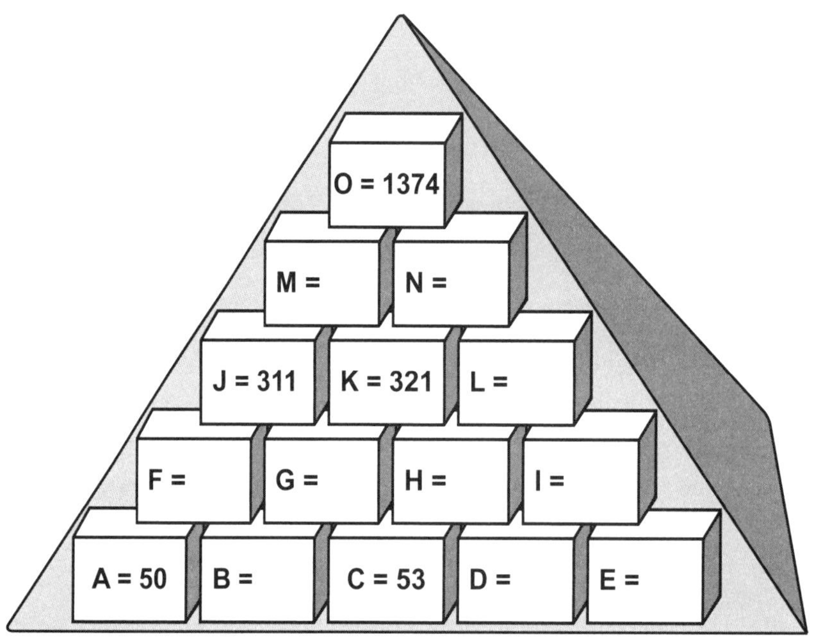

33 In this puzzle, an amateur coin collector has been out with his metal detector, searching for booty. He didn't have time to dig up all the coins he found, so has made a grid map, showing their locations, in the hope that if he loses the map, at least no-one else will understand it…

Those squares containing numbers are empty, but where a number appears in a square, it indicates how many coins are located in the squares (up to a maximum of eight) surrounding the numbered one, touching it at any corner or side. There is only one coin in any individual square.

Place a circle into every square containing a coin.

2		2			1			0	
	2			3					
				4	3	2			
	5						1		1
							1		
3		3	2		2			0	
	3	2		1		3			1
			2					2	
		2							2
	0				1	2	3		

LEVEL 3

34 Given that the letters are valued 1-26 according to their places in the alphabet, can you crack the mystery code to reveal the missing letter?

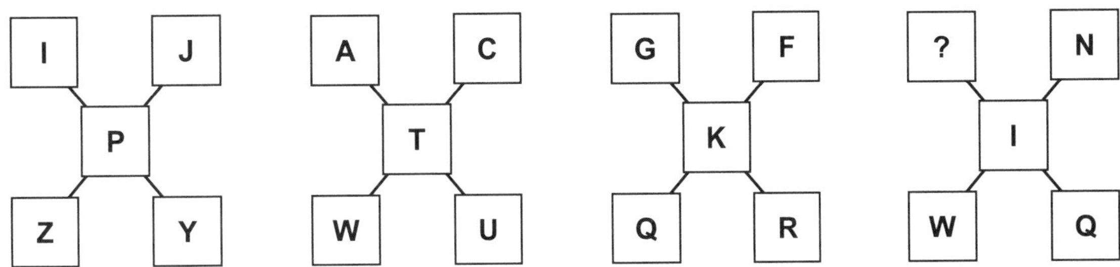

35 Place all twelve of the pieces into the grid. Any may be rotated or flipped over, but none may touch another, not even diagonally. The numbers outside the grid refer to the number of consecutive black squares; and each block is separated from the others by at least one white square. For instance, "3 2" could refer to a row with none, one or more white squares, then three black squares, then at least one white square, then two more black squares, followed by any number of white squares.

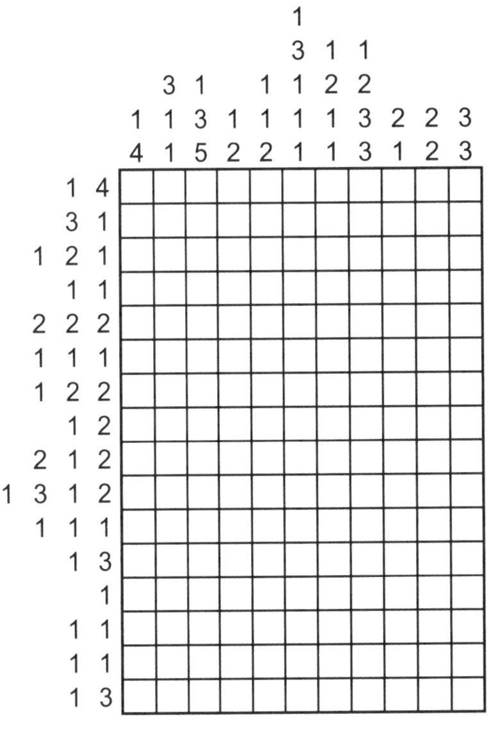

LEVEL 3

36 Each of the eight segments of the spider's web should be filled with a different number from 1 to 8, in such a way that every ring also contains a different number from 1 to 8.

The segments run from the outside of the spider's web to the middle, and the rings run all the way around.

Some numbers are already in place. Can you fill in the rest?

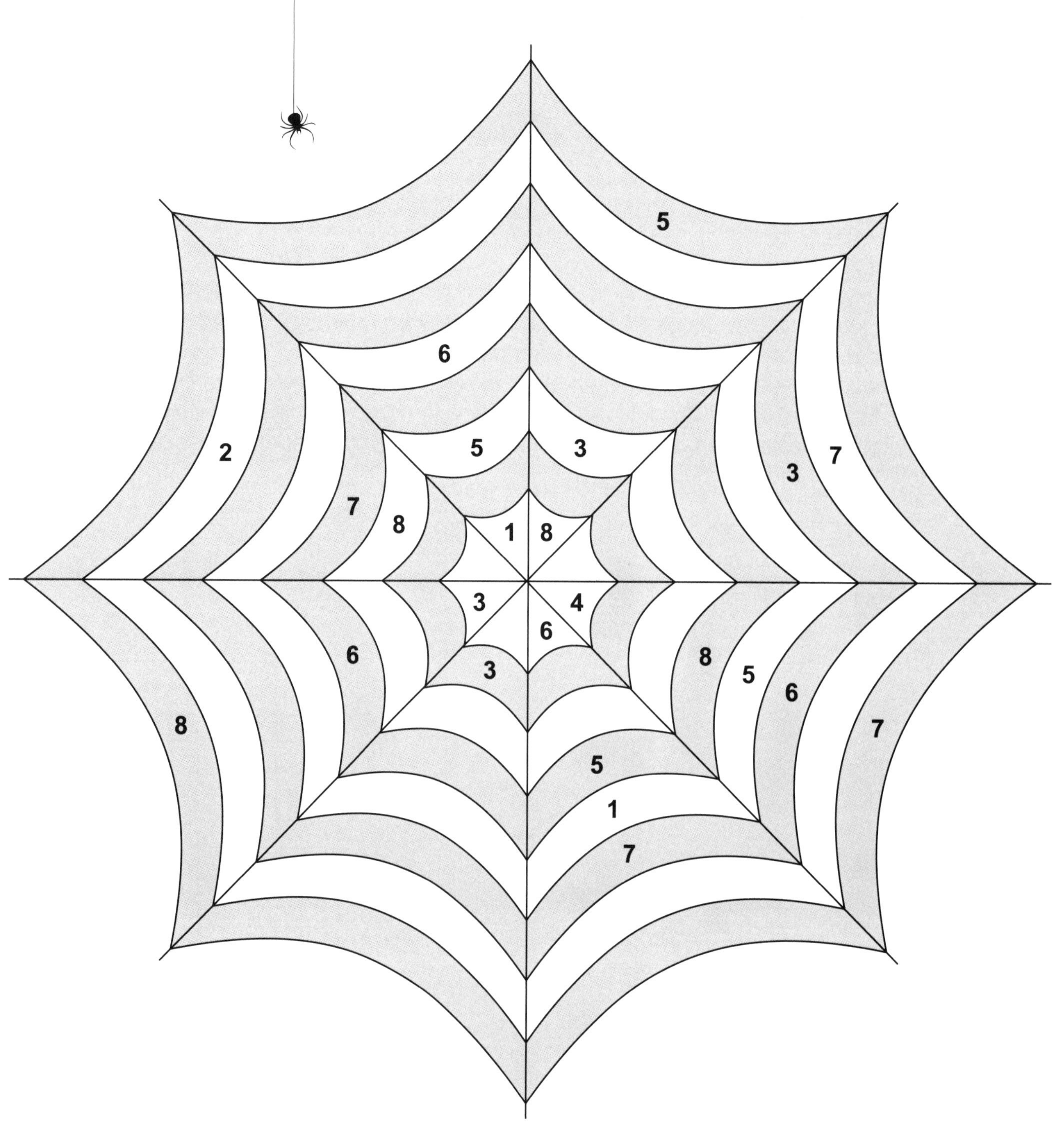

37 Every row and column in this grid originally contained one heart, one club, one diamond, one spade, and two blank squares, although not necessarily in that order.

Every symbol with a black arrow refers to the first of the four symbols encountered in the direction of the arrow. Every symbol with a white arrow refers to the second of the four symbols encountered in the direction of the arrow.

Can you complete the original grid?

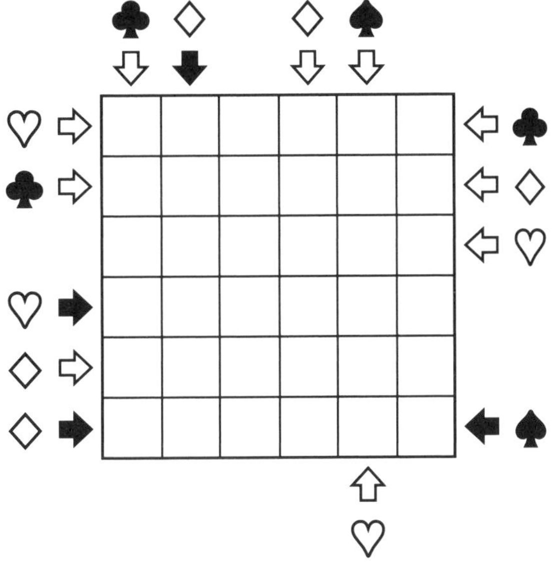

38 Fill the grid so that every horizontal row and vertical column contains the numbers 1-5. Any arrows in the grid always point toward a square that contains a lower number.

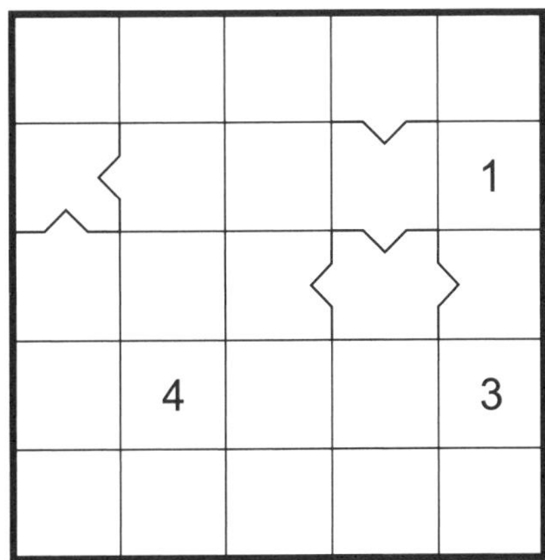

LEVEL 3

39

With the starter already given, can you fit all of the remaining listed numbers into this grid? Take care, this puzzle may not be as easy as it looks!

11	326	761	6030	85462
21	347	779	8199	90605
44	433	812	13273	130684
69	456	929	14679	169021
79	499	1222	22173	317463
92	526	2837	27039	321506
128	542	4240	29307	852544
197	596	4559	30190	991315
206	609	4937	38113	4171563
230	629	5363 ✓	49049	4688651
258	747	5683	54782	6772403
325	750	5780	79801	9478273

40

The grid should be filled with numbers from 1 to 6, so that each number appears just once in every row and column.

The clues refer to the digit totals in the squares, e.g. A 1 2 3 = 6 means that the numbers in squares A1, A2 and A3 add up to 6.

1. B C D 3 = 10
2. A B C 4 = 7
3. E F 5 = 6
4. C D 6 = 10
5. A 5 6 = 11
6. B 5 6 = 4
7. C 1 2 = 4
8. D 4 5 = 9
9. E 2 3 = 11
10. F 1 2 = 10
11. A B 1 = 6

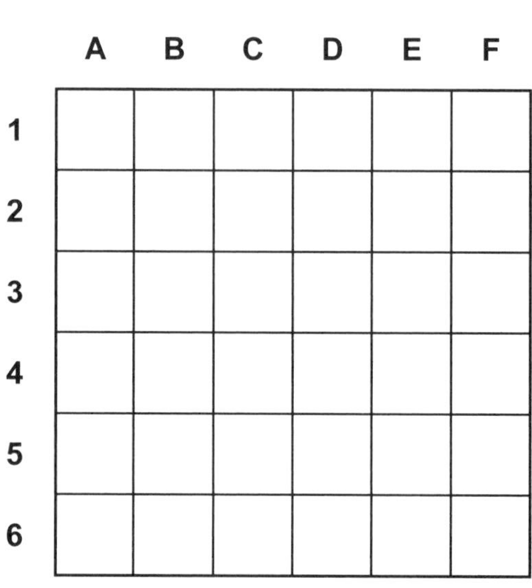

LEVEL 3

41 The object of this puzzle is to trace a single path from the top left corner to the bottom right corner of the grid, moving through all of the cells in either a horizontal, vertical, or diagonal direction.

Every cell must be entered once only, and your path should take you through the numbers in the sequence 1-2-3-4-1-2-3-4, etc.

Can you find the way?

1	4	1	2	3	2	2	3
3	2	3	3	4	1	4	1
4	2	1	1	4	2	4	1
2	1	2	4	4	1	3	2
1	3	3	1	4	3	3	1
2	4	2	3	1	2	2	4
3	1	2	1	4	3	4	3
4	3	4	2	3	1	2	4

42 A standard set of 28 dominoes has been laid out as shown. Can you draw in the edges of them all?

The check-box is provided as an aid and the domino already placed will help.

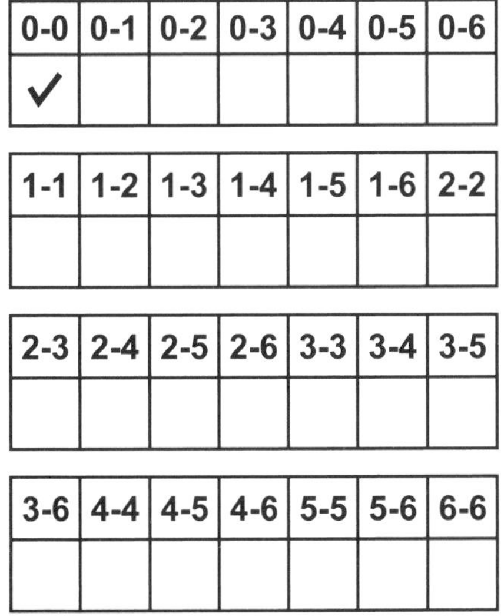

0-0	0-1	0-2	0-3	0-4	0-5	0-6
✓						

1-1	1-2	1-3	1-4	1-5	1-6	2-2

2-3	2-4	2-5	2-6	3-3	3-4	3-5

3-6	4-4	4-5	4-6	5-5	5-6	6-6

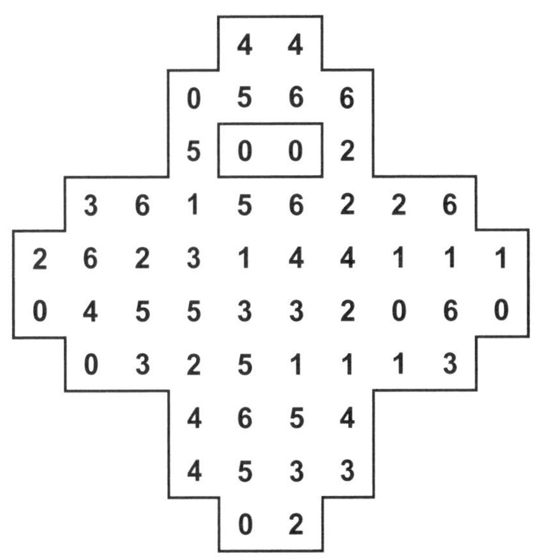

LEVEL 3

43

Draw a single continuous loop, by connecting the dots. No line may cross the path of another.

The figure inside each set of any four surrounding dots indicates the total number of surrounding lines.

3		1	1	1			3		
	1		0		1		3		2
2	1	3							2
				0			3		1
	2	1		2	1	1	1	2	
						3	1		
	3		2			1	0		3
3		1	1	0		1	2		
				1		1	2		3
	1	0							2
3			1						1
3		1			3		1	0	

44

Place the eight tiles into the puzzle grid so that all adjacent numbers on each tile match up.

Tiles may be rotated through 360 degrees, but none may be flipped over.

3	3
4	1

2	3
4	2

2	4
3	1

2	2
4	3

2	1
4	1

2	4
4	2

1	1
3	3

4	1
2	4

				2	2
				3	1

LEVEL 3

45 Which of the four lettered alternatives (A, B, C, or D) fits most logically into the empty square?

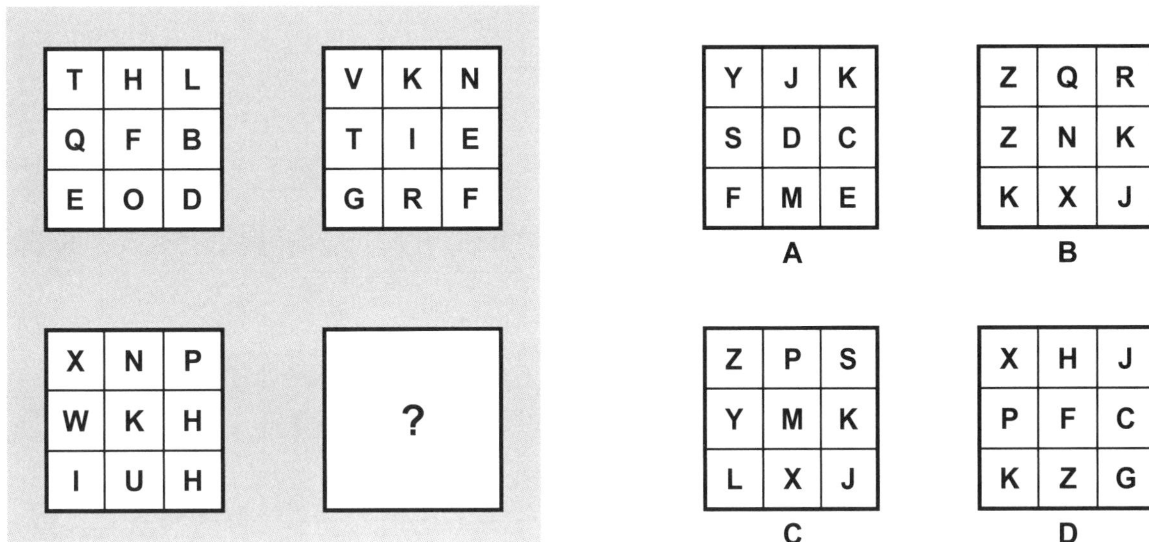

46 Which four pieces can be fitted together to form an exact copy of this shape?

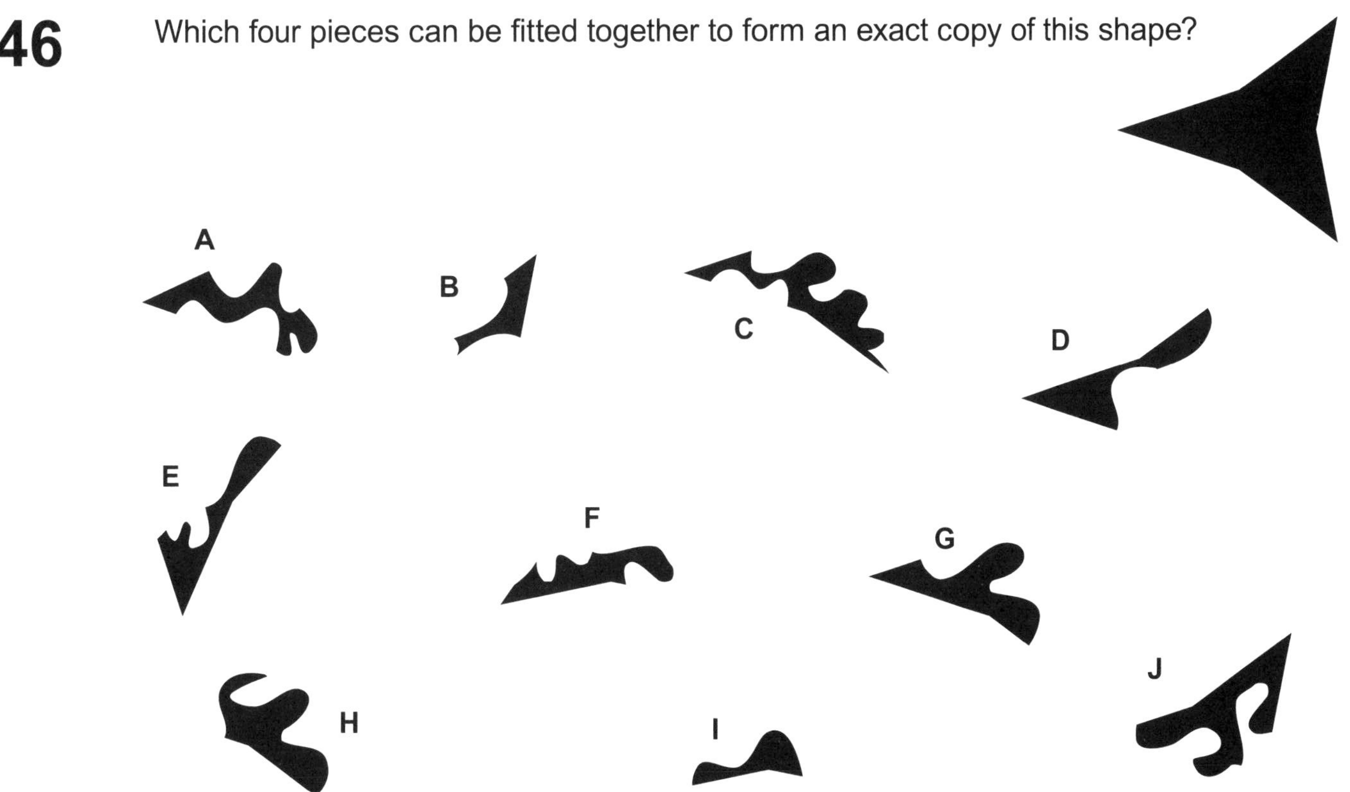

LEVEL 3

47 Twelve L-shapes need to be inserted in the grid, and each L has one hole in it.

There are three pieces of each of the four kinds shown here, and any piece may be turned or flipped over before being put in the grid. No pieces of the same kind touch, even at a corner.

The pieces fit together so well that you cannot see any spaces between them; only the holes show.

Can you tell where the Ls are?

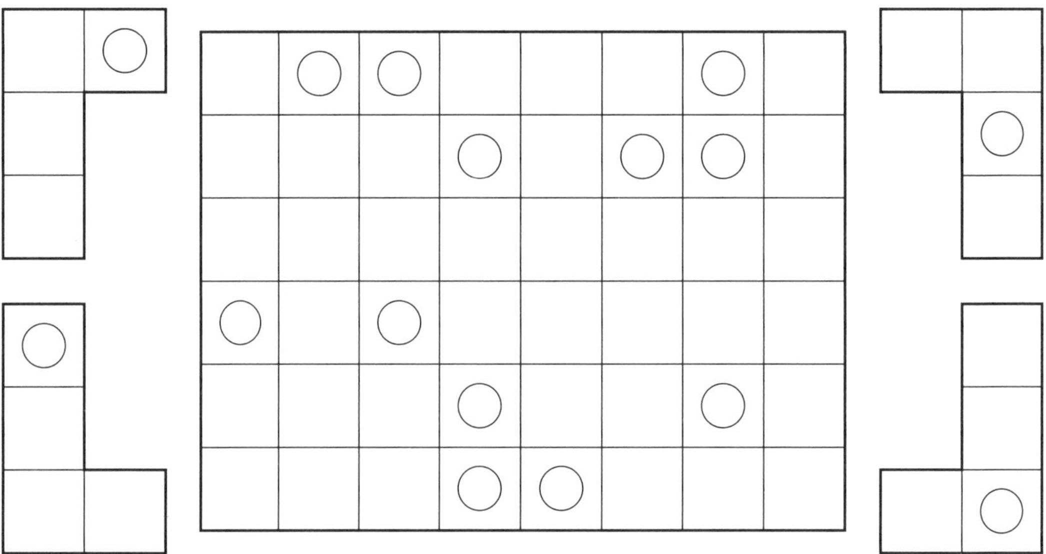

48 Each symbol stands for a different number. In order to reach the correct total at the end of each row and column, what is the value of the circle, cross, pentagon, square and star?

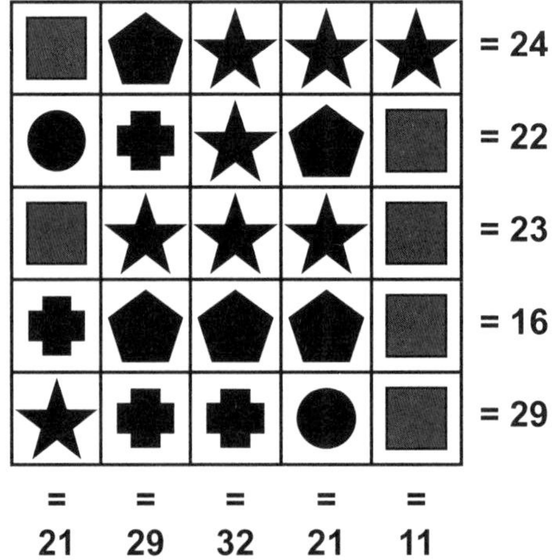

LEVEL 3

49 Each of the small squares in the grid below contains either A, B, or C. Each row, column, and diagonal line of six squares has exactly two of each letter. Can you tell the letter in each square?

Across

1 Each C is directly next to and left of an A

3 The Cs are further right than the As

4 The Cs are further left than the As

5 The Cs are next to each other

Down

2 Each C is directly next to and below a B

3 The Bs are between the Cs

4 The Bs are between the Cs

6 Each C is directly next to and below a B

	1	2	3	4	5	6
1						
2						
3						
4						
5						
6						

50 Which is the odd one out?

LEVEL 3

51 The chart gives directions to a hidden treasure behind the central black square in the grid. Move the indicated number of spaces north, south, east, and west (eg 4N means move four squares north) stopping at every square once only to arrive there. At which square should you start?

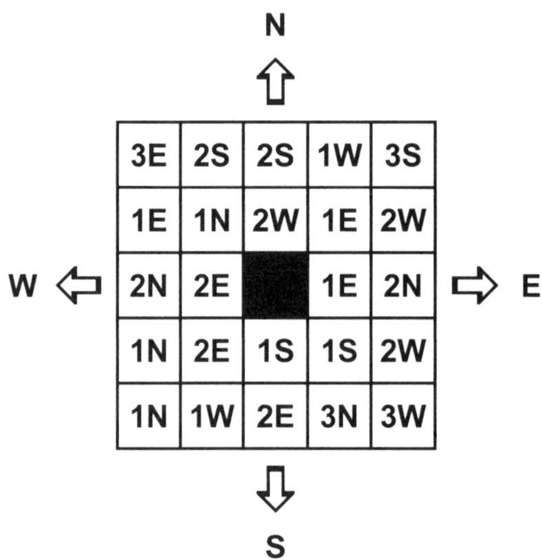

52 What number should replace the question mark?

26	2
14	2

45	80
25	5

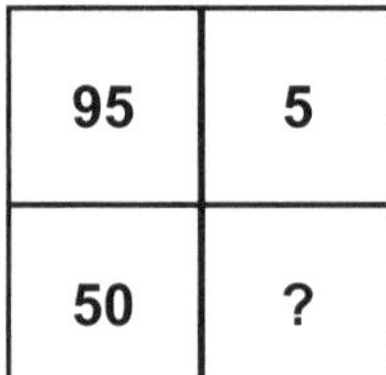

LEVEL 3

53 In the grid below, what number should replace the question mark?

23	25	22	26	21	27	?
15	17	14	18	13	19	12
31	33	30	34	29	35	28
18	20	17	21	16	22	15
26	28	25	29	24	30	23
29	31	28	32	27	33	26
30	32	29	33	28	34	27

54 The blank squares below should be filled with whole numbers between 1 and 30 inclusive, any of which may occur more than once, or not at all.

The numbers in every horizontal row add up to the totals on the right, as do the two long diagonal lines; while those in every vertical column add up to the totals along the bottom.

							117
15		8	14		20	13	104
	17		30	1		18	122
2	7			12		27	98
25	5	21	26		3		123
4	9	17	23	19	5		88
20	15			3	9	12	99
12		30	28	18		20	126
88	98	128	167	73	76	130	121

LEVEL 3

55

Can you place the hexagons into the grid, so that where any hexagon touches another along a straight line, the number in both triangles is the same? No rotation of any hexagon is allowed!

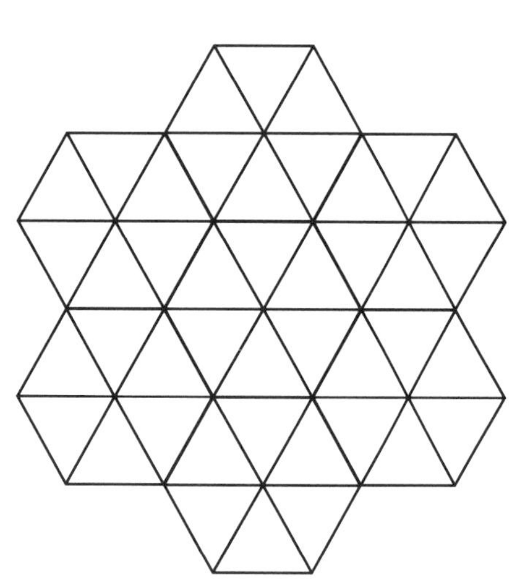

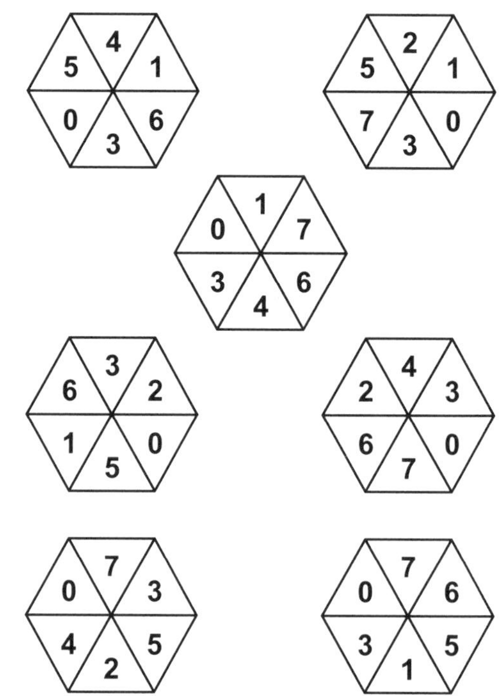

56

Can you place the vessels into the diagram? Some parts of vessels or sea squares have already been filled in. A number to the right or below a row or column refers to the number of occupied squares in that row or column.

Any vessel may be positioned horizontally or vertically, but no part of a vessel touches part of any other vessel, either horizontally, vertically, or diagonally.

Empty Area of Sea: ≈

Aircraft Carrier: ◀■■▶

Battleships: ◀■▶ ◀■▶

Cruisers: ◀▶ ◀▶ ◀▶

Submarines: ● ● ● ●

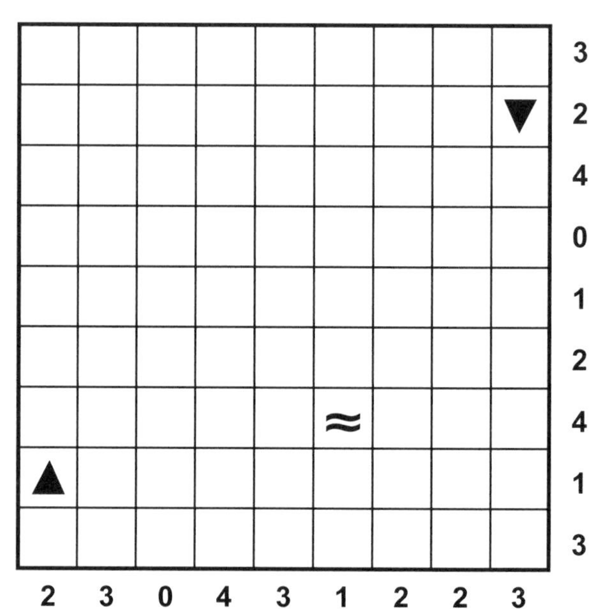

LEVEL 3

57 Each horizontal row and vertical column should contain different shapes and different numbers.

Every square will contain one number and one shape, and no combination may be repeated anywhere else in the puzzle.

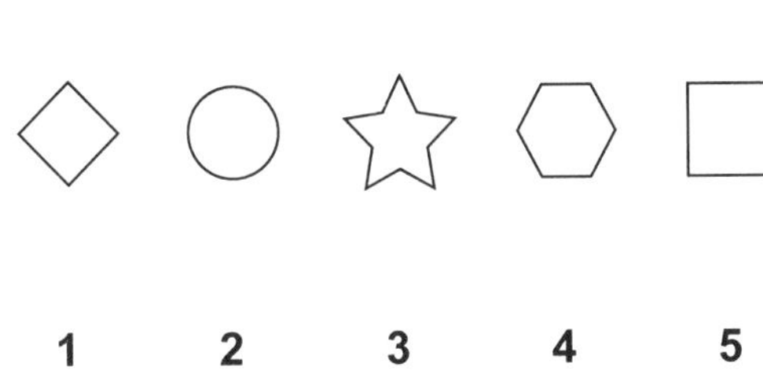

3	□ 4		○	
	○	□ 3		
□ 1	◇ 2			
	☆		3	2
		1		4

58 In the diagram below, what letter should replace the question mark?

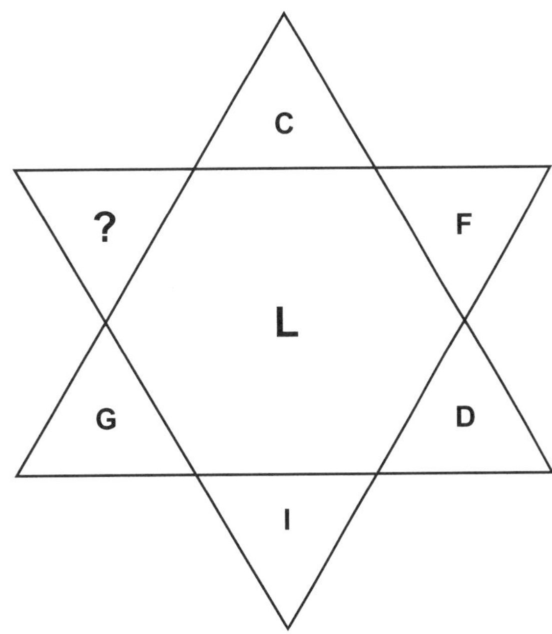

LEVEL 3

59

Every brick in this pyramid contains a number which is the sum of the two numbers below it, so that F=A+B, etc.

Just work out the missing numbers!

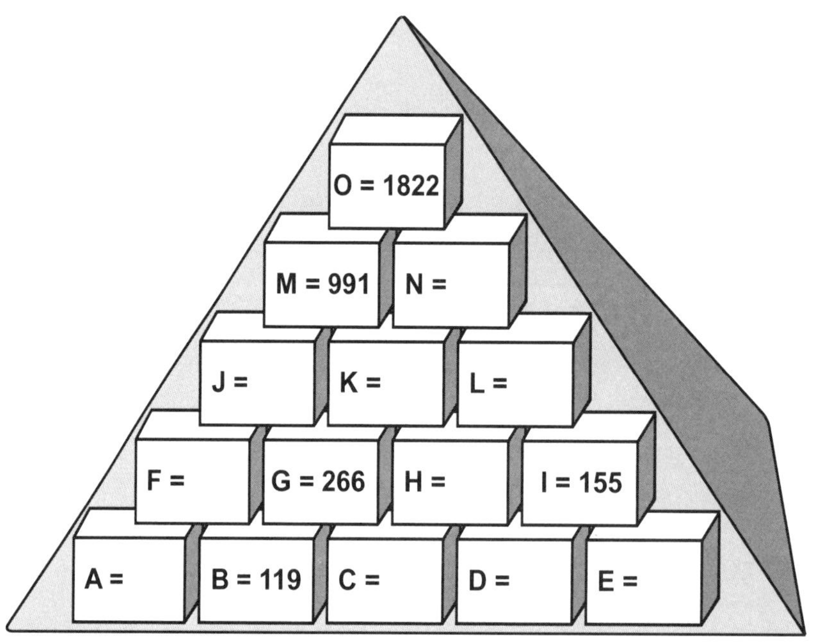

60

In this puzzle, an amateur coin collector has been out with his metal detector, searching for booty. He didn't have time to dig up all the coins he found, so has made a grid map, showing their locations, in the hope that if he loses the map, at least no-one else will understand it…

Those squares containing numbers are empty, but where a number appears in a square, it indicates how many coins are located in the squares (up to a maximum of eight) surrounding the numbered one, touching it at any corner or side. There is only one coin in any individual square.

Place a circle into every square containing a coin.

	0	1			1	2			
					2				1
	3	2				2		2	1
2		4		1	0	2			1
	3		3		2			3	
0			3					3	2
						4	1	3	
2						3		2	
		2	0				1		

LEVEL 3

61 Given that the letters are valued 1-26 according to their places in the alphabet, can you crack the mystery code to reveal the missing letter?

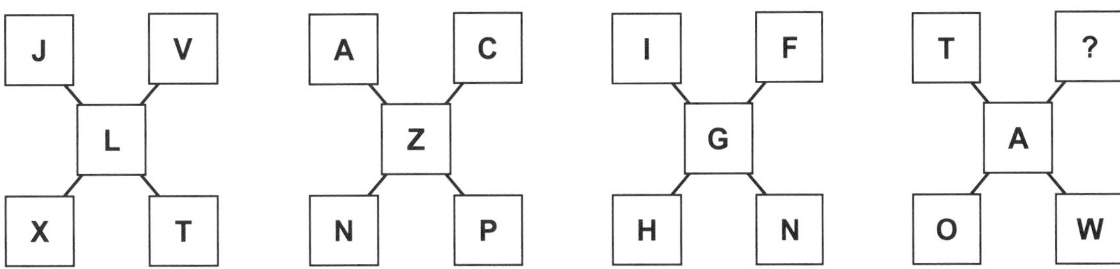

62 Place all twelve of the pieces into the grid. Any may be rotated or flipped over, but none may touch another, not even diagonally. The numbers outside the grid refer to the number of consecutive black squares; and each block is separated from the others by at least one white square. For instance, "3 2" could refer to a row with none, one or more white squares, then three black squares, then at least one white square, then two more black squares, followed by any number of white squares.

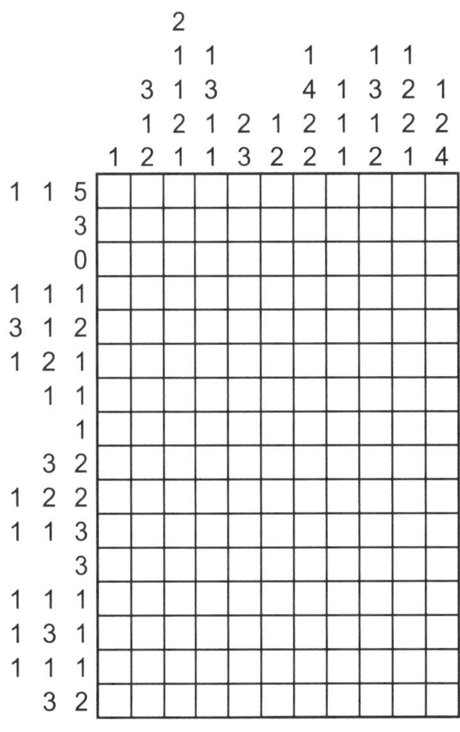

LEVEL 3

63 Each of the eight segments of the spider's web should be filled with a different number from 1 to 8, in such a way that every ring also contains a different number from 1 to 8.

The segments run from the outside of the spider's web to the middle, and the rings run all the way around.

Some numbers are already in place. Can you fill in the rest?

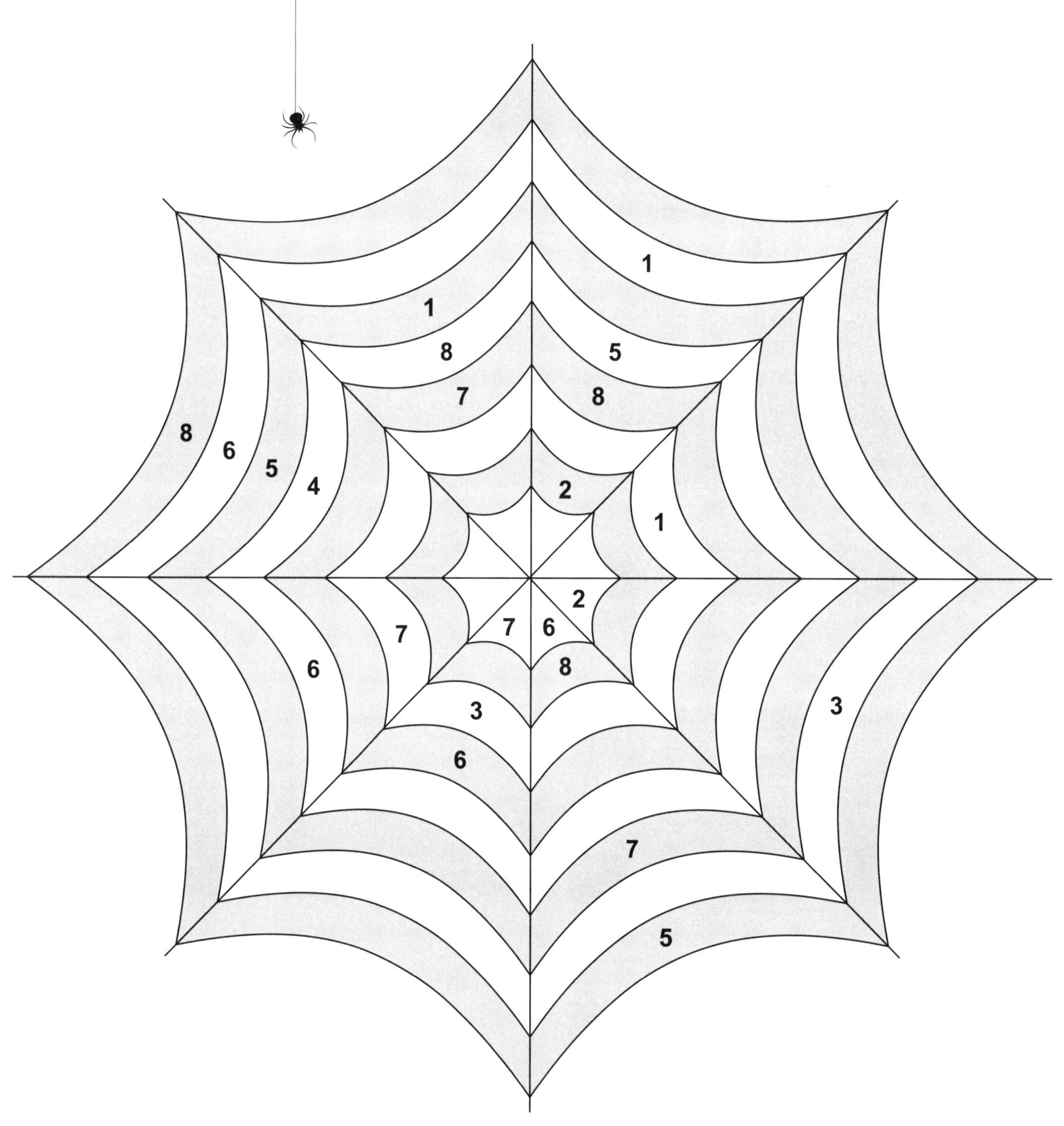

LEVEL 3

64 Every row and column in this grid originally contained one heart, one club, one diamond, one spade, and two blank squares, although not necessarily in that order.

Every symbol with a black arrow refers to the first of the four symbols encountered in the direction of the arrow. Every symbol with a white arrow refers to the second of the four symbols encountered in the direction of the arrow.

Can you complete the original grid?

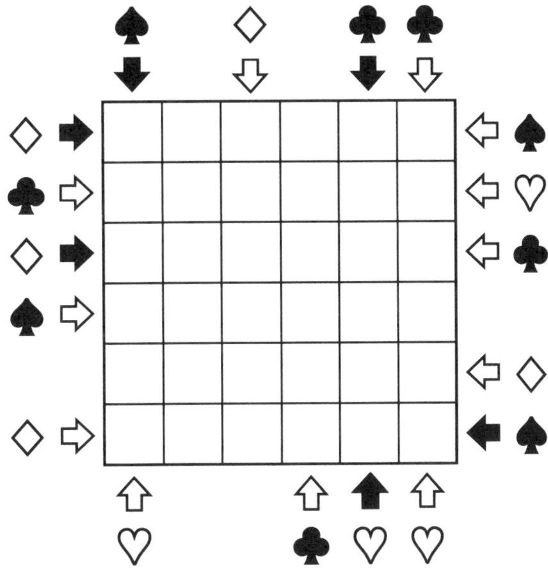

65 Fill the grid so that every horizontal row and vertical column contains the numbers 1-5. Any arrows in the grid always point toward a square that contains a lower number.

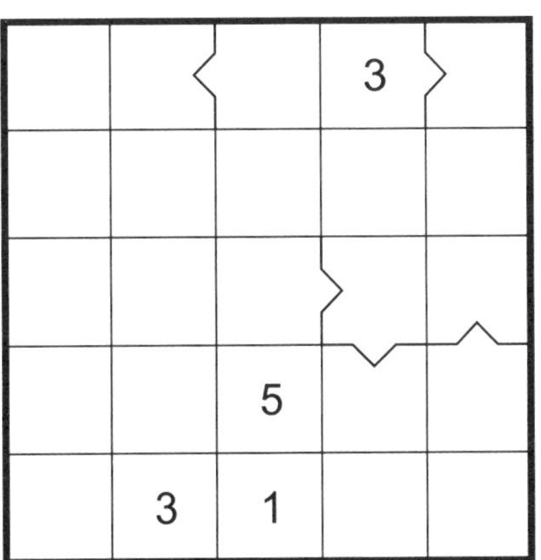

LEVEL 3

66

With the starters already given, can you fit all of the remaining listed numbers into this grid? Take care, this puzzle may not be as easy as it looks!

18	224	6031	32550	72830
27	316	6354	32672 ✓	76249
50	344	7023	35565	80669
60	454	8213	40000	94080
76	474	16882	45582	106772
82	712	19805	57802	111591
90	811	21250	58030	669849
99	849	21747	58710	788752
130	915	23104	59784	2846099
139	940	27465	60019	2932297
164	1544	31061	61673	
179	4855	31863	62981	

67

The grid should be filled with numbers from 1 to 6, so that each number appears just once in every row and column.

The clues refer to the digit totals in the squares, e.g. A 1 2 3 = 6 means that the numbers in squares A1, A2 and A3 add up to 6.

1. E 4 5 = 8
2. F 5 6 = 7
3. A B C 1 = 7
4. C D 2 = 7
5. C D E 3 = 8
6. C D 4 = 10
7. A B 5 = 4
8. D E 6 = 6
9. A 2 3 = 3
10. B 2 3 = 11
11. C 5 6 = 7

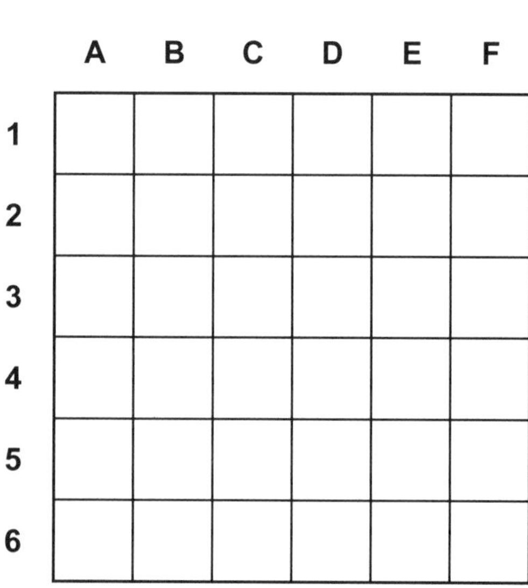

LEVEL 3

68

The object of this puzzle is to trace a single path from the top left corner to the bottom right corner of the grid, moving through all of the cells in either a horizontal, vertical, or diagonal direction.

Every cell must be entered once only, and your path should take you through the numbers in the sequence 1-2-3-4-1-2-3-4, etc.

Can you find the way?

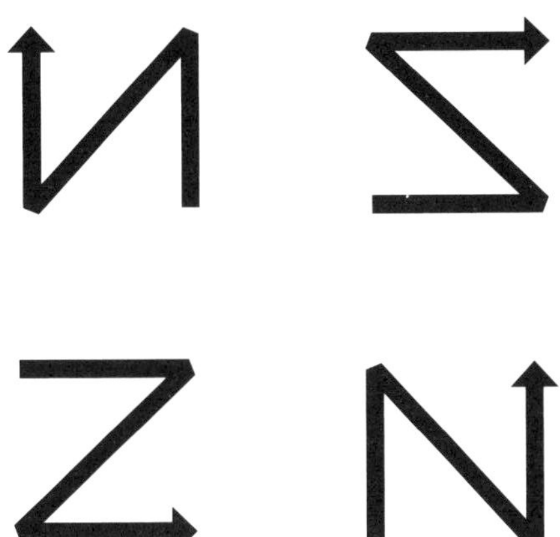

1	2	4	3	2	1	4	3
4	3	2	1	4	3	2	4
3	1	4	1	2	2	2	1
2	1	1	3	3	1	4	3
4	2	2	4	1	2	3	4
3	3	4	1	1	1	2	1
4	2	3	2	4	4	2	3
1	3	4	1	2	3	3	4

69

A standard set of 28 dominoes has been laid out as shown. Can you draw in the edges of them all?

The check-box is provided as an aid and the domino already placed will help.

0-0	0-1	0-2	0-3	0-4	0-5	0-6

1-1	1-2	1-3	1-4	1-5	1-6	2-2
	✓					

2-3	2-4	2-5	2-6	3-3	3-4	3-5

3-6	4-4	4-5	4-6	5-5	5-6	6-6

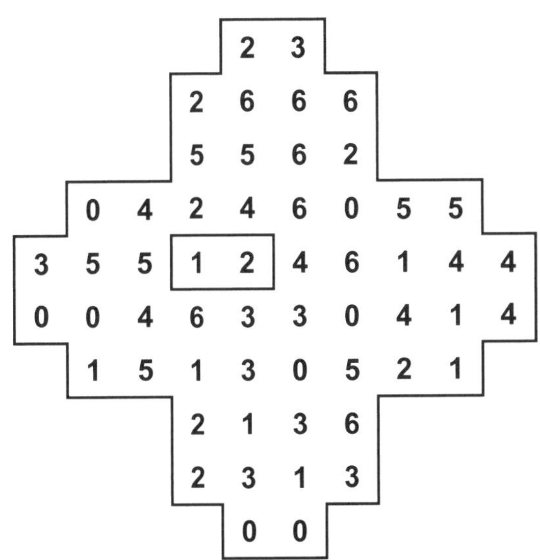

LEVEL 3

70

Draw a single continuous loop, by connecting the dots. No line may cross the path of another.

The figure inside each set of any four surrounding dots indicates the total number of surrounding lines.

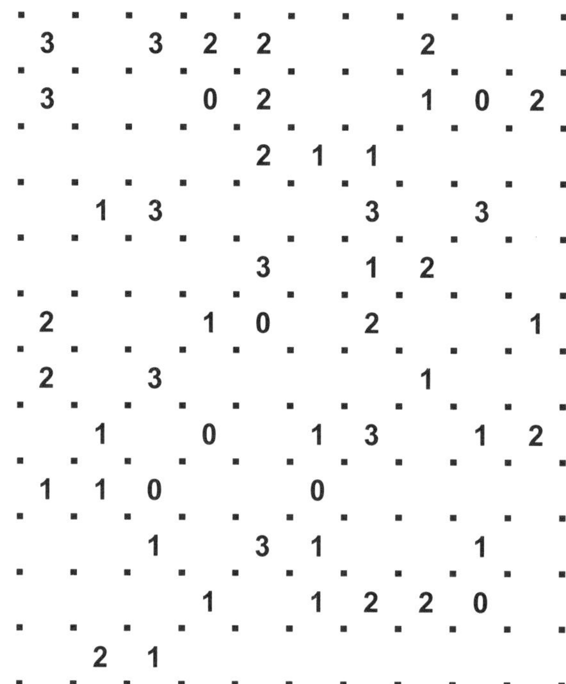

71

Place the eight tiles into the puzzle grid so that all adjacent numbers on each tile match up.

Tiles may be rotated through 360 degrees, but none may be flipped over.

4	4
1	2

2	3
1	2

1	3
4	4

1	2
4	3

2	4
1	3

1	2
2	1

4	3
4	4

1	3
2	3

3	3				
4	1				

LEVEL 3

72

Every oval shape in this diagram contains a different letter of the alphabet from A to K inclusive.

Use the clues to determine their locations. Reference in the clues to "due" means in any location along the same horizontal or vertical line.

1. The B is next to and east of the J, which is further east than the D.
2. The C is next to and east of the K, which is next to and north of the E, which is further north than the A.
3. The H is due north of the G, which is next to and east of the A, which is due north of the F.
4. The I is further west than the H.

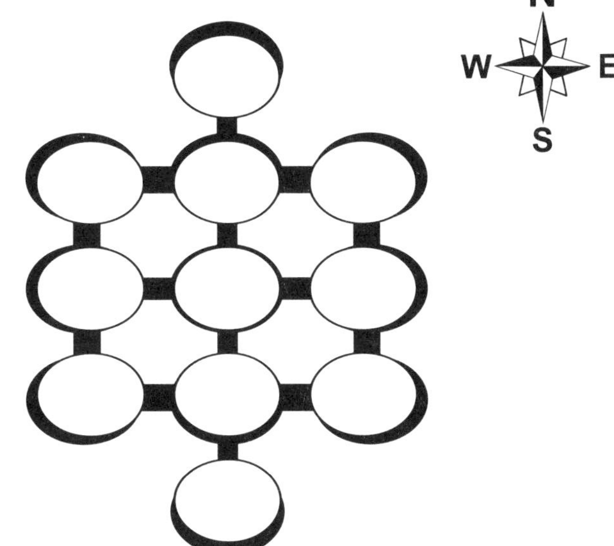

73

Draw walls to partition the grid into areas (some walls are already drawn in for you).

Each area must contain two circles, area sizes must match those numbers shown next to the grid, and each "+" must be linked to at least two walls.

2, 3, 3, 5, 6, 6

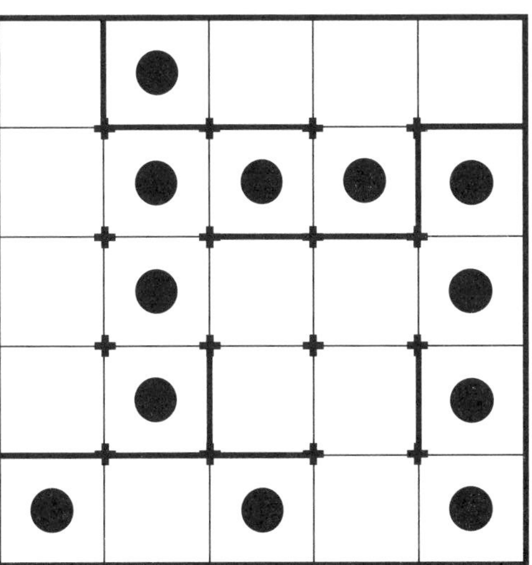

74 Twelve L-shapes need to be inserted in the grid, and each L has one hole in it.

There are three pieces of each of the four kinds shown here, and any piece may be turned or flipped over before being put in the grid. No pieces of the same kind touch, even at a corner.

The pieces fit together so well that you cannot see any spaces between them; only the holes show.

Can you tell where the Ls are?

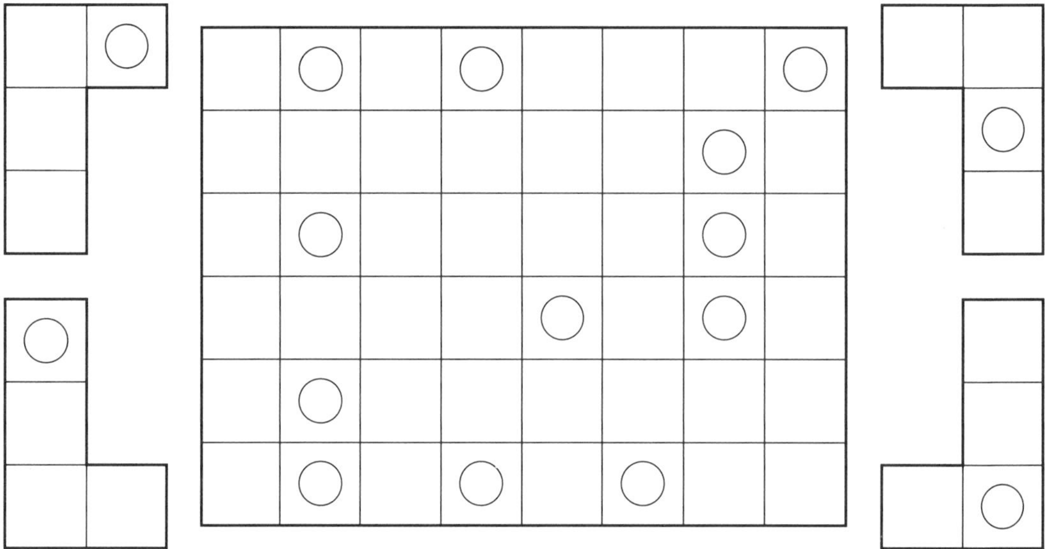

75 Fill the three empty circles with the symbols +, –, and x in some order, to make a sum that totals the central number. Each symbol must be used once, and calculations are made in the direction of travel (clockwise).

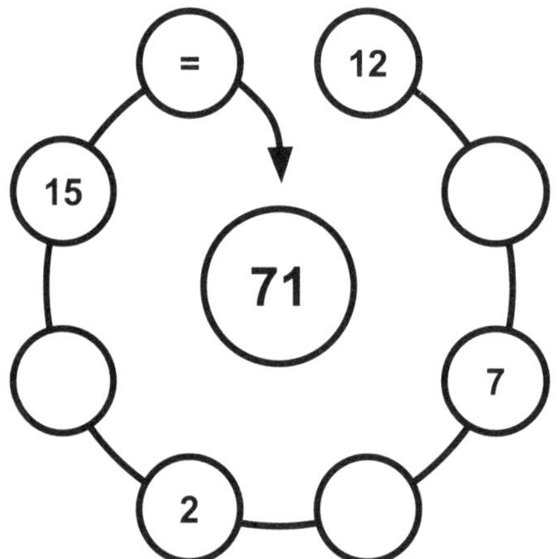

LEVEL 3

76 Each of the small squares in the grid below contains either A, B, or C. Each row, column, and diagonal line of six squares has exactly two of each letter. Can you tell the letter in each square?

Across

1 The Bs are next to each other
2 The Bs are between the Cs
3 The Bs are between the Cs
5 The As are between the Bs
6 The Cs are further right than the As

Down

1 The Bs are lower than the Cs
2 The Cs are next to each other
3 The As are lower than the Bs
4 The As are lower than the Bs
6 The Cs are lower than the As

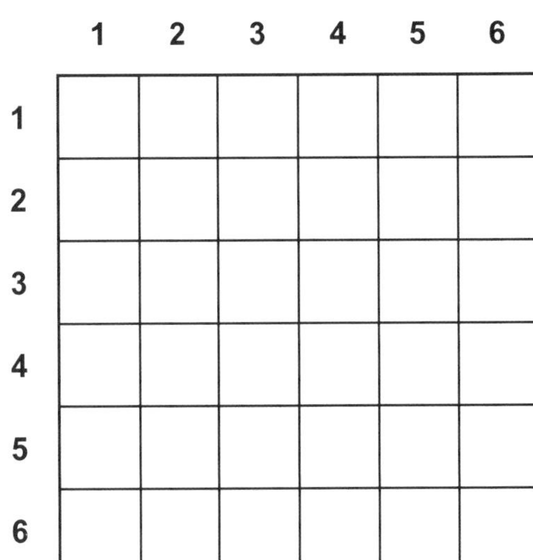

77 Using the numbers below, complete these six equations (three reading across and three reading downwards).

Every number is used once.

1 2 3 4 5
6 7 8 9

	x		x		=	30
–	■	x	■	+		
	x		–		=	7
x	■	+	■	x		
	x		x		=	84
=		=		=		
28		11		56		

78 The chart gives directions to a hidden treasure behind the central black square in the grid. Move the indicated number of spaces north, south, east, and west (eg 4N means move four squares north) stopping at every square once only to arrive there. At which square should you start?

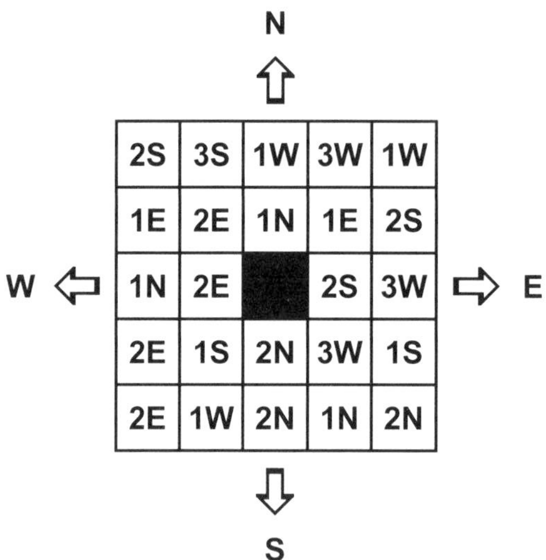

79 The numbers at the top and on the left side show the quantity of single-digit numbers (1-9) used in that row and column. The numbers at the bottom and on the right show the sum of the digits. A number may appear more than once in a row or column, but no numbers are in squares that touch, even at a corner.

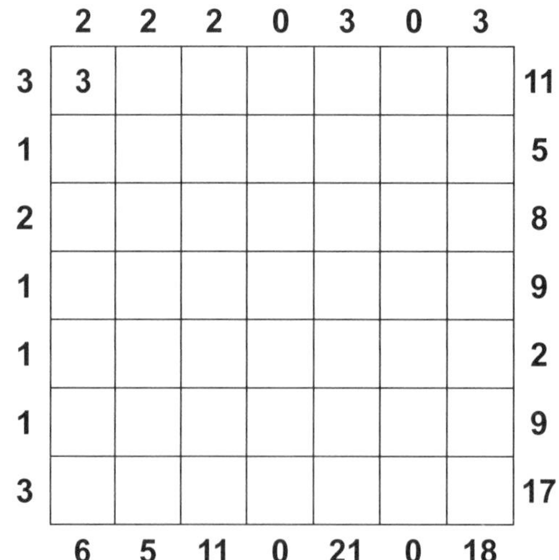

LEVEL 3

80 In the square below, change the positions of six numbers, one per horizontal row, vertical column, and long diagonal line of six smaller squares, in such a way that the numbers in each row, column, and long diagonal line total exactly 228. Any number may appear more than once in a row, column or line.

58	38	23	32	62	40
51	38	30	26	46	45
37	59	38	44	20	38
41	55	38	29	18	44
19	38	53	43	38	13
30	25	32	51	52	24

81 The blank squares below should be filled with whole numbers between 1 and 30 inclusive, any of which may occur more than once, or not at all.

The numbers in every horizontal row add up to the totals on the right, as do the two long diagonal lines; while those in every vertical column add up to the totals along the bottom.

							107
	17		2	6	15	10	93
13	28	16	9		18		139
30		26	17	12		25	142
	20			8	7	22	118
1	11	27		19	2		88
4	15			22	14	17	107
2	30	29	12			18	102
88	142	150	104	100	72	133	142

LEVEL 4

1 Can you place the hexagons into the grid, so that where any hexagon touches another along a straight line, the number in both triangles is the same? No rotation of any hexagon is allowed!

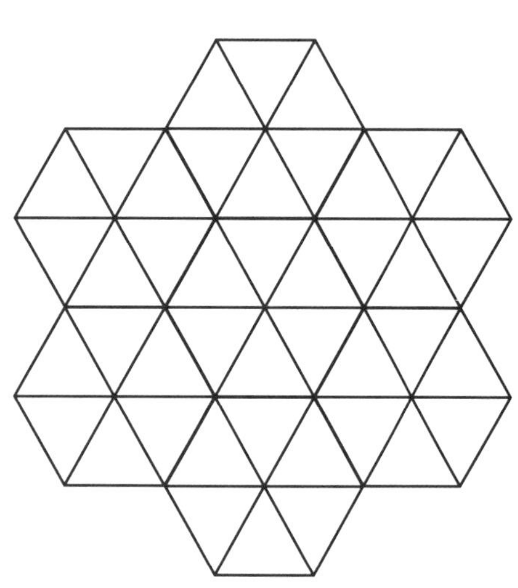

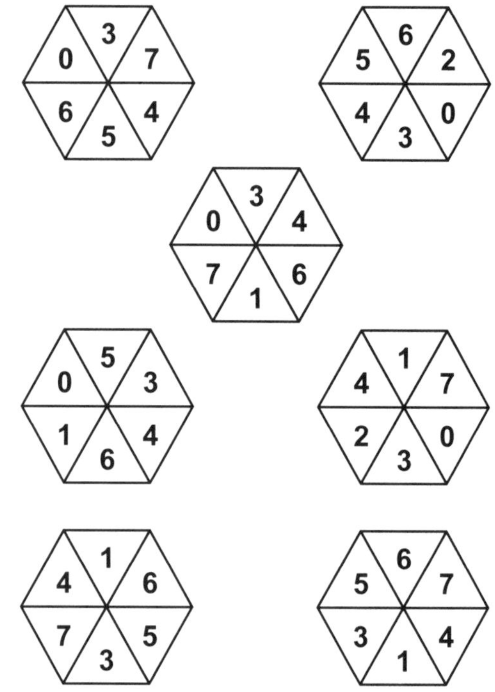

2 Can you place the vessels into the diagram? Some parts of vessels or sea squares have already been filled in. A number to the right or below a row or column refers to the number of occupied squares in that row or column.

Any vessel may be positioned horizontally or vertically, but no part of a vessel touches part of any other vessel, either horizontally, vertically, or diagonally.

Empty Area of Sea: ≈

Aircraft Carrier:

Battleships:

Cruisers:

Submarines:

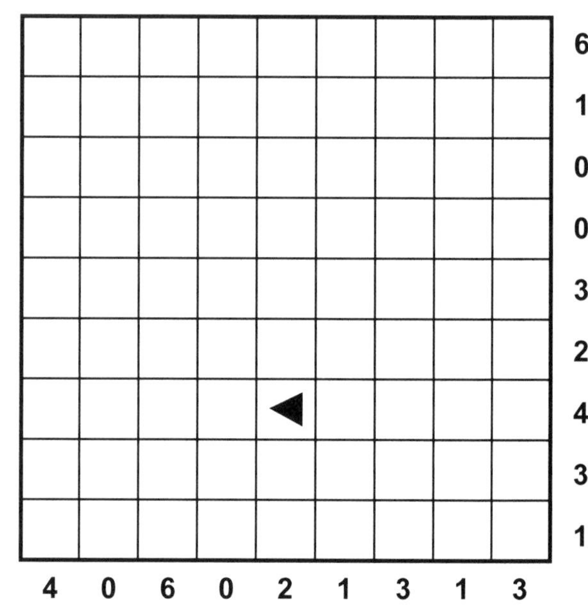

3 Each horizontal row and vertical column should contain different shapes and different numbers.

Every square will contain one number and one shape, and no combination may be repeated anywhere else in the puzzle.

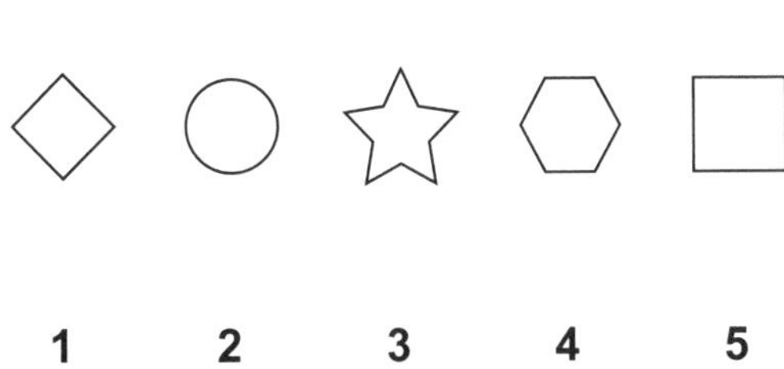

		○		1
			○ 5	2
3	1	□	2	
○	⬡			
2	☆			3

4 In the diagram below, what letter should replace the question mark?

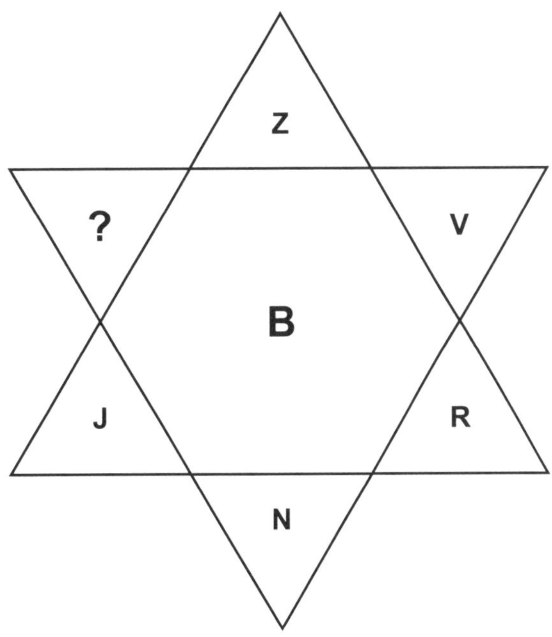

LEVEL 4

5 Every brick in this pyramid contains a number which is the sum of the two numbers below it, so that F=A+B, etc.

Just work out the missing numbers!

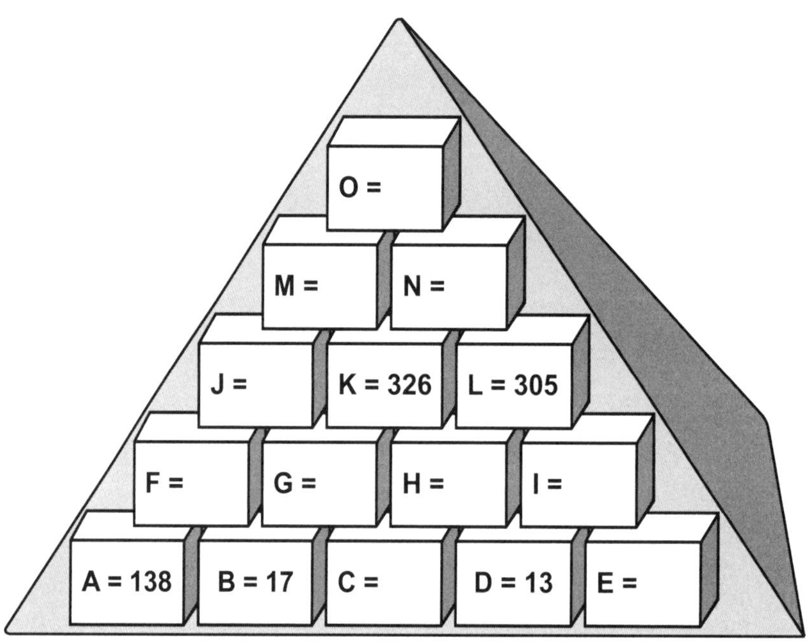

6 In this puzzle, an amateur coin collector has been out with his metal detector, searching for booty. He didn't have time to dig up all the coins he found, so has made a grid map, showing their locations, in the hope that if he loses the map, at least no-one else will understand it…

Those squares containing numbers are empty, but where a number appears in a square, it indicates how many coins are located in the squares (up to a maximum of eight) surrounding the numbered one, touching it at any corner or side. There is only one coin in any individual square.

Place a circle into every square containing a coin.

1		2						2	
			3		0	1			4
1	4								
1				1					
						2	2	4	
		0		1		1		3	2
	1			1					
	0				1	0	2		
						2			1
	0			4				0	

LEVEL 4

7 Given that the letters are valued 1-26 according to their places in the alphabet, can you crack the mystery code to reveal the missing letter?

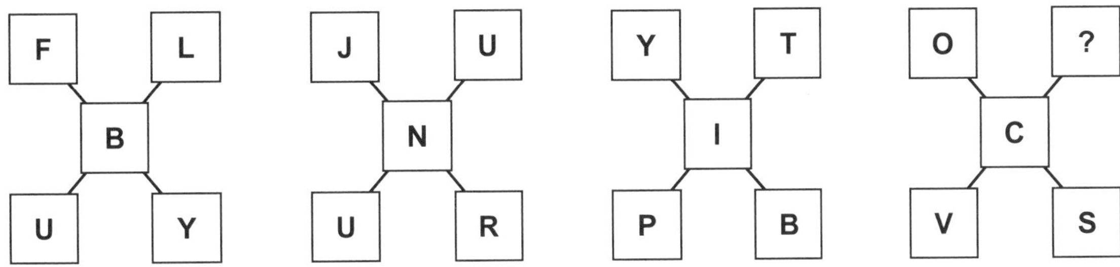

8 Place all twelve of the pieces into the grid. Any may be rotated or flipped over, but none may touch another, not even diagonally. The numbers outside the grid refer to the number of consecutive black squares; and each block is separated from the others by at least one white square. For instance, "3 2" could refer to a row with none, one or more white squares, then three black squares, then at least one white square, then two more black squares, followed by any number of white squares.

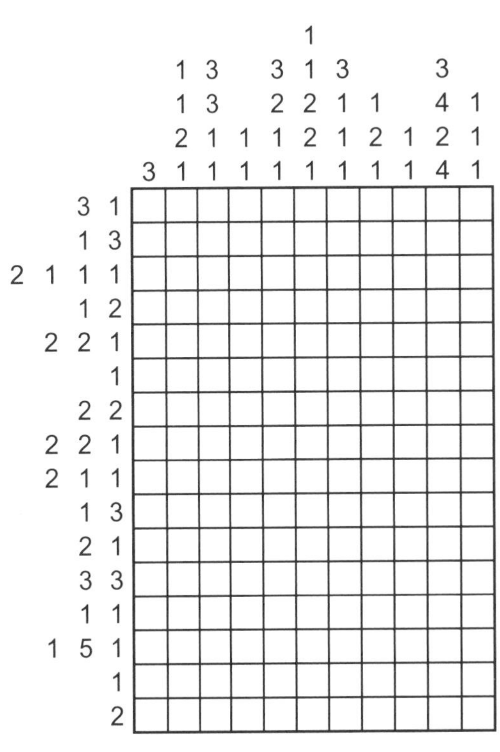

LEVEL 4

9 Each of the eight segments of the spider's web should be filled with a different number from 1 to 8, in such a way that every ring also contains a different number from 1 to 8.

The segments run from the outside of the spider's web to the middle, and the rings run all the way around.

Some numbers are already in place. Can you fill in the rest?

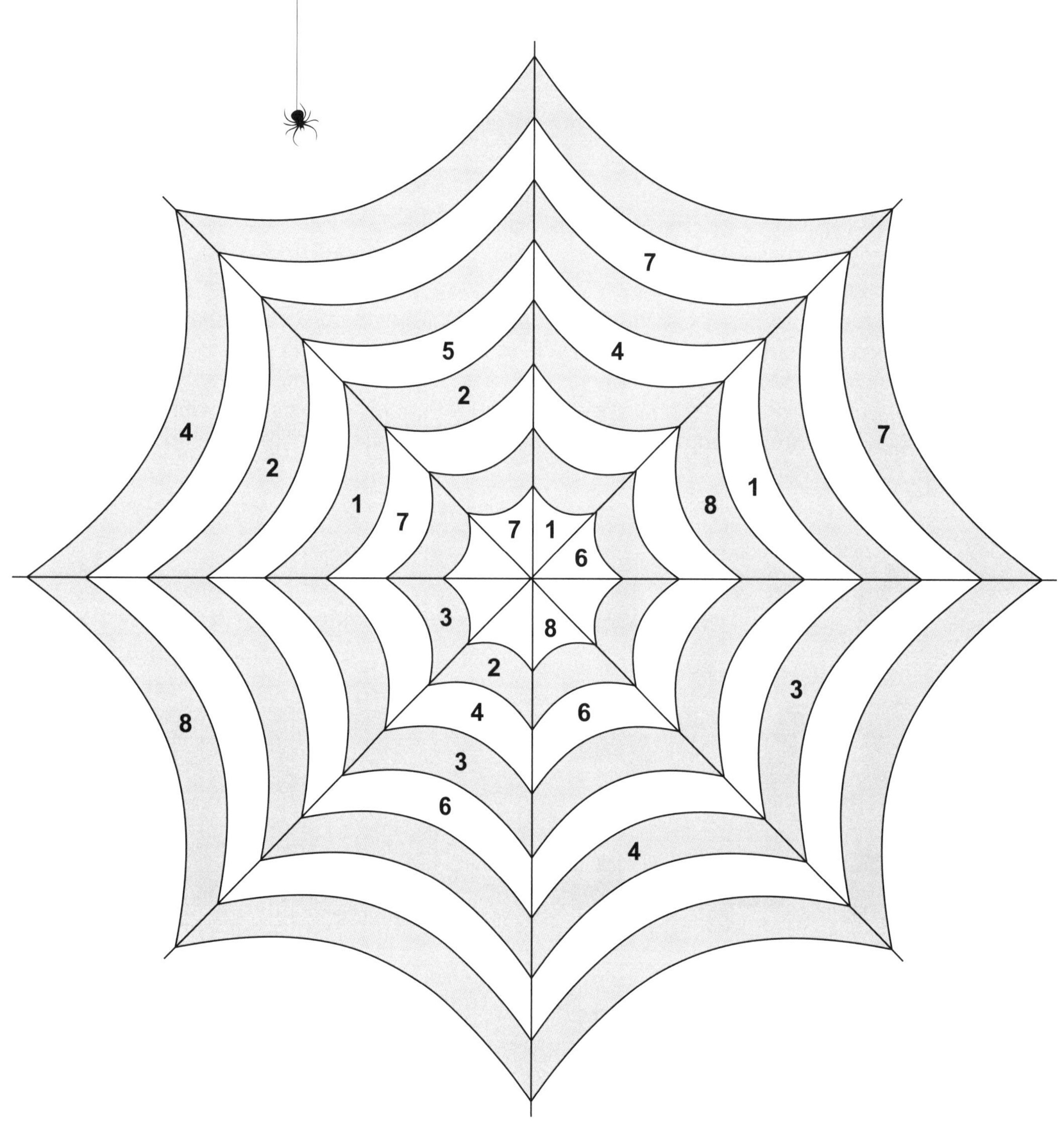

LEVEL 4

10 Every row and column in this grid originally contained one heart, one club, one diamond, one spade, and two blank squares, although not necessarily in that order.

Every symbol with a black arrow refers to the first of the four symbols encountered in the direction of the arrow. Every symbol with a white arrow refers to the second of the four symbols encountered in the direction of the arrow.

Can you complete the original grid?

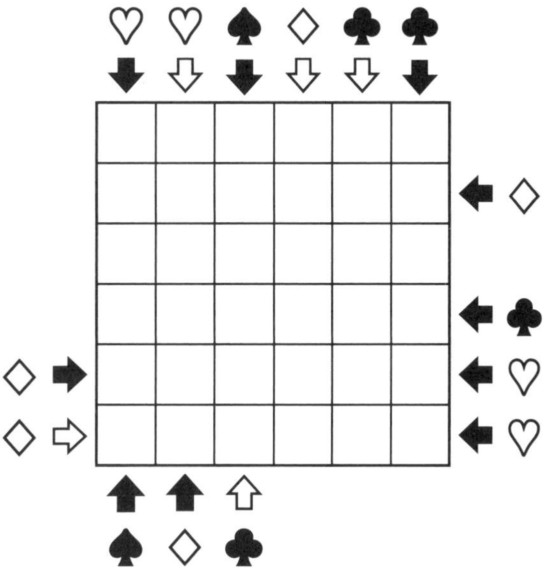

11 Fill the grid so that every horizontal row and vertical column contains the numbers 1-5. Any arrows in the grid always point toward a square that contains a lower number.

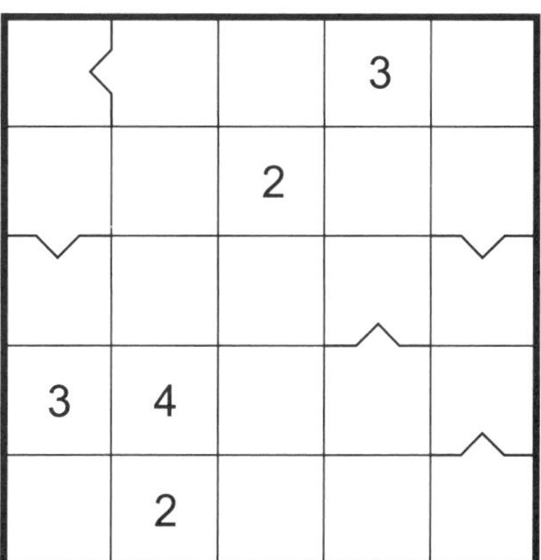

LEVEL 4

12

With the starter already given, can you fit all of the remaining listed numbers into this grid? Take care, this puzzle may not be as easy as it looks!

14	421	897	4196	42656
28	438	906	4694	46603
45	457	914	6015	52376
56	507	926	6110	53291
60	510	950	6153	65085
93	674	955	6789	68690
198	738	1409	14699	71643
260	753	2006	20204	90874
286	771	2618 ✓	27815	174486
317	780	3274	31906	276772
352	832	3475	37666	343596
354	859	3683	38911	526990

13

The grid should be filled with numbers from 1 to 6, so that each number appears just once in every row and column.

The clues refer to the digit totals in the squares, e.g. A 1 2 3 = 6 means that the numbers in squares A1, A2 and A3 add up to 6.

1 D E 5 = 6
2 C D 6 = 11
3 A 3 4 5 = 13
4 B 4 5 6 = 9
5 C 3 4 = 4
6 D 3 4 = 6
7 E 1 2 = 5
8 F 4 5 = 5
9 B C 1 = 11
10 A B 2 = 10
11 E F 3 = 11

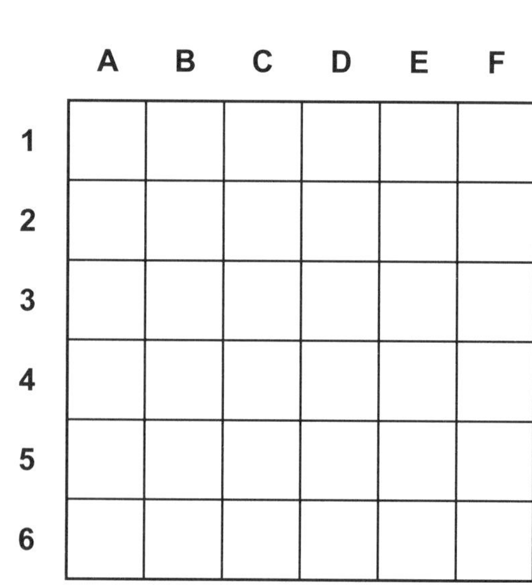

LEVEL 4

14 The object of this puzzle is to trace a single path from the top left corner to the bottom right corner of the grid, moving through all of the cells in either a horizontal, vertical, or diagonal direction.

Every cell must be entered once only, and your path should take you through the numbers in the sequence 1-2-3-4-1-2-3-4, etc.

Can you find the way?

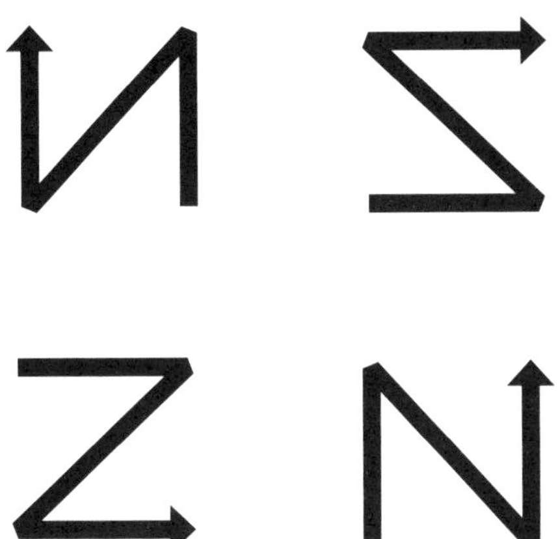

1	3	3	4	1	3	4	1
2	4	4	2	2	3	4	2
1	2	3	1	1	2	3	1
2	3	2	1	4	4	3	2
1	3	4	2	3	3	4	4
4	1	1	4	2	2	1	1
4	2	4	3	1	3	2	3
3	1	2	3	2	1	4	4

15 A standard set of 28 dominoes has been laid out as shown. Can you draw in the edges of them all?

The check-box is provided as an aid and the domino already placed will help.

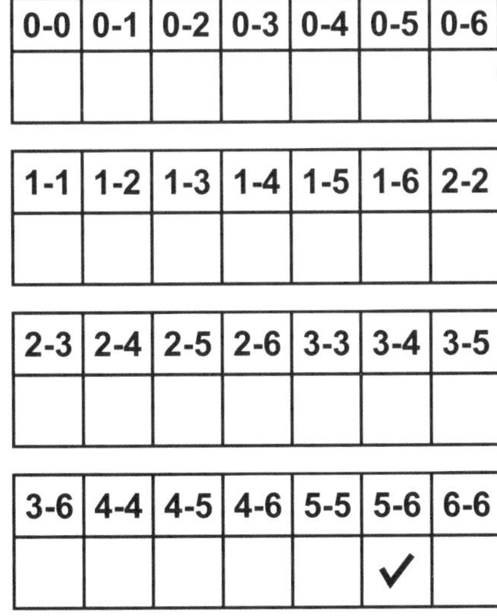

0-0	0-1	0-2	0-3	0-4	0-5	0-6

1-1	1-2	1-3	1-4	1-5	1-6	2-2

2-3	2-4	2-5	2-6	3-3	3-4	3-5

3-6	4-4	4-5	4-6	5-5	5-6	6-6
					✓	

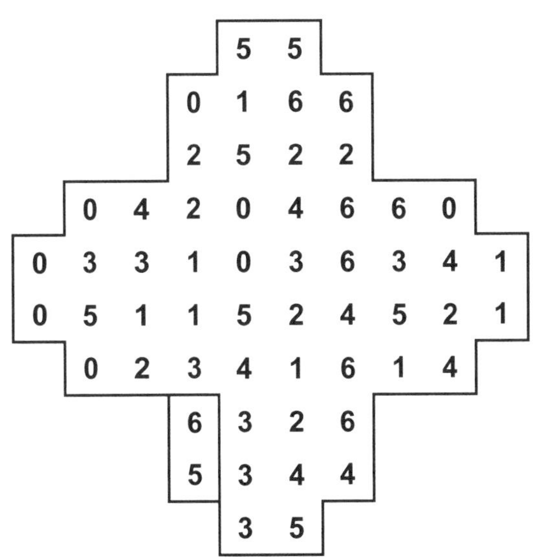

LEVEL 4

16

Draw a single continuous loop, by connecting the dots. No line may cross the path of another.

The figure inside each set of any four surrounding dots indicates the total number of surrounding lines.

		1		3		0		1	
3	1					2	2	1	
2	0		3			1			1
1					1				
3		3					0		1
1			1			3			
		1	1		3		0		
			2	2		3			3
		2	2			1			
2	1		1				2		
	2				1	1	3		
	1		2	1	1		3		1

17

Place the eight tiles into the puzzle grid so that all adjacent numbers on each tile match up.

Tiles may be rotated through 360 degrees, but none may be flipped over.

1	4
1	2

4	1
4	1

2	2
3	1

1	1
1	3

4	2
3	3

1	2
2	2

4	1
2	4

1	2
3	3

		3	1		
		4	2		

LEVEL 4

18 Every oval shape in this diagram contains a different letter of the alphabet from A to K inclusive.

Use the clues to determine their locations. Reference in the clues to "due" means in any location along the same horizontal or vertical line.

1 The A is further north than the B, which is further east than the F, which is next to and south of the H.

2 The C is next to and north of the J, which is further east than the G.

3 The D is further north than the E.

4 The G is due west of the D, which is next to and south of the I, which is further south than the J.

4 The K is next to and west of the I, which is due south of the A.

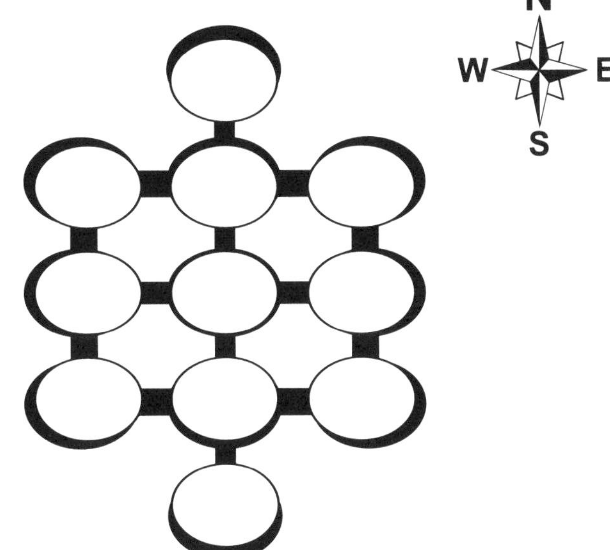

19 Draw walls to partition the grid into areas (some walls are already drawn in for you).

Each area must contain two circles, area sizes must match those numbers shown next to the grid, and each "+" must be linked to at least two walls.

3, 4, 4, 7, 7

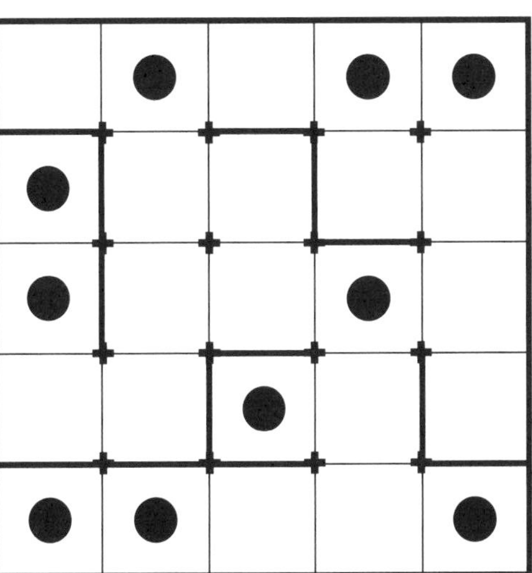

LEVEL 4

20 Twelve L-shapes need to be inserted in the grid, and each L has one hole in it.

There are three pieces of each of the four kinds shown here, and any piece may be turned or flipped over before being put in the grid. No pieces of the same kind touch, even at a corner.

The pieces fit together so well that you cannot see any spaces between them; only the holes show.

Can you tell where the Ls are?

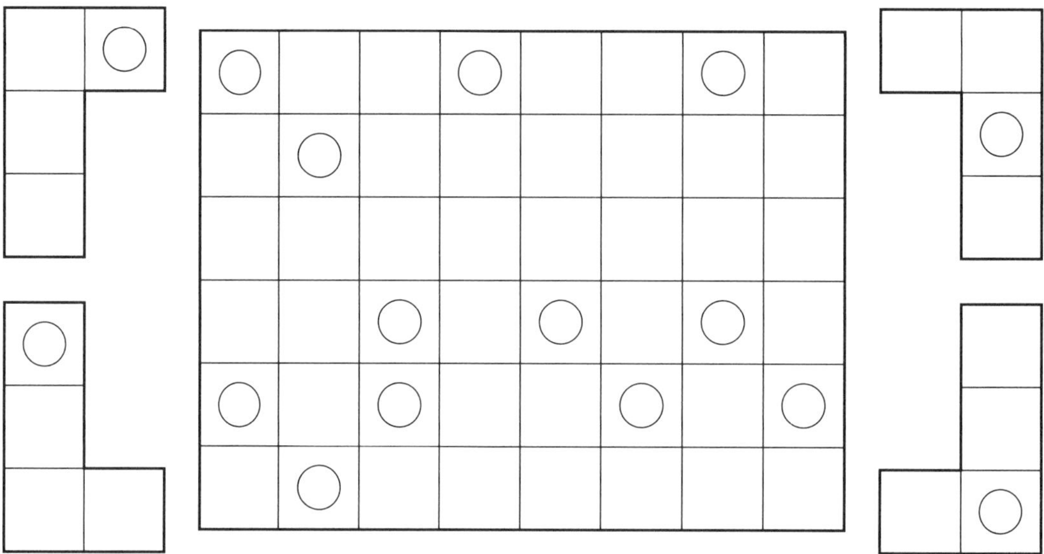

21 Fill the three empty circles with the symbols +, –, and x in some order, to make a sum that totals the central number. Each symbol must be used once, and calculations are made in the direction of travel (clockwise).

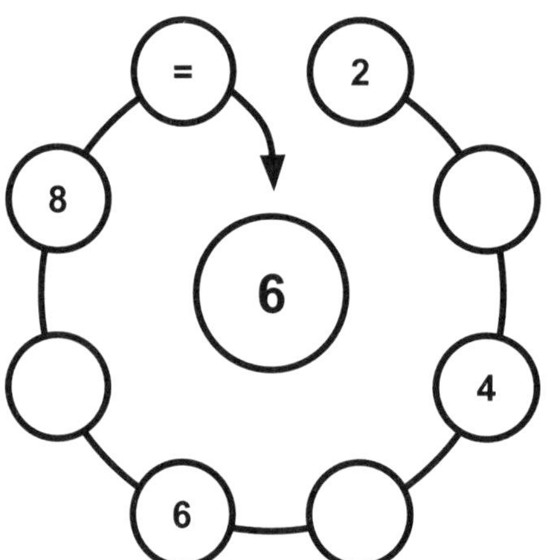

LEVEL 4

22

Each of the small squares in the grid below contains either A, B, or C. Each row, column, and diagonal line of six squares has exactly two of each letter. Can you tell the letter in each square?

Across

3 The As are further left than the Cs
4 The As are between the Cs
5 The Cs are between the As
6 The As are between the Cs

Down

1 The As are between the Bs
2 The Cs are next to each other
3 Each A is directly next to and below a C
5 The Bs are between the As
6 The As are next to each other

	1	2	3	4	5	6
1						
2						
3						
4						
5						
6						

23

Using the numbers below, complete these six equations (three reading across and three reading downwards).

Every number is used once.

1 2 3 4 5
6 7 8 9

	+		+		=	15
x	■	x	■	+		
	x		x		=	192
–	■	x	■	–		
	+		x		=	20
=		=		=		
19		378		9		

LEVEL 4

24 The chart gives directions to a hidden treasure behind the central black square in the grid. Move the indicated number of spaces north, south, east, and west (eg 4N means move four squares north) stopping at every square once only to arrive there. At which square should you start?

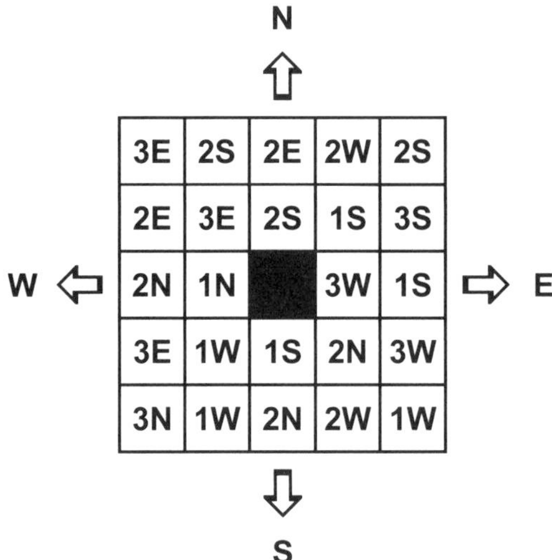

25 The numbers at the top and on the left side show the quantity of single-digit numbers (1-9) used in that row and column. The numbers at the bottom and on the right show the sum of the digits. A number may appear more than once in a row or column, but no numbers are in squares that touch, even at a corner.

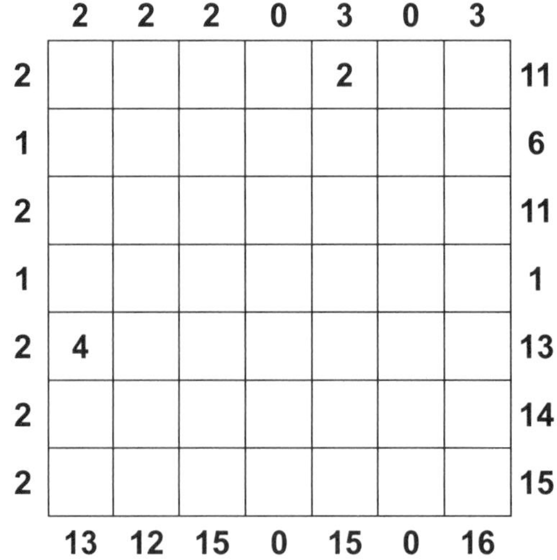

LEVEL 4

26

In the square below, change the positions of six numbers, one per horizontal row, vertical column, and long diagonal line of six smaller squares, in such a way that the numbers in each row, column, and long diagonal line total exactly 234. Any number may appear more than once in a row, column or line.

39	30	33	44	51	47
33	39	22	33	39	43
40	61	39	27	29	45
29	53	39	51	20	15
36	47	36	40	63	44
67	36	40	42	39	13

27

The blank squares below should be filled with whole numbers between 1 and 30 inclusive, any of which may occur more than once, or not at all.

The numbers in every horizontal row add up to the totals on the right, as do the two long diagonal lines; while those in every vertical column add up to the totals along the bottom.

							126
	8	28	30		5	21	113
19	13			7	12	11	113
16	29	8	3	26			134
	15	17		12	10	20	97
18		6	11	10	27		118
6	28		3		22	18	104
19	20	10		4		1	85
102	138	109	101	79	121	114	83

LEVEL 4

28 Can you place the hexagons into the grid, so that where any hexagon touches another along a straight line, the number in both triangles is the same? No rotation of any hexagon is allowed!

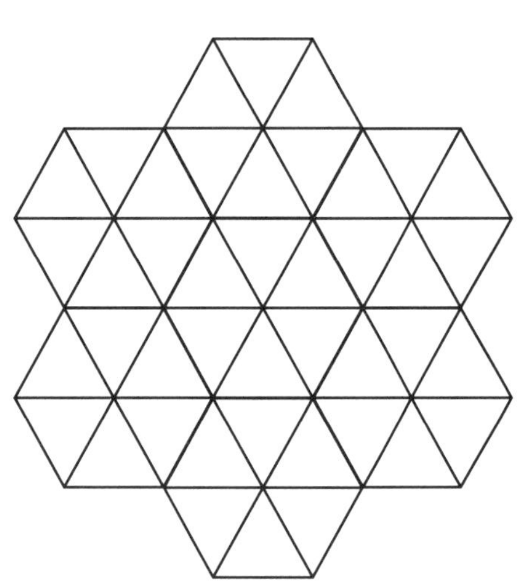

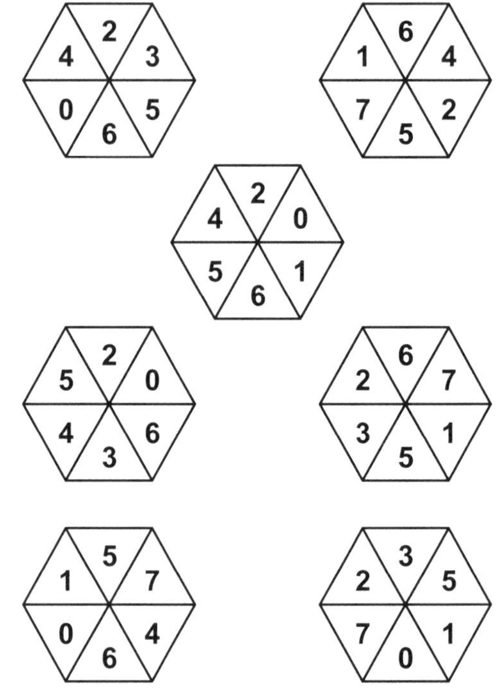

29 Can you place the vessels into the diagram? Some parts of vessels or sea squares have already been filled in. A number to the right or below a row or column refers to the number of occupied squares in that row or column.

Any vessel may be positioned horizontally or vertically, but no part of a vessel touches part of any other vessel, either horizontally, vertically, or diagonally.

Empty Area of Sea: ≈

Aircraft Carrier: ◀■■▶

Battleships: ◀■▶ ◀■▶

Cruisers: ◀▶ ◀▶ ◀▶

Submarines: ● ● ● ●

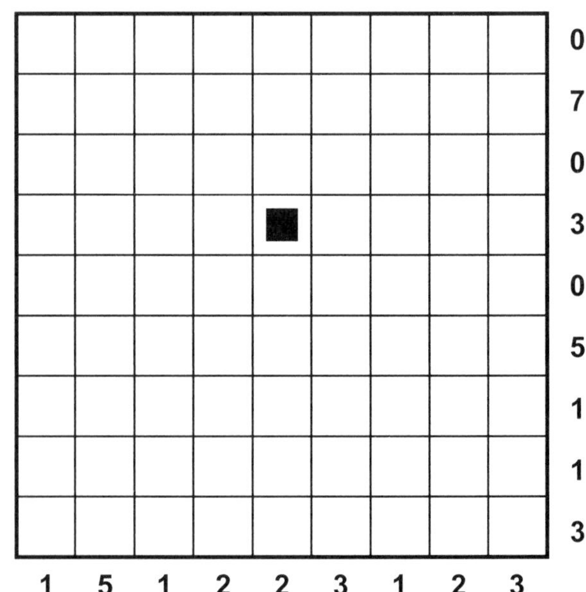

LEVEL 4

30 Each horizontal row and vertical column should contain different shapes and different numbers.

Every square will contain one number and one shape, and no combination may be repeated anywhere else in the puzzle.

1 2 3 4 5

		4		
		3		5
1				3
			4	

31 Which of the four lettered alternatives (A, B, C, or D) fits most logically into the empty square?

25	16	31
12	23	13
13	27	22

15	8	26
14	29	25
34	15	16

18	13	21
23	2	27
41	26	11

?

31	12	19
17	24	16
13	22	20

A

29	10	17
7	33	21
15	20	30

B

28	11	16
8	33	20
15	19	29

C

29	12	16
17	24	16
19	22	28

D

LEVEL 4

32 Every brick in this pyramid contains a number which is the sum of the two numbers below it, so that F=A+B, etc.

Just work out the missing numbers!

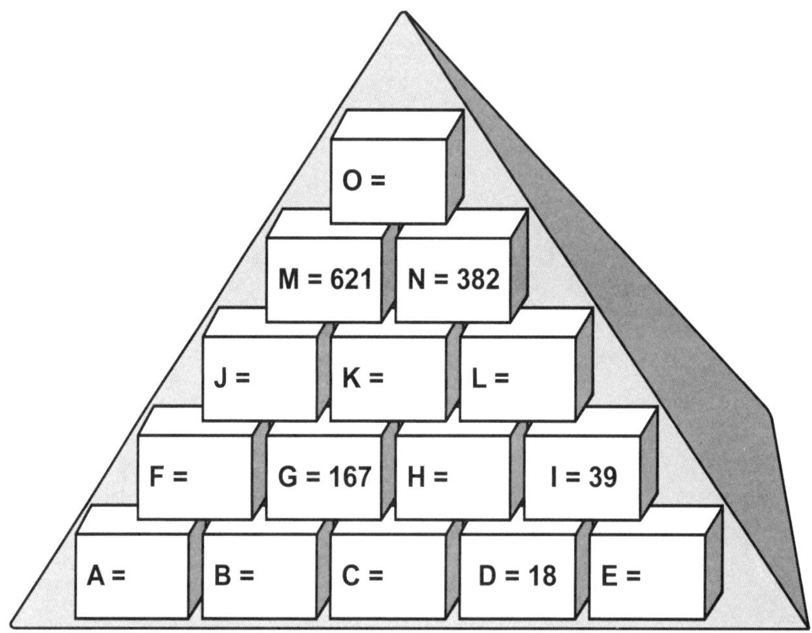

33 In this puzzle, an amateur coin collector has been out with his metal detector, searching for booty. He didn't have time to dig up all the coins he found, so has made a grid map, showing their locations, in the hope that if he loses the map, at least no-one else will understand it…

Those squares containing numbers are empty, but where a number appears in a square, it indicates how many coins are located in the squares (up to a maximum of eight) surrounding the numbered one, touching it at any corner or side. There is only one coin in any individual square.

Place a circle into every square containing a coin.

	3	1	2		2			2	
			3	3			1		
	3						1	1	
				2	2	2			
	1	1			1				0
	1		0					3	
		1	2		2	3		2	
2							3		2
	3			4	4				
	2		1					2	

LEVEL 4

34

Given that the letters are valued 1-26 according to their places in the alphabet, can you crack the mystery code to reveal the missing letter?

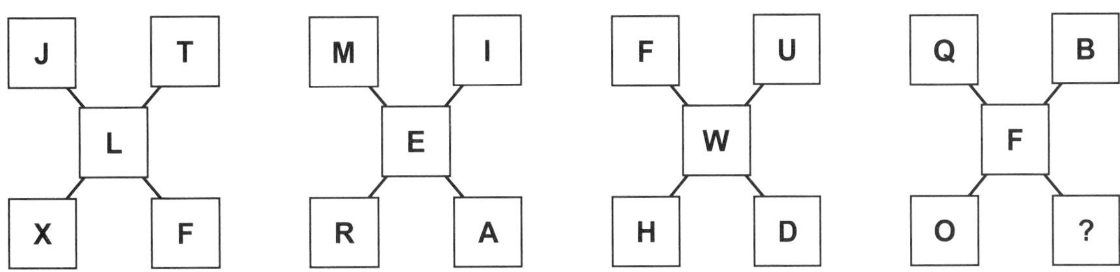

35

Place all twelve of the pieces into the grid. Any may be rotated or flipped over, but none may touch another, not even diagonally. The numbers outside the grid refer to the number of consecutive black squares; and each block is separated from the others by at least one white square. For instance, "3 2" could refer to a row with none, one or more white squares, then three black squares, then at least one white square, then two more black squares, followed by any number of white squares.

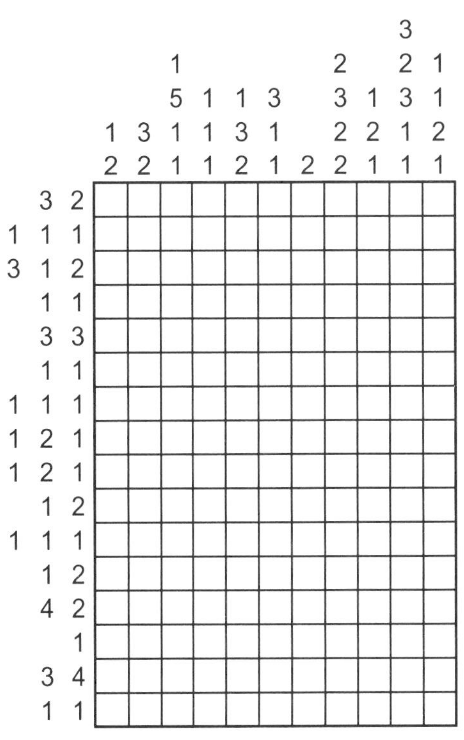

LEVEL 4

36 Each of the eight segments of the spider's web should be filled with a different number from 1 to 8, in such a way that every ring also contains a different number from 1 to 8.

The segments run from the outside of the spider's web to the middle, and the rings run all the way around.

Some numbers are already in place. Can you fill in the rest?

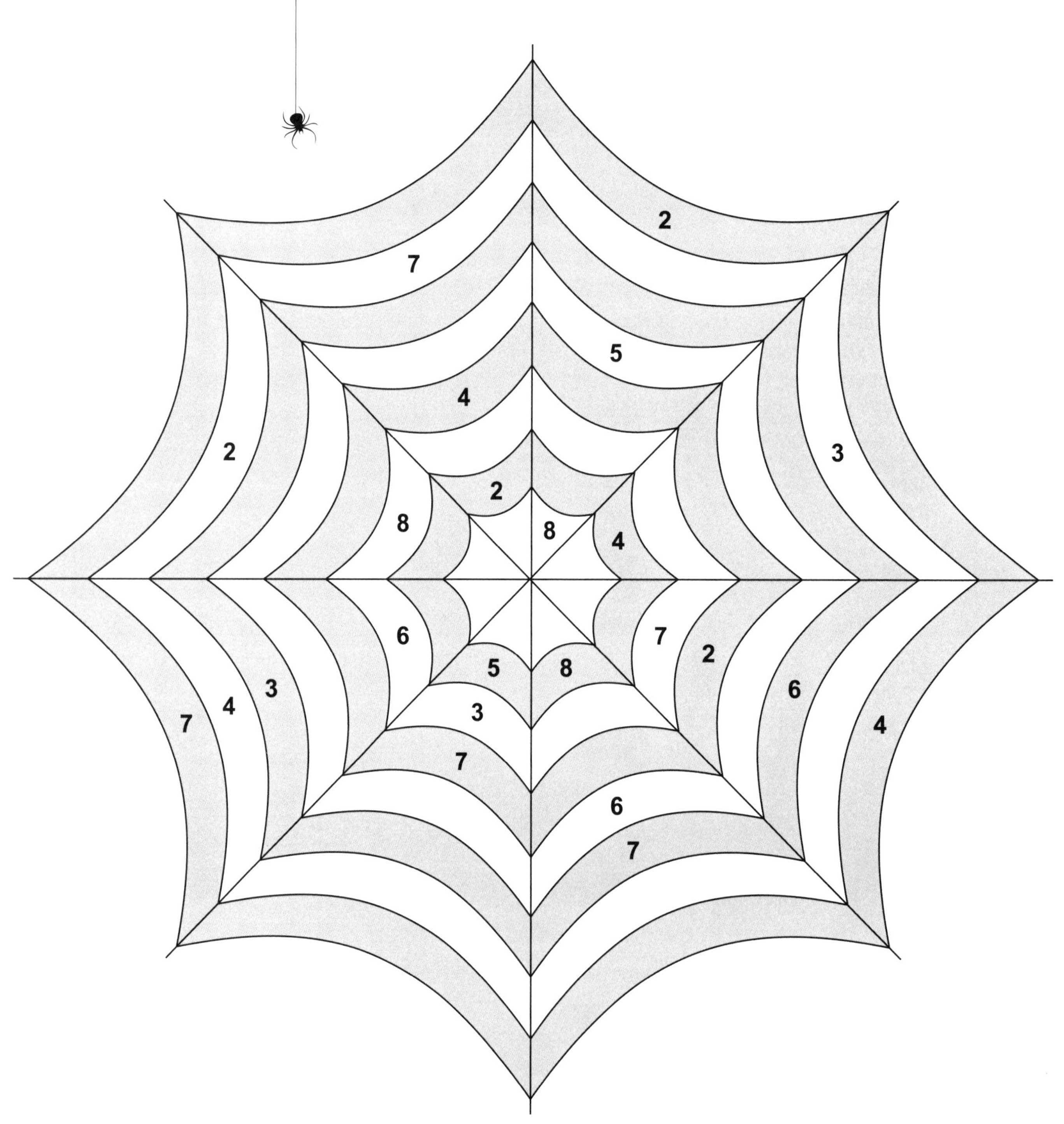

37

Every row and column in this grid originally contained one heart, one club, one diamond, one spade, and two blank squares, although not necessarily in that order.

Every symbol with a black arrow refers to the first of the four symbols encountered in the direction of the arrow. Every symbol with a white arrow refers to the second of the four symbols encountered in the direction of the arrow.

Can you complete the original grid?

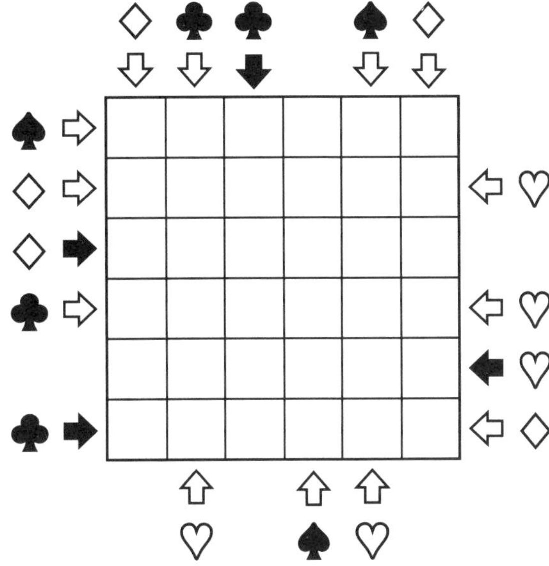

38

Fill the grid so that every horizontal row and vertical column contains the numbers 1-5. Any arrows in the grid always point toward a square that contains a lower number.

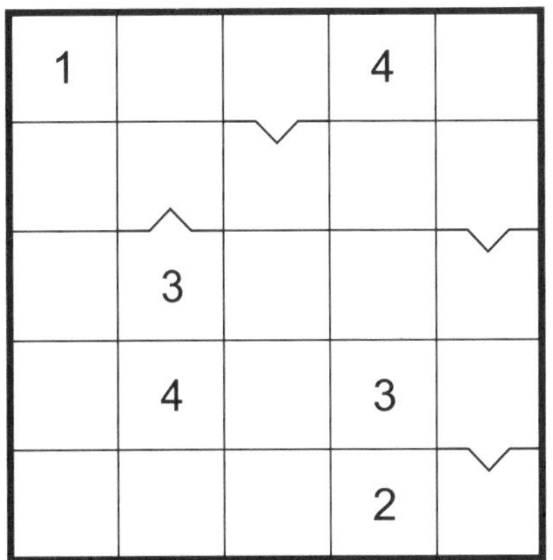

LEVEL 4

39

With the starter already given, can you fit all of the remaining listed numbers into this grid? Take care, this puzzle may not be as easy as it looks!

19	175	815	11430	78609
21	240	973	15990	90825
27	295	1173	25931	94091
32	402	1203	35345	95246
33	425	1522	35902	103856
38	448	2038	39432	104116
41	534	2163	40266	149932
52	596	4263	43195	346079
67	598	5520	56401	380595
83	621	6561	60989	420231
88	789	8135	65623 ✓	539160
95	812	8743	72025	679884

40

The grid should be filled with numbers from 1 to 6, so that each number appears just once in every row and column.

The clues refer to the digit totals in the squares, e.g. A 1 2 3 = 6 means that the numbers in squares A1, A2 and A3 add up to 6.

1 D 3 4 = 6
2 A B 3 = 10
3 A 4 5 6 = 6
4 B C 4 = 8
5 B 5 6 = 6
6 C 1 2 3 = 7
7 A B 1 = 6
8 F 5 6 = 7
9 A B 2 = 11
10 C D 5 = 8
11 E 3 4 = 6

	A	B	C	D	E	F
1						
2						
3						
4						
5						
6						

LEVEL 4

41 The object of this puzzle is to trace a single path from the top left corner to the bottom right corner of the grid, moving through all of the cells in either a horizontal, vertical, or diagonal direction.

Every cell must be entered once only, and your path should take you through the numbers in the sequence 1-2-3-4-1-2-3-4, etc.

Can you find the way?

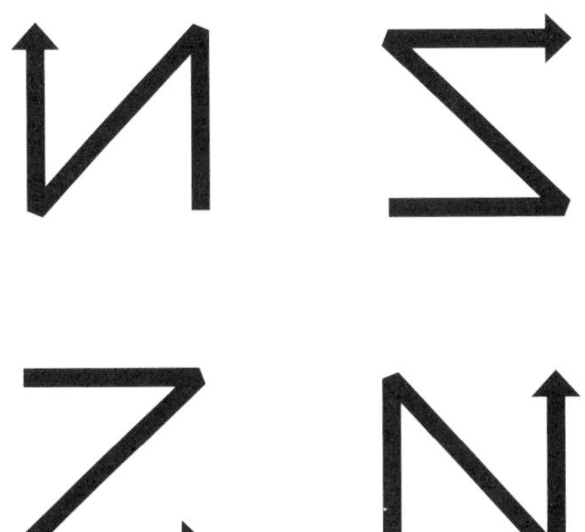

1	2	4	3	4	1	4	3
4	1	3	1	2	1	1	2
1	3	2	4	2	4	2	4
4	2	3	4	1	3	1	3
1	3	1	4	3	2	2	3
2	2	3	2	1	3	2	4
4	3	3	2	3	4	3	1
1	2	1	4	4	1	2	4

42 A standard set of 28 dominoes has been laid out as shown. Can you draw in the edges of them all?

The check-box is provided as an aid and the domino already placed will help.

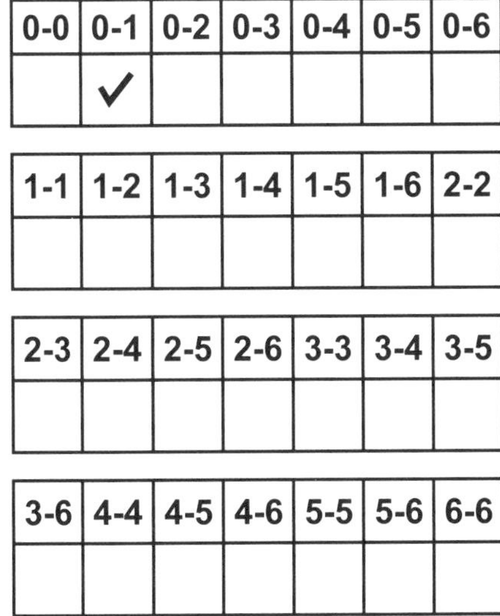

0-0	0-1	0-2	0-3	0-4	0-5	0-6
	✓					

1-1	1-2	1-3	1-4	1-5	1-6	2-2

2-3	2-4	2-5	2-6	3-3	3-4	3-5

3-6	4-4	4-5	4-6	5-5	5-6	6-6

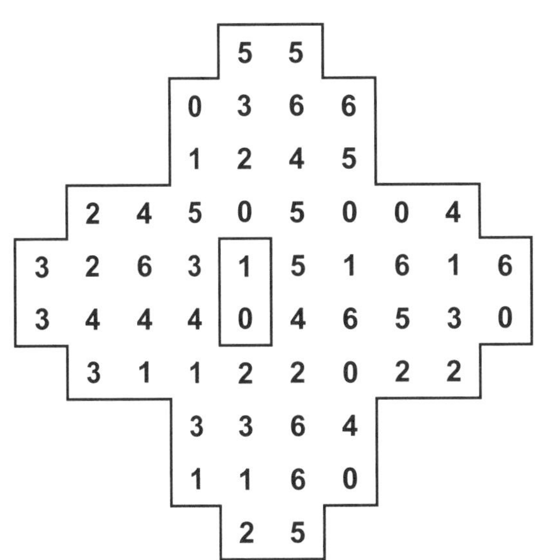

LEVEL 4

43

Draw a single continuous loop, by connecting the dots. No line may cross the path of another.

The figure inside each set of any four surrounding dots indicates the total number of surrounding lines.

	1		1	1		2		1	
	1	0			1		2	2	3
	0				0				1
	1		1					0	
1		2	2	2		1			3
2			1			3	1		
		1						3	
1	3	2	2		2	2		1	
3	2		3			2	0	2	
2		0			3	1			
		3				3	1		
	2							3	

44

Place the eight tiles into the puzzle grid so that all adjacent numbers on each tile match up.

Tiles may be rotated through 360 degrees, but none may be flipped over.

2	3
3	2

3	1
4	2

1	4
3	2

3	3
2	2

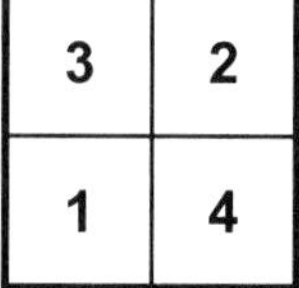

3	2
1	4

4	1
3	2

3	4
2	4

3	2
3	1

		3	3		
		4	3		

LEVEL 4

45 What number should replace the question mark?

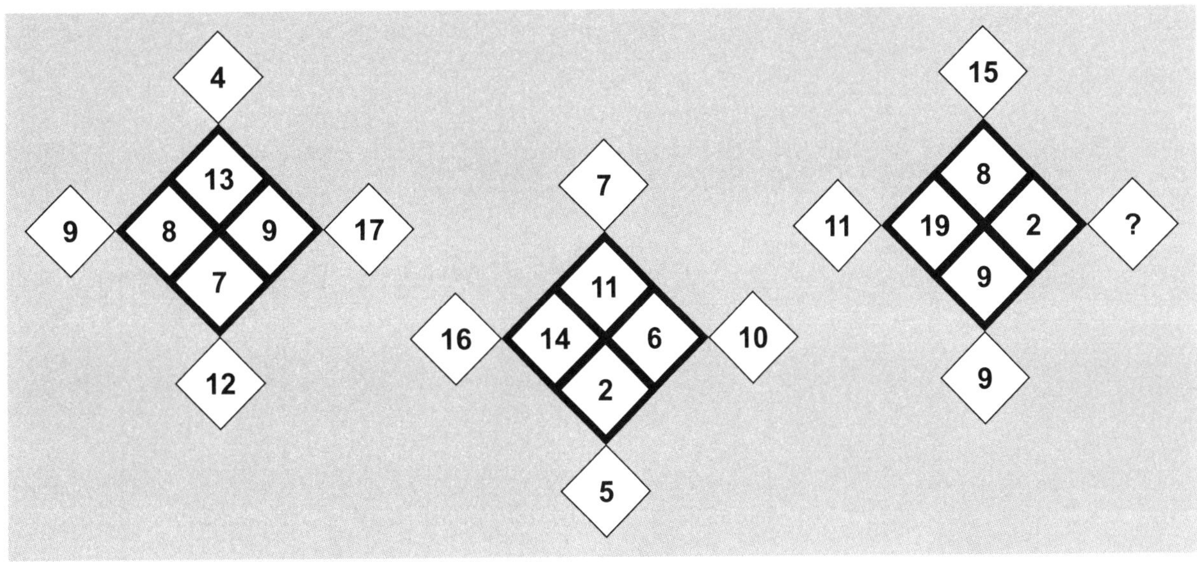

46 Which four pieces can be fitted together to form an exact copy of this shape?

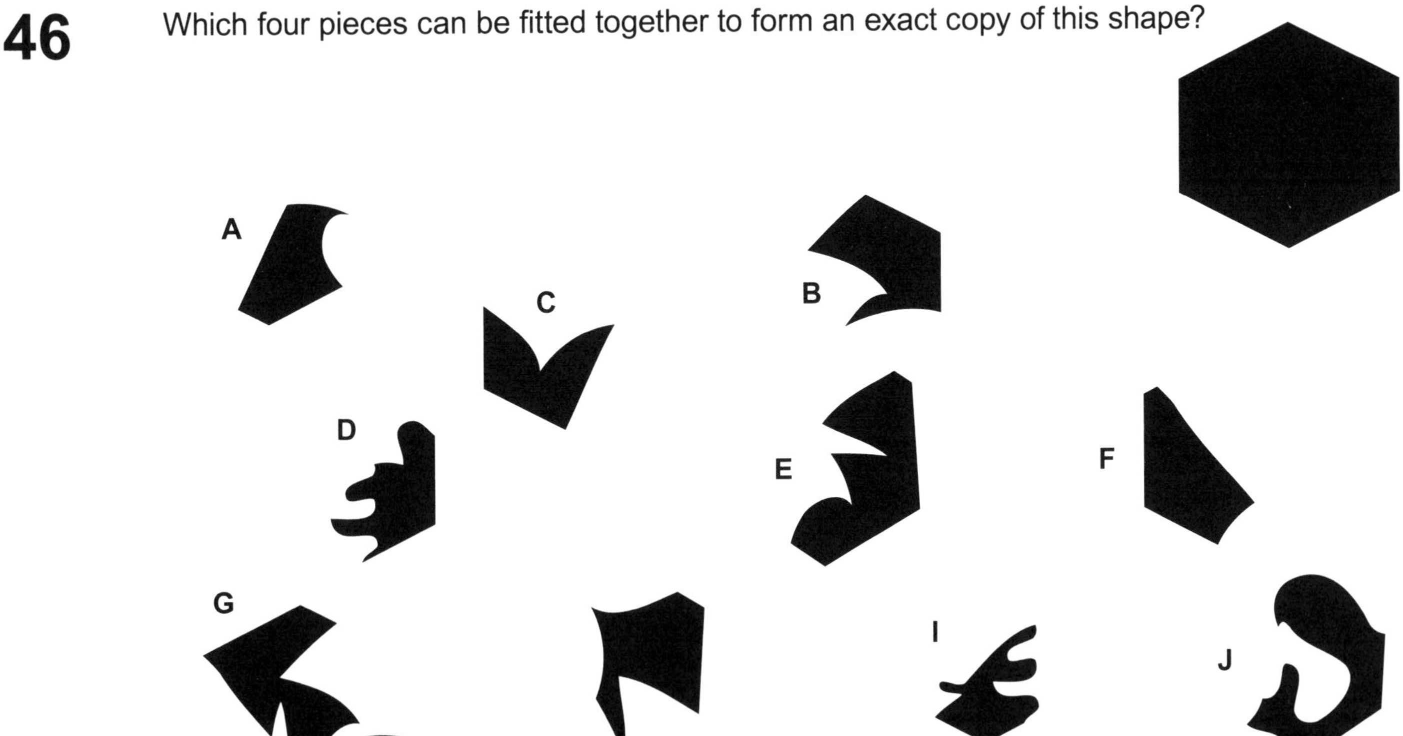

LEVEL 4

47 Twelve L-shapes need to be inserted in the grid, and each L has one hole in it.

There are three pieces of each of the four kinds shown here, and any piece may be turned or flipped over before being put in the grid. No pieces of the same kind touch, even at a corner.

The pieces fit together so well that you cannot see any spaces between them; only the holes show.

Can you tell where the Ls are? One shape is already in place.

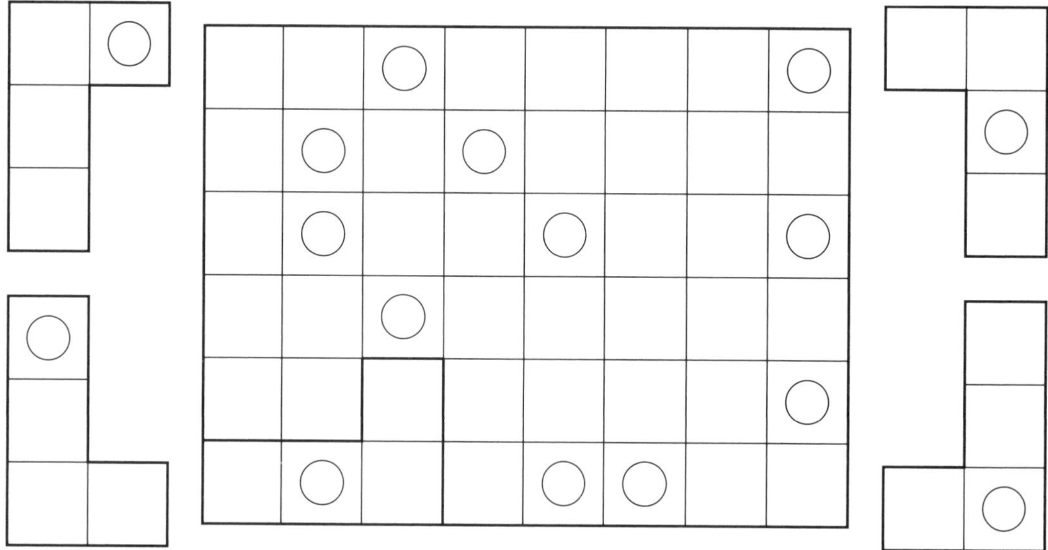

48 Each symbol stands for a different number. In order to reach the correct total at the end of each row and column, what is the value of the circle, cross, pentagon, square and star?

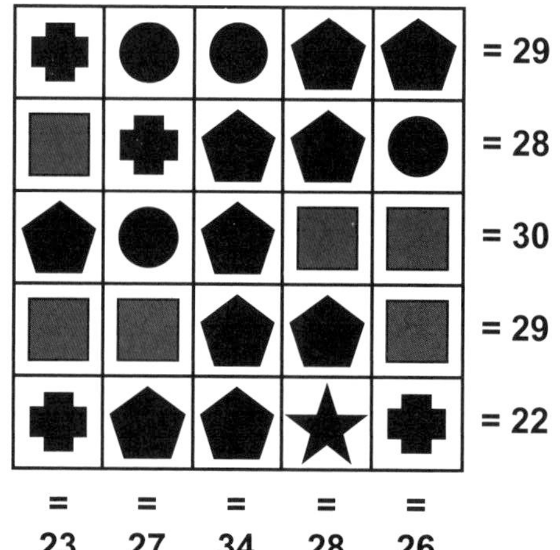

LEVEL 4

49 Each of the small squares in the grid below contains either A, B, or C. Each row, column, and diagonal line of six squares has exactly two of each letter. Can you tell the letter in each square?

Across

1 The As are next to each other
2 The Bs are further right than the As
3 The Cs are between the Bs
5 The As are further right than the Cs
6 The Bs are next to each other

Down

1 The Cs are lower than the Bs
2 The Cs are between the Bs
3 The Bs are lower than the As
4 The Cs are higher than the As
5 The Bs are next to each other
6 The Cs are lower than the Bs

	1	2	3	4	5	6
1						
2						
3						
4						
5						
6						

50 Which is the odd one out?

A

B

C

D

E

F

LEVEL 4

51 The chart gives directions to a hidden treasure behind the central black square in the grid. Move the indicated number of spaces north, south, east, and west (eg 4N means move four squares north) stopping at every square once only to arrive there. At which square should you start?

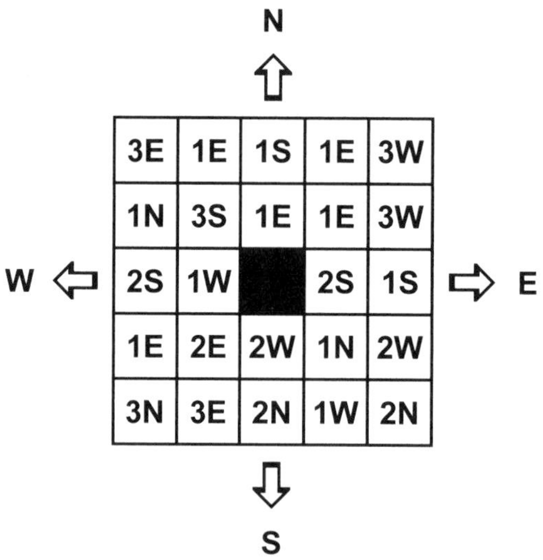

3E	1E	1S	1E	3W
1N	3S	1E	1E	3W
2S	1W		2S	1S
1E	2E	2W	1N	2W
3N	3E	2N	1W	2N

52 What number should replace the question mark?

11	17	8
6	8	13
9	12	10
4	2	1
7	6	3
5	9	?

LEVEL 4

53

In the grid below, what number should replace the question mark?

4	12	24	19	1	16	9
7	10	3	12	7	5	1
11	22	27	31	8	21	10
18	32	30	43	15	26	11
29	54	57	?	23	47	21
47	86	87	117	38	73	32
76	140	144	191	61	120	53

54

The blank squares below should be filled with whole numbers between 1 and 30 inclusive, any of which may occur more than once, or not at all.

The numbers in every horizontal row add up to the totals on the right, as do the two long diagonal lines; while those in every vertical column add up to the totals along the bottom.

							133
	16	26	22	6	3	30	114
7	14	9			23	2	108
1	10	14		26		4	97
	2	11	10	14	27		108
8		19	30	26		4	120
5	23		15		14	29	116
		4	16	27	11		77
54	89	96	134	141	128	98	94

55

Can you place the hexagons into the grid, so that where any hexagon touches another along a straight line, the number in both triangles is the same? No rotation of any hexagon is allowed!

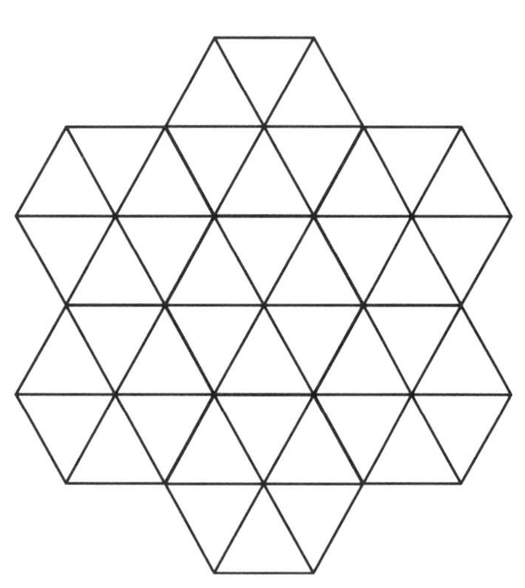

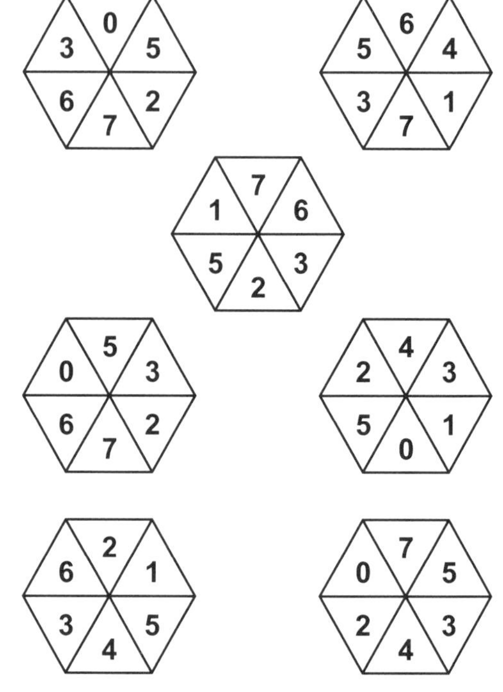

56

Can you place the vessels into the diagram? Some parts of vessels or sea squares have already been filled in. A number to the right or below a row or column refers to the number of occupied squares in that row or column.

Any vessel may be positioned horizontally or vertically, but no part of a vessel touches part of any other vessel, either horizontally, vertically, or diagonally.

Empty Area of Sea: ≈

Aircraft Carrier: ◀■■▶

Battleships: ◀■▶ ◀■▶

Cruisers: ◀▶ ◀▶ ◀▶

Submarines: ● ● ● ●

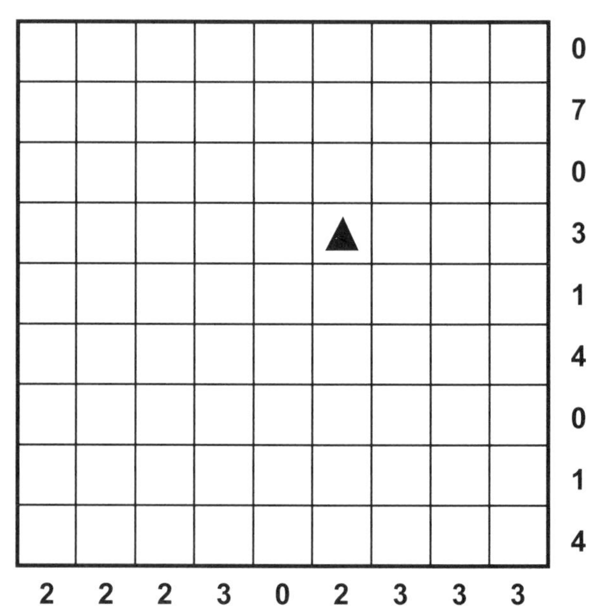

LEVEL 4

57 Each horizontal row and vertical column should contain different shapes and different numbers.

Every square will contain one number and one shape, and no combination may be repeated anywhere else in the puzzle.

1	2	3	4	5

	3		4	2
		3	5	
	2	1		

58 In the diagram below, what number should replace the question mark?

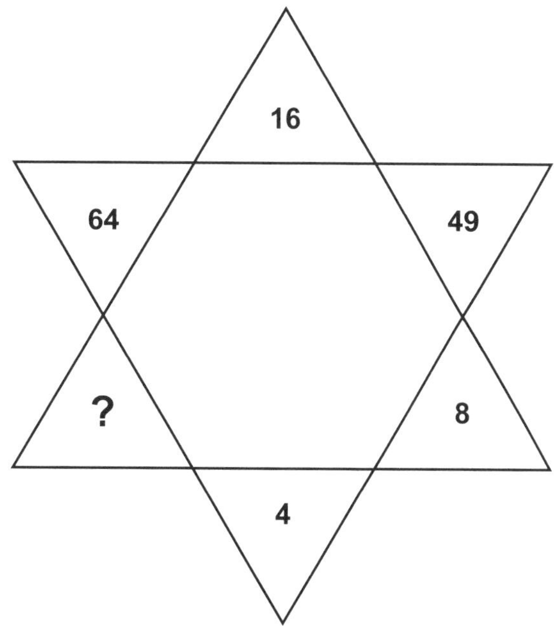

LEVEL 4

59 Every brick in this pyramid contains a number which is the sum of the two numbers below it, so that F=A+B, etc.

Just work out the missing numbers!

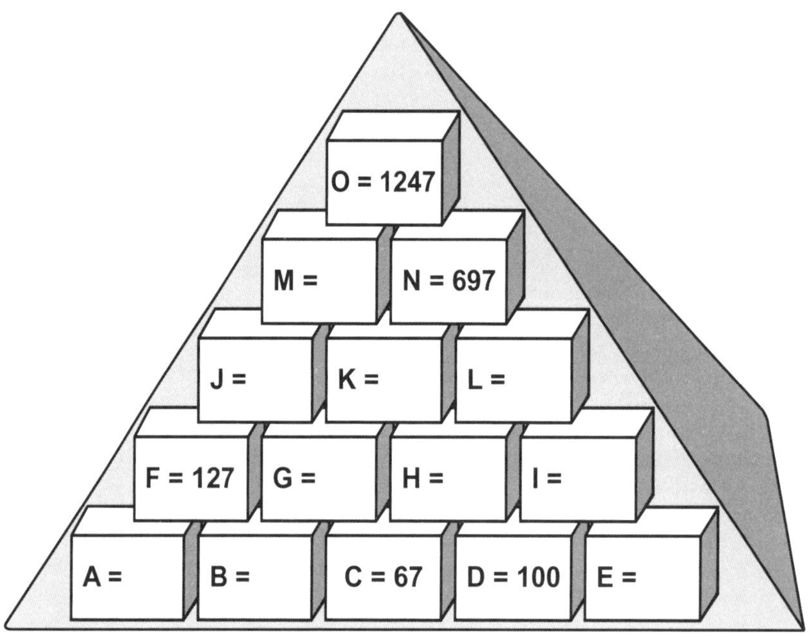

60 In this puzzle, an amateur coin collector has been out with his metal detector, searching for booty. He didn't have time to dig up all the coins he found, so has made a grid map, showing their locations, in the hope that if he loses the map, at least no-one else will understand it…

Those squares containing numbers are empty, but where a number appears in a square, it indicates how many coins are located in the squares (up to a maximum of eight) surrounding the numbered one, touching it at any corner or side. There is only one coin in any individual square.

Place a circle into every square containing a coin.

			2			2	2		0
4				2					
2				2		2			
			1		3		1	1	
0								2	
	2	2					3	2	
2				2	3	3			
	5			2				1	
	4					3			
1	2			1			0	0	

LEVEL 4

61 Given that the letters are valued 1-26 according to their places in the alphabet, can you crack the mystery code to reveal the missing letter?

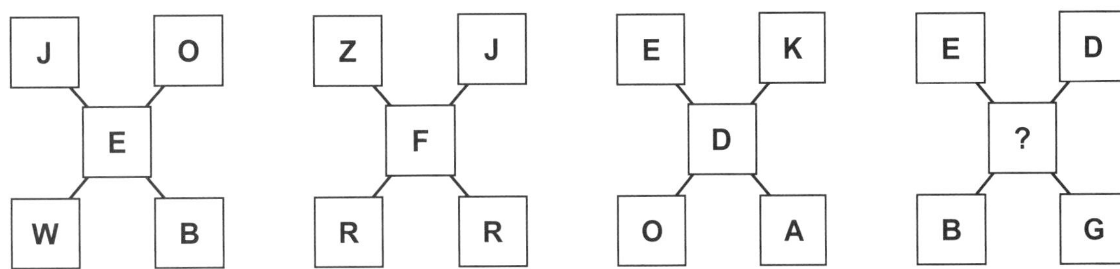

62 Place all twelve of the pieces into the grid. Any may be rotated or flipped over, but none may touch another, not even diagonally. The numbers outside the grid refer to the number of consecutive black squares; and each block is separated from the others by at least one white square. For instance, "3 2" could refer to a row with none, one or more white squares, then three black squares, then at least one white square, then two more black squares, followed by any number of white squares.

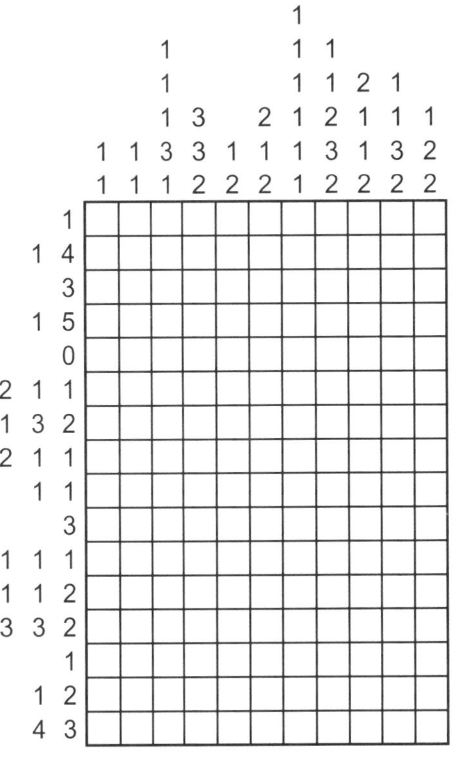

LEVEL 4

63 Each of the eight segments of the spider's web should be filled with a different number from 1 to 8, in such a way that every ring also contains a different number from 1 to 8.

The segments run from the outside of the spider's web to the middle, and the rings run all the way around.

Some numbers are already in place. Can you fill in the rest?

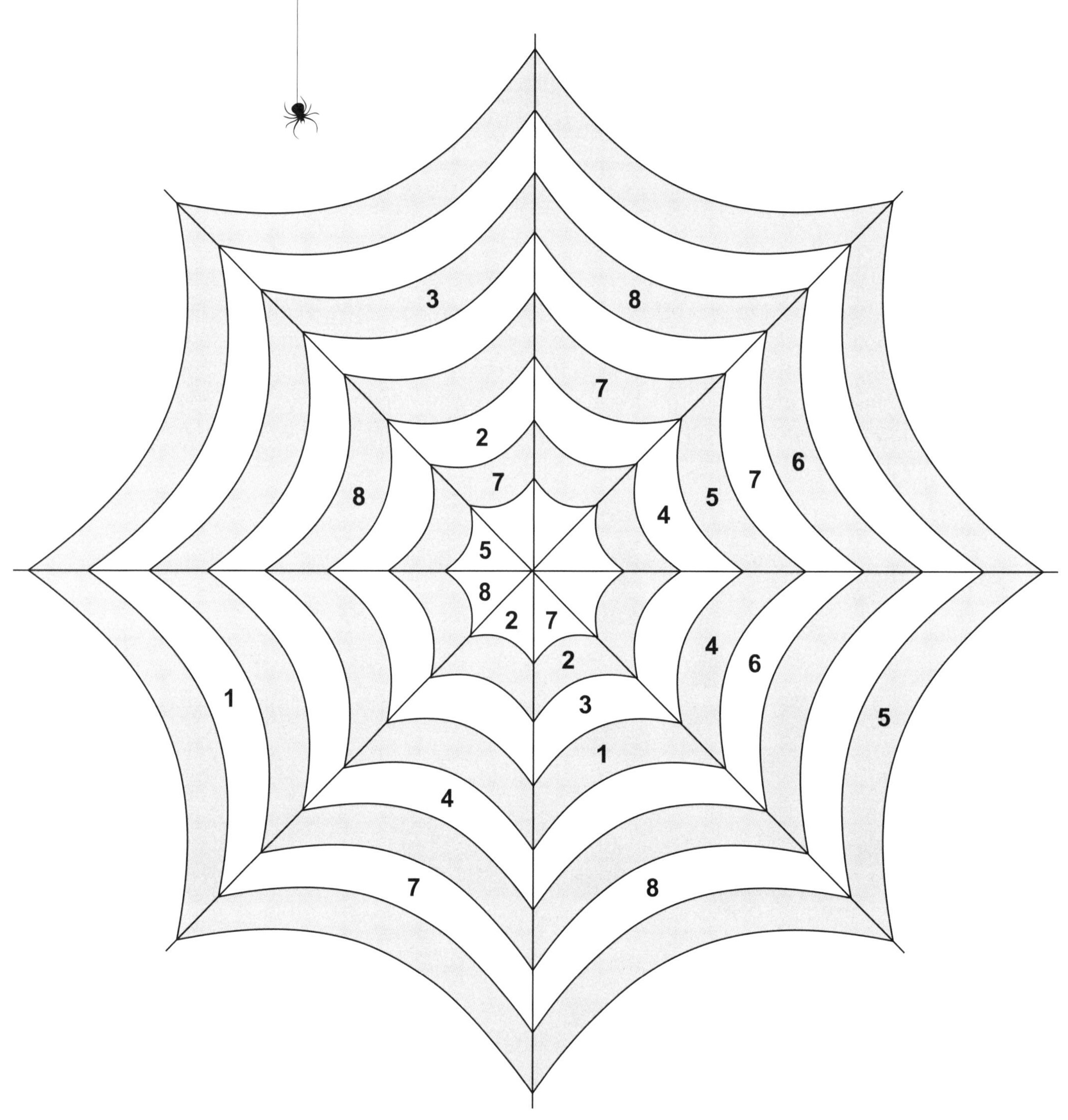

64 Every row and column in this grid originally contained one heart, one club, one diamond, one spade, and two blank squares, although not necessarily in that order.

Every symbol with a black arrow refers to the first of the four symbols encountered in the direction of the arrow. Every symbol with a white arrow refers to the second of the four symbols encountered in the direction of the arrow.

Can you complete the original grid?

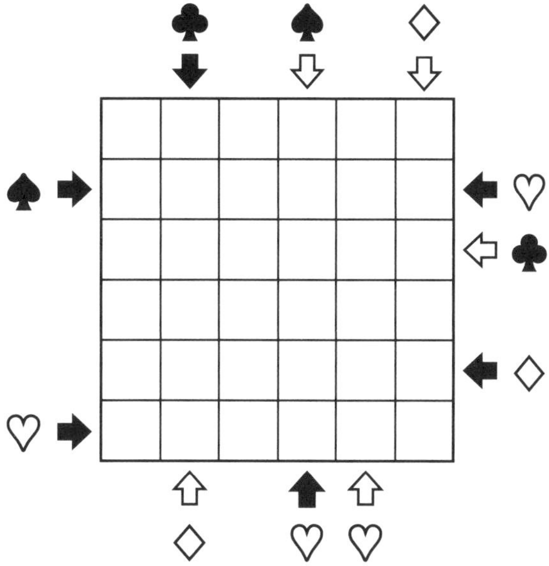

65 Fill the grid so that every horizontal row and vertical column contains the numbers 1-5. Any arrows in the grid always point toward a square that contains a lower number.

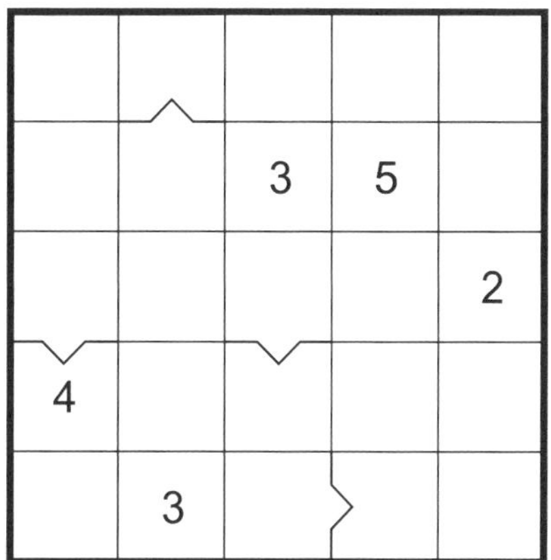

LEVEL 4

66

With the starter already given, can you fit all of the remaining listed numbers into this grid? Take care, this puzzle may not be as easy as it looks!

23	275	912	6586	163288
41	292	923	7023	224015
45	349	939	7236	303417
50	450	1003	9314	589487
54	451	1467	9345	609977
56	464	4018	9357	2618155
82	526	4478	9532	4333749
84	617	4637	13273	4692448
114	628	4897	30121	5214545
123	743 ✓	5045	36889	5568021
138	855	5610	41242	6143857
223	884	6515	127284	7254362

67

The grid should be filled with numbers from 1 to 6, so that each number appears just once in every row and column.

The clues refer to the digit totals in the squares, e.g. A 1 2 3 = 6 means that the numbers in squares A1, A2 and A3 add up to 6.

1 D E 2 = 6
2 E 4 5 6 = 12
3 D 3 4 = 8
4 A B 4 = 8
5 E F 3 = 5
6 A 5 6 = 4
7 B C D 5 = 13
8 F 1 2 = 9
9 B C 6 = 5
10 B 1 2 = 6
11 C D 1 = 7
12 C 2 3 = 4

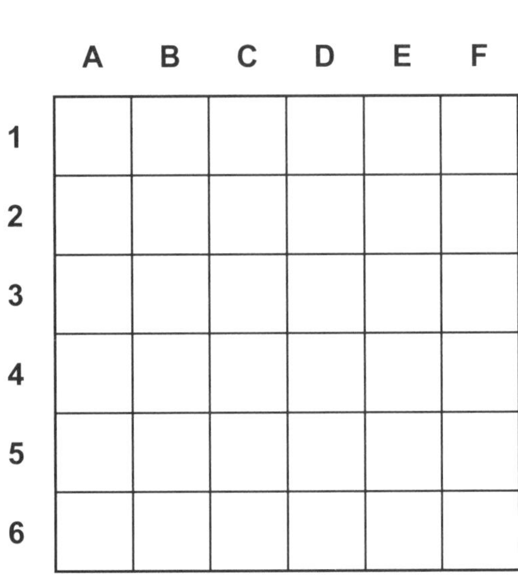

LEVEL 4

68 The object of this puzzle is to trace a single path from the top left corner to the bottom right corner of the grid, moving through all of the cells in either a horizontal, vertical, or diagonal direction.

Every cell must be entered once only, and your path should take you through the numbers in the sequence 1-2-3-4-1-2-3-4, etc.

Can you find the way?

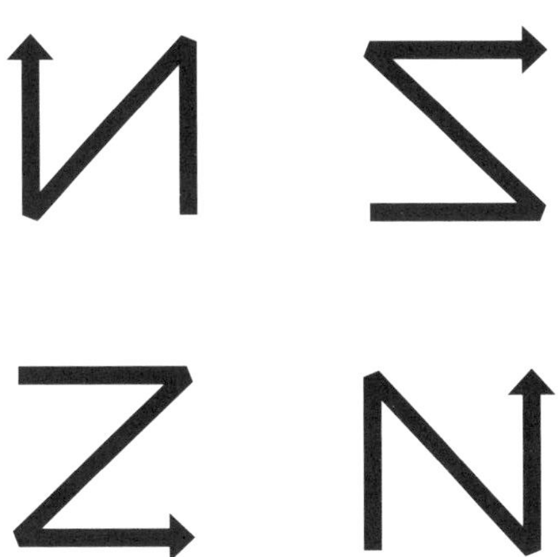

1	2	3	2	1	4	4	2
3	4	3	4	1	3	3	1
2	4	1	2	2	4	3	2
1	2	3	1	1	2	4	1
3	3	2	4	1	3	2	3
4	1	4	2	4	2	4	1
3	1	1	1	3	4	3	3
4	2	2	3	4	1	2	4

69 A standard set of 28 dominoes has been laid out as shown. Can you draw in the edges of them all?

The check-box is provided as an aid and the domino already placed will help.

0-0	0-1	0-2	0-3	0-4	0-5	0-6
						✓

1-1	1-2	1-3	1-4	1-5	1-6	2-2

2-3	2-4	2-5	2-6	3-3	3-4	3-5

3-6	4-4	4-5	4-6	5-5	5-6	6-6

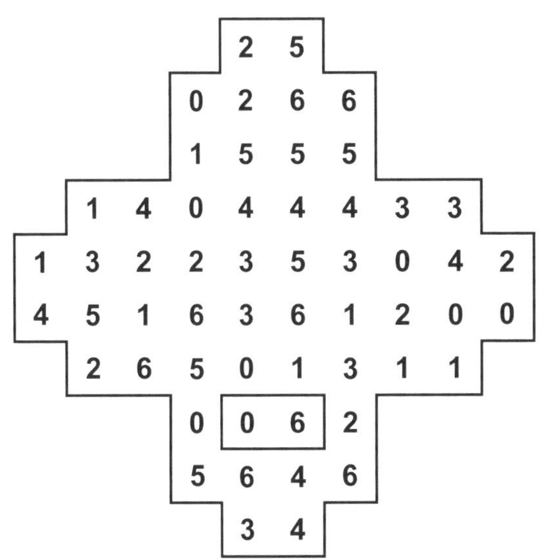

LEVEL 4

70

Draw a single continuous loop, by connecting the dots. No line may cross the path of another.

The figure inside each set of any four surrounding dots indicates the total number of surrounding lines.

	0	2			1		2	3	
1								1	
		1			1	2	1		1
	2	3		0			2		1
2			1					1	
2	1		2			3	2		
2	0				2		0	1	2
1				2	1			3	
1	1	0				2		1	2
		1	1		1	1			
3			2			1		0	
	1		2	1			3	2	

71

Place the eight tiles into the puzzle grid so that all adjacent numbers on each tile match up.

Tiles may be rotated through 360 degrees, but none may be flipped over.

1	2
2	1

2	1
4	4

4	2
3	1

4	1
4	3

2	3
1	1

3	2
1	2

4	4
2	1

2	4
3	3

		2	4		
		2	4		

LEVEL 4

72 Every oval shape in this diagram contains a different letter of the alphabet from A to K inclusive.

Use the clues to determine their locations. Reference in the clues to "due" means in any location along the same horizontal or vertical line.

1 The A is due south of the G and due west of the F.

2 The E is due south of the J and due east of the C.

3 The F is due south of the H and due west of the K.

4 The H is due south of the B and due west of the E.

5 The I is due north of both the B and the D.

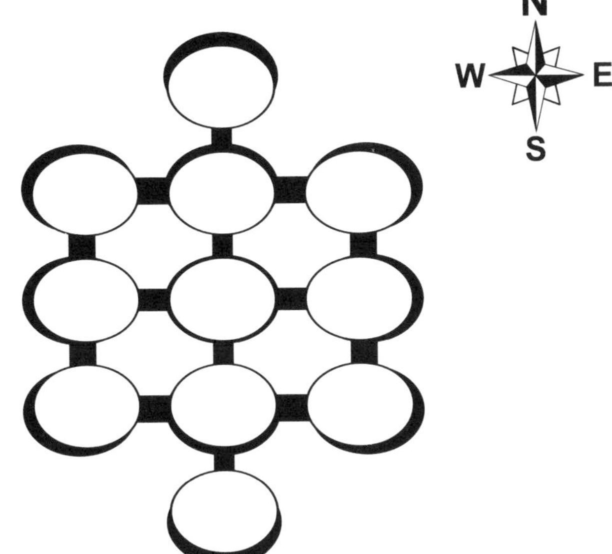

73 Draw walls to partition the grid into areas (some walls are already drawn in for you).

Each area must contain two circles, area sizes must match those numbers shown next to the grid, and each "+" must be linked to at least two walls.

2, 3, 3, 5, 6, 6

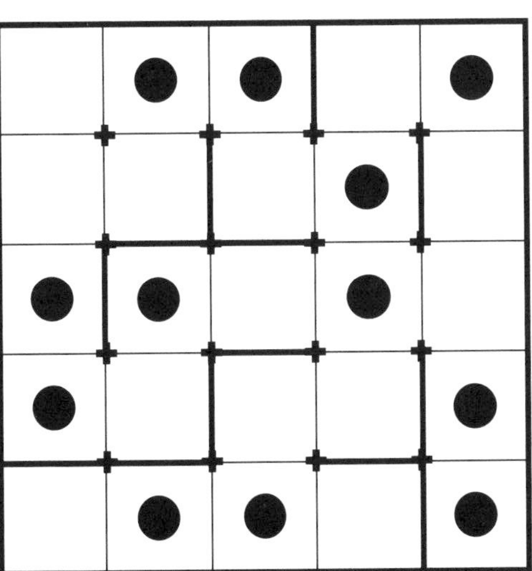

74 Twelve L-shapes need to be inserted in the grid, and each L has one hole in it.

There are three pieces of each of the four kinds shown here, and any piece may be turned or flipped over before being put in the grid. No pieces of the same kind touch, even at a corner.

The pieces fit together so well that you cannot see any spaces between them; only the holes show.

Can you tell where the Ls are?

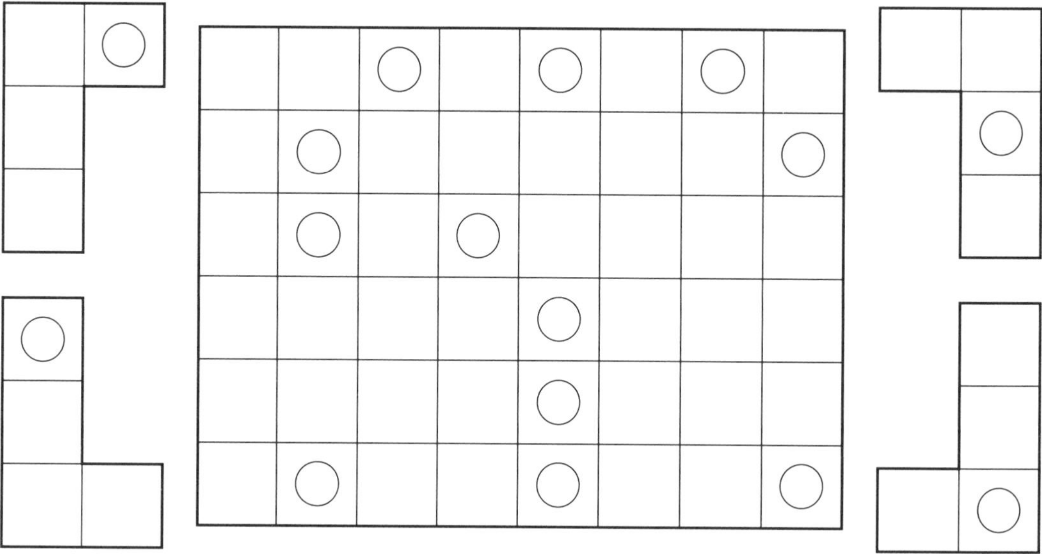

75 Fill the three empty circles with the symbols +, –, and x in some order, to make a sum that totals the central number. Each symbol must be used once, and calculations are made in the direction of travel (clockwise).

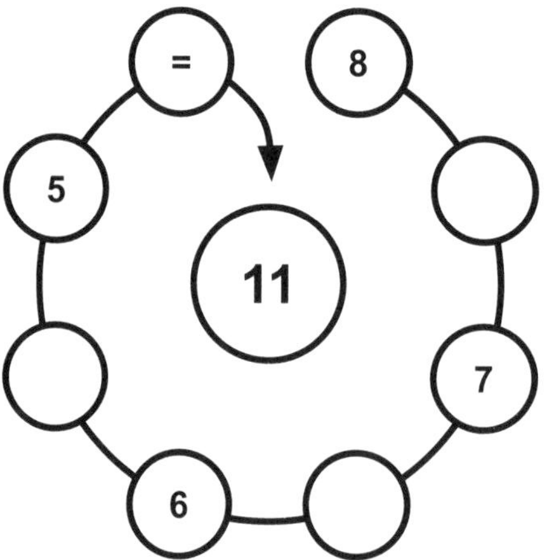

LEVEL 4

76 Each of the small squares in the grid below contains either A, B, or C. Each row, column, and diagonal line of six squares has exactly two of each letter. Can you tell the letter in each square?

Across

3 The Cs are between the Bs

4 Each B is directly next to and right of an A

Down

1 The Cs are lower than the Bs

2 The Cs are lower than the As

3 The Cs are between the Bs

4 The Bs are between the As

6 The Cs are lower than the As

	1	2	3	4	5	6
1						
2						
3						
4						
5						
6						

77 Using the numbers below, complete these six equations (three reading across and three reading downwards).

Every number is used once.

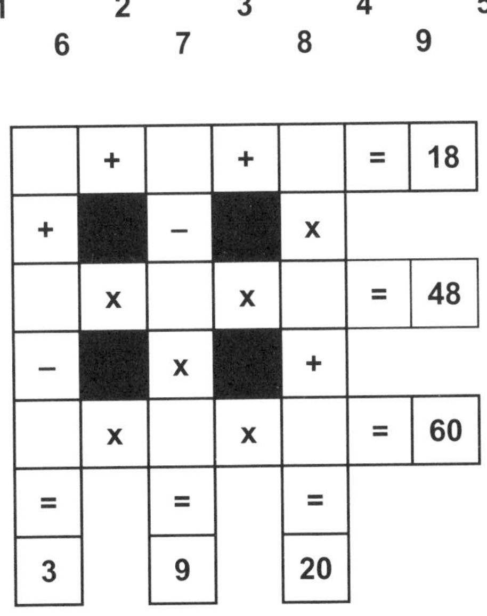

LEVEL 4

78 The chart gives directions to a hidden treasure behind the central black square in the grid. Move the indicated number of spaces north, south, east, and west (eg 4N means move four squares north) stopping at every square once only to arrive there. At which square should you start?

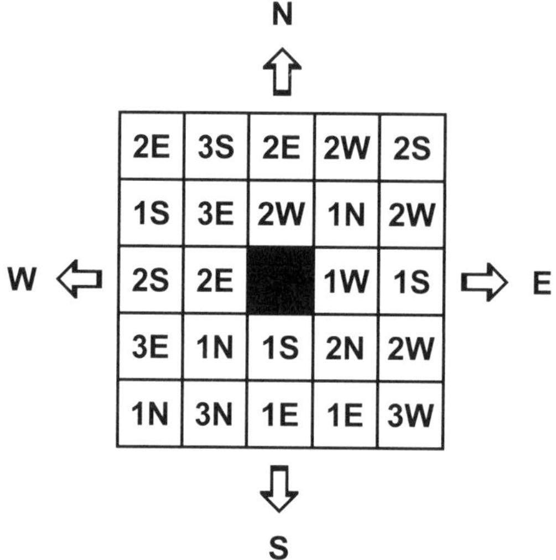

79 The numbers at the top and on the left side show the quantity of single-digit numbers (1-9) used in that row and column. The numbers at the bottom and on the right show the sum of the digits. A number may appear more than once in a row or column, but no numbers are in squares that touch, even at a corner.

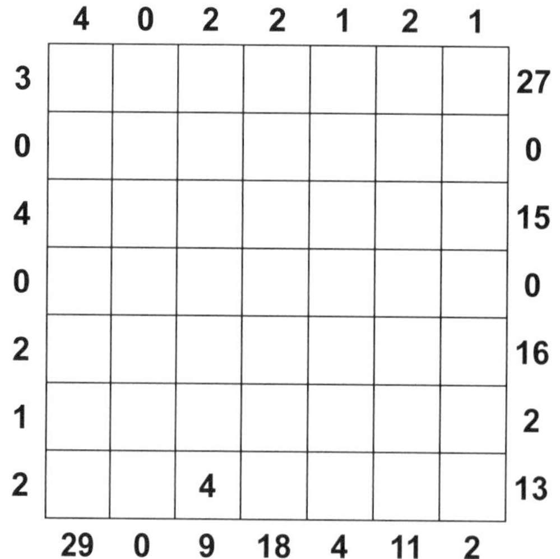

LEVEL 4

80

In the square below, change the positions of six numbers, one per horizontal row, vertical column, and long diagonal line of six smaller squares, in such a way that the numbers in each row, column, and long diagonal line total exactly 257. Any number may appear more than once in a row, column or line.

23	34	38	39	48	60
75	42	32	25	47	39
67	72	42	24	25	37
25	63	47	51	23	39
22	16	62	60	63	40
48	40	42	49	56	27

81

The blank squares below should be filled with whole numbers between 1 and 30 inclusive, any of which may occur more than once, or not at all.

The numbers in every horizontal row add up to the totals on the right, as do the two long diagonal lines; while those in every vertical column add up to the totals along the bottom.

							76
14	17		21	24	19	4	107
13	7	11				20	111
27	21	10		6		19	93
9		28	11	8	3		91
		5	14		24	15	107
29	13		15	23	10		111
	9	14		25	4	27	98
111	92	80	82	141	92	120	105

LEVEL 5

1 Can you place the hexagons into the grid, so that where any hexagon touches another along a straight line, the number in both triangles is the same? No rotation of any hexagon is allowed!

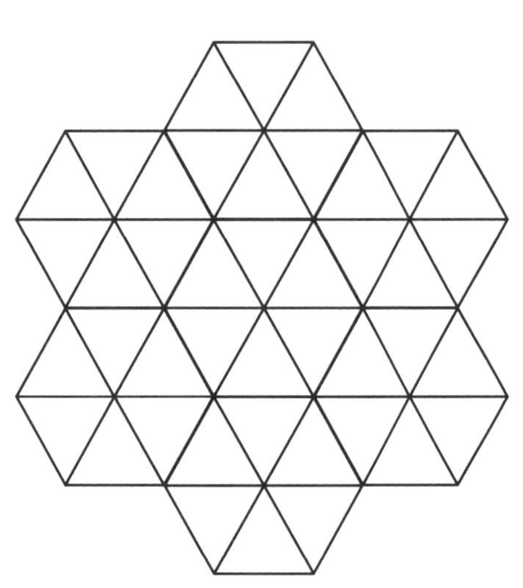

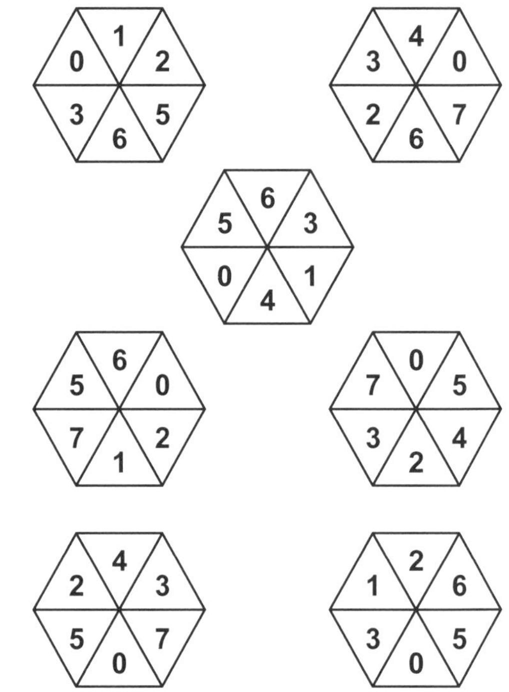

2 Can you place the vessels into the diagram? Some parts of vessels or sea squares have already been filled in. A number to the right or below a row or column refers to the number of occupied squares in that row or column.

Any vessel may be positioned horizontally or vertically, but no part of a vessel touches part of any other vessel, either horizontally, vertically, or diagonally.

Empty Area of Sea: ≈

Aircraft Carrier: ◀■■▶

Battleships: ◀■▶ ◀■▶

Cruisers: ◀▶ ◀▶ ◀▶

Submarines: ● ● ● ●

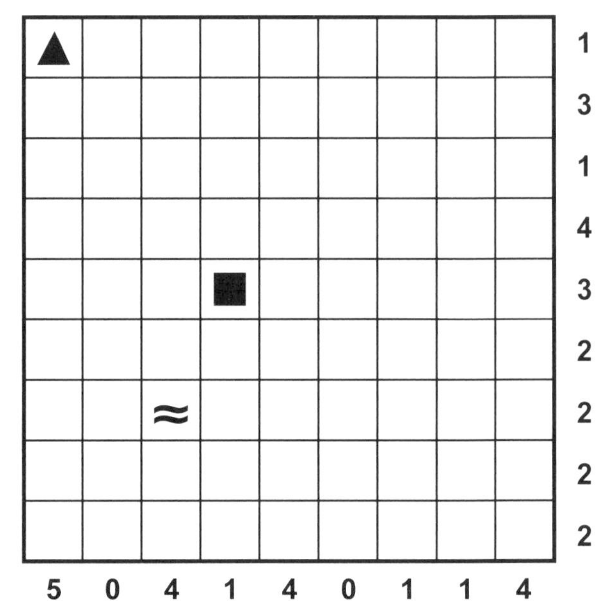

LEVEL 5

3 Each horizontal row and vertical column should contain different shapes and different numbers.

Every square will contain one number and one shape, and no combination may be repeated anywhere else in the puzzle.

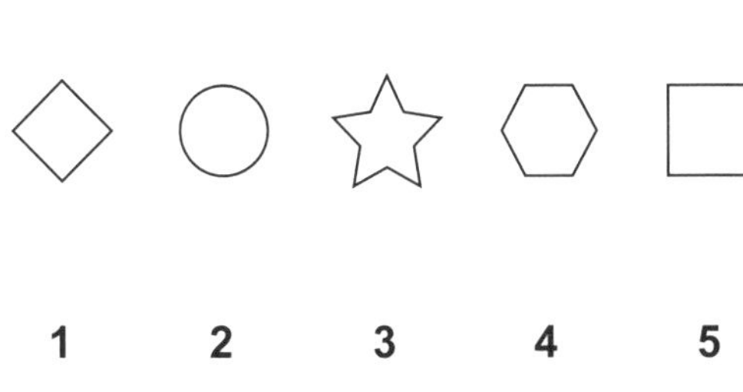

		⬡ 1	□	
⬡			○	◇
		5	3	
4	□			
◇			⬡	2

4 In the diagram below, what number should replace the question mark?

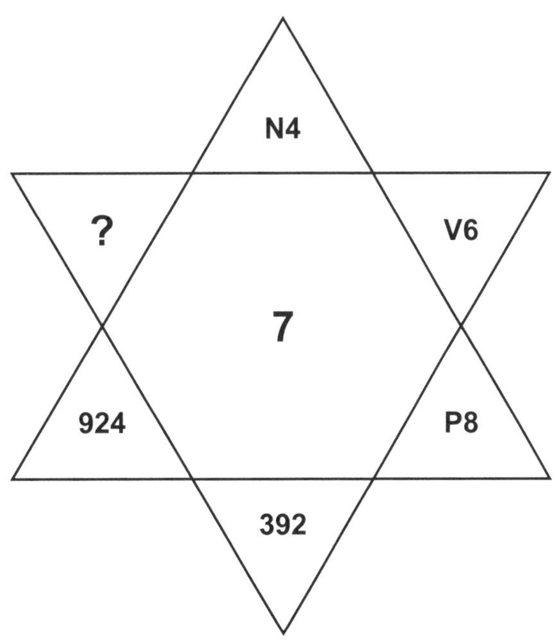

LEVEL 5

5 Every brick in this pyramid contains a number which is the sum of the two numbers below it, so that F=A+B, etc.

Just work out the missing numbers!

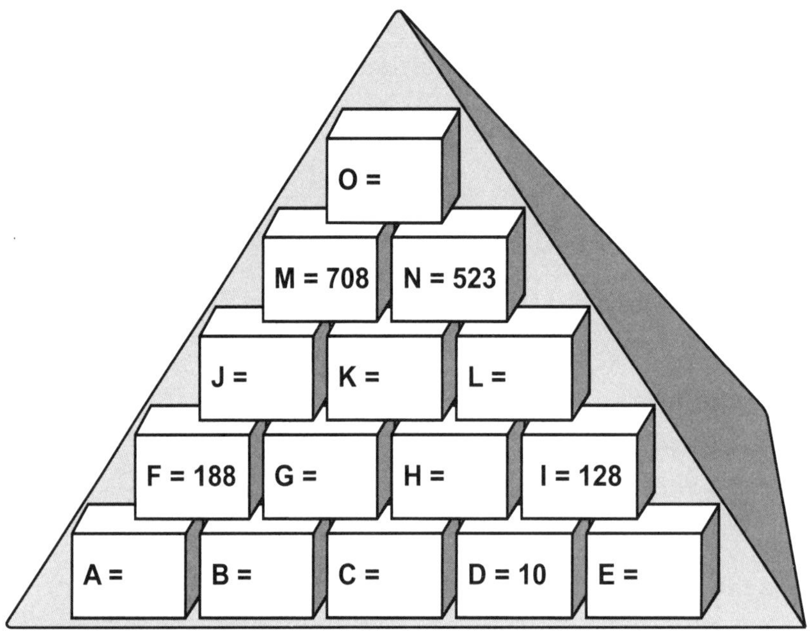

6 In this puzzle, an amateur coin collector has been out with his metal detector, searching for booty. He didn't have time to dig up all the coins he found, so has made a grid map, showing their locations, in the hope that if he loses the map, at least no-one else will understand it…

Those squares containing numbers are empty, but where a number appears in a square, it indicates how many coins are located in the squares (up to a maximum of eight) surrounding the numbered one, touching it at any corner or side. There is only one coin in any individual square.

Place a circle into every square containing a coin.

	1					2		1	
2			3						1
	2	1			3		3		0
		1		1					0
0			2	2	1		2		
	3								
						2		2	
	3		1			2	1		
	4	4	4		3			1	
					2			0	

LEVEL 5

7 Given that the letters are valued 1-26 according to their places in the alphabet, can you crack the mystery code to reveal the missing letter?

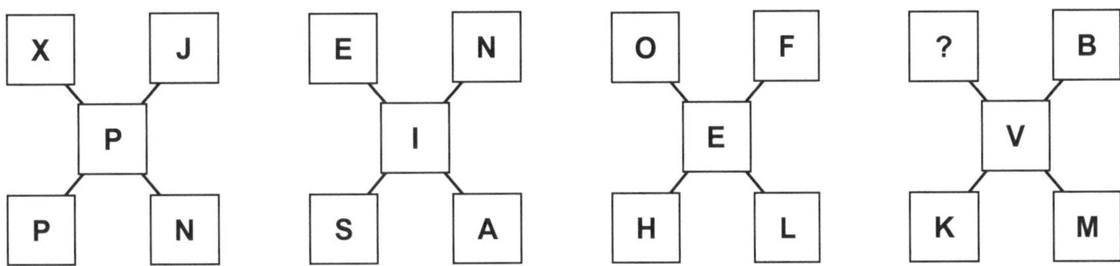

8 Place all twelve of the pieces into the grid. Any may be rotated or flipped over, but none may touch another, not even diagonally. The numbers outside the grid refer to the number of consecutive black squares; and each block is separated from the others by at least one white square. For instance, "3 2" could refer to a row with none, one or more white squares, then three black squares, then at least one white square, then two more black squares, followed by any number of white squares.

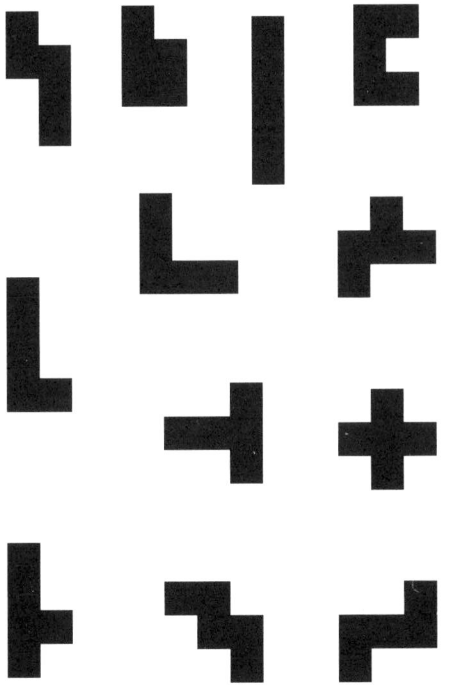

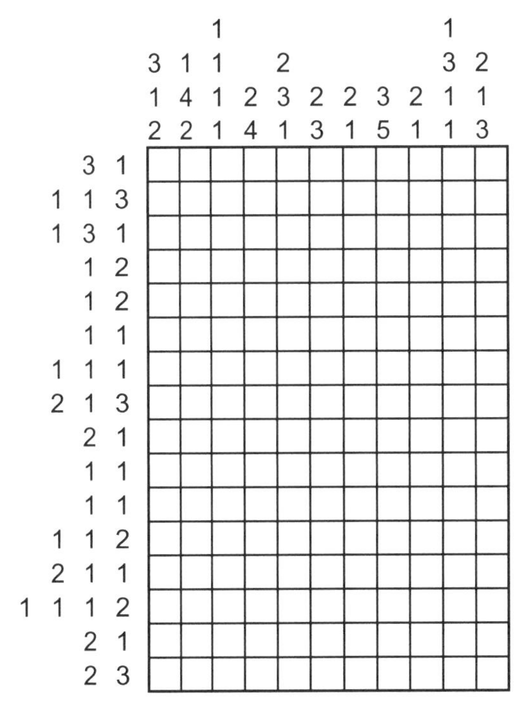

LEVEL 5

9 Each of the eight segments of the spider's web should be filled with a different number from 1 to 8, in such a way that every ring also contains a different number from 1 to 8.

The segments run from the outside of the spider's web to the middle, and the rings run all the way around.

Some numbers are already in place. Can you fill in the rest?

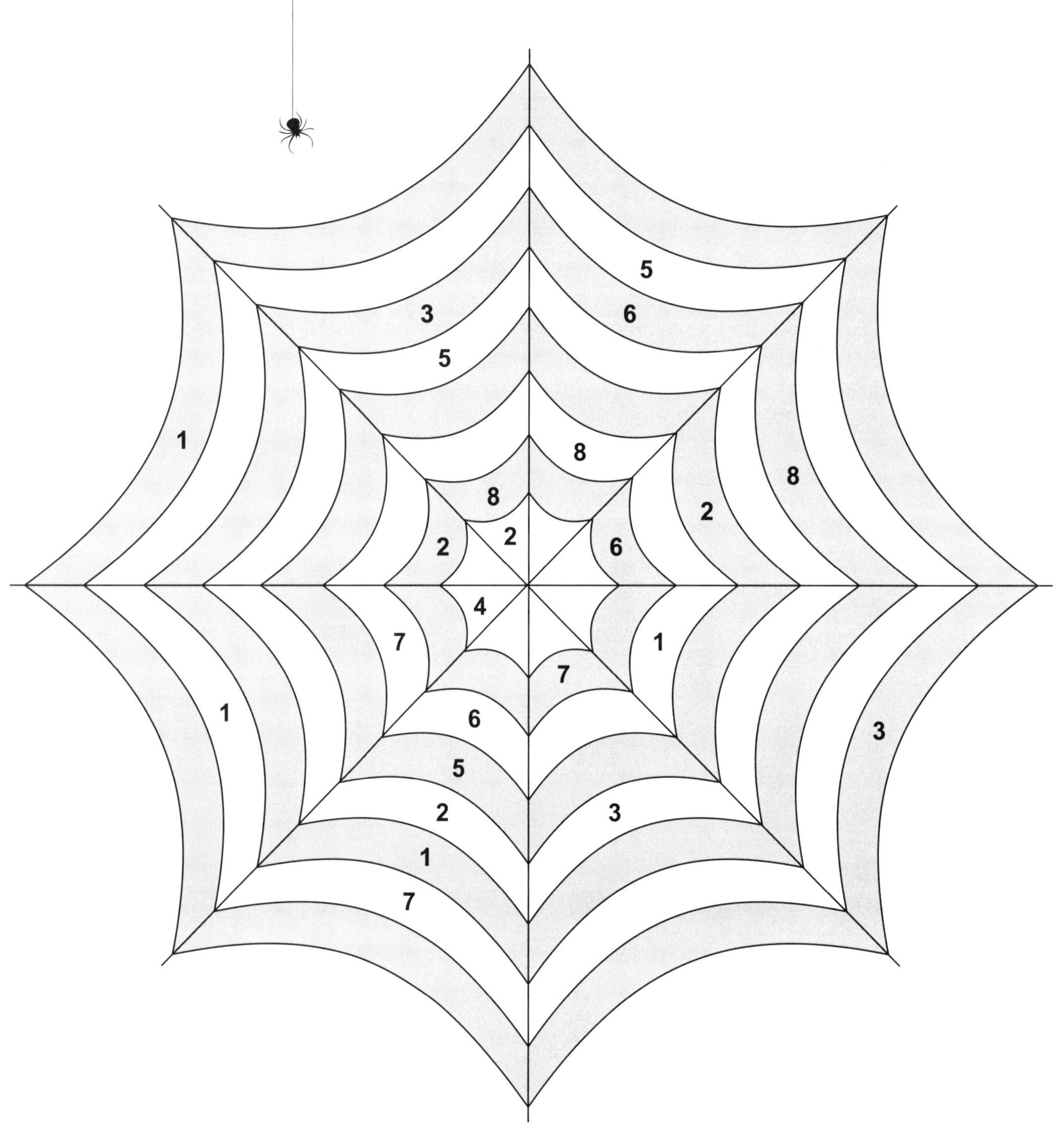

10 Every row and column in this grid originally contained one heart, one club, one diamond, one spade, and two blank squares, although not necessarily in that order.

Every symbol with a black arrow refers to the first of the four symbols encountered in the direction of the arrow. Every symbol with a white arrow refers to the second of the four symbols encountered in the direction of the arrow.

Can you complete the original grid?

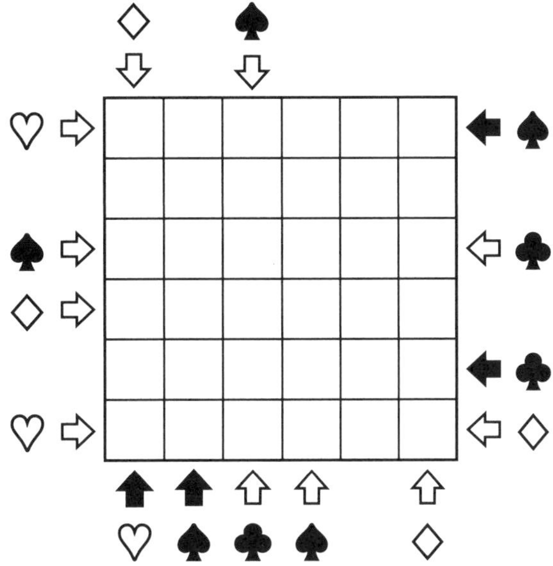

11 Fill the grid so that every horizontal row and vertical column contains the numbers 1-5. Any arrows in the grid always point toward a square that contains a lower number.

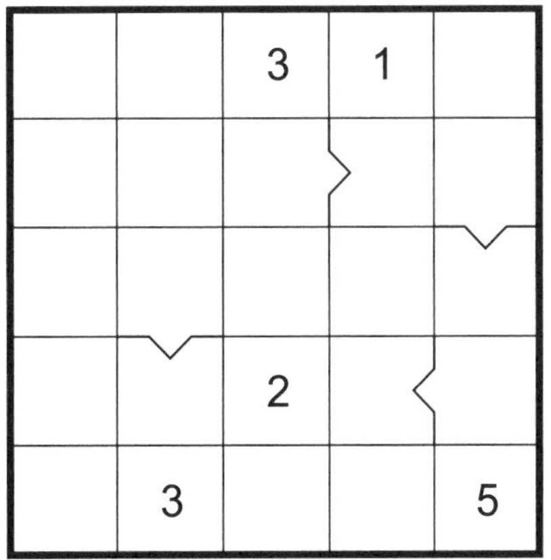

LEVEL 5

12

With the starter already given, can you fit all of the remaining listed numbers into this grid? Take care, this puzzle may not be as easy as it looks!

11	325	960	6715	82341
20	333	987	7023	95950
21	366	1146	7223	136783
23	456	3383 ✓	7411	203392
24	507	3597	7445	254256
34	510	3887	7530	258636
61	633	5071	8322	364483
62	740	5593	9235	527993
89	782	6271	9338	533718
93	789	6424	9708	630005
123	826	6444	33914	694812
203	881	6546	49193	813320

13

The grid should be filled with numbers from 1 to 6, so that each number appears just once in every row and column.

The clues refer to the digit totals in the squares, e.g. A 1 2 3 = 6 means that the numbers in squares A1, A2 and A3 add up to 6.

1 D E 1 = 8
2 D 2 3 = 9
3 A B 2 = 5
4 A B 3 = 10
5 A 4 5 6 = 9
6 B 4 5 6 = 13
7 C D 5 = 5
8 F 5 6 = 7
9 C D 6 = 3
10 C 2 3 = 5
11 E 2 3 = 7

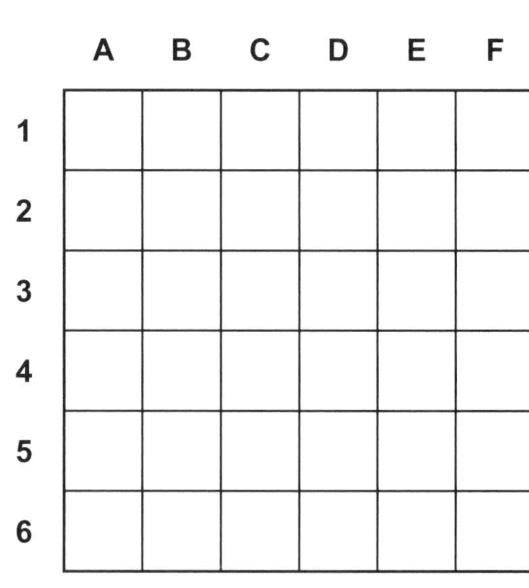

LEVEL 5

14 The object of this puzzle is to trace a single path from the top left corner to the bottom right corner of the grid, moving through all of the cells in either a horizontal, vertical, or diagonal direction.

Every cell must be entered once only, and your path should take you through the numbers in the sequence 1-2-3-4-1-2-3-4, etc.

Can you find the way?

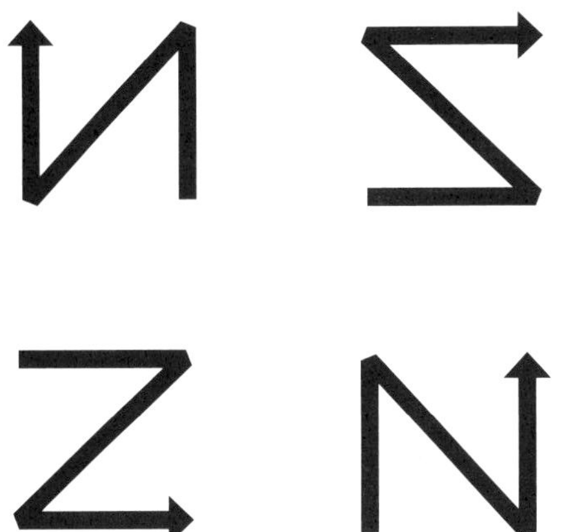

1	2	3	2	3	4	2	3
1	4	1	1	4	2	1	4
4	2	2	3	1	3	1	2
3	1	3	1	4	3	4	3
4	2	4	2	4	2	1	4
2	3	4	3	3	1	1	3
3	1	2	3	4	2	2	3
4	1	2	1	4	1	2	4

15 A standard set of 28 dominoes has been laid out as shown. Can you draw in the edges of them all?

The check-box is provided as an aid and the domino already placed will help.

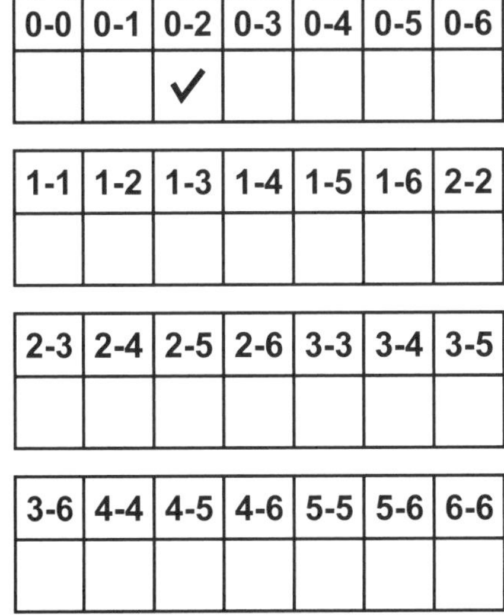

0-0	0-1	0-2	0-3	0-4	0-5	0-6
		✓				

1-1	1-2	1-3	1-4	1-5	1-6	2-2

2-3	2-4	2-5	2-6	3-3	3-4	3-5

3-6	4-4	4-5	4-6	5-5	5-6	6-6

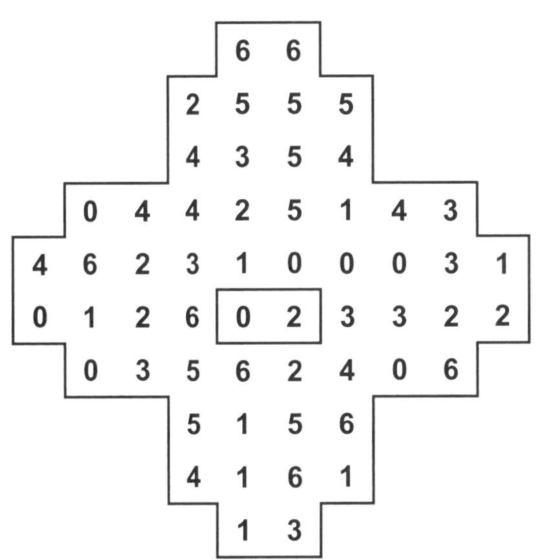

LEVEL 5

16

Draw a single continuous loop, by connecting the dots. No line may cross the path of another.

The figure inside each set of any four surrounding dots indicates the total number of surrounding lines.

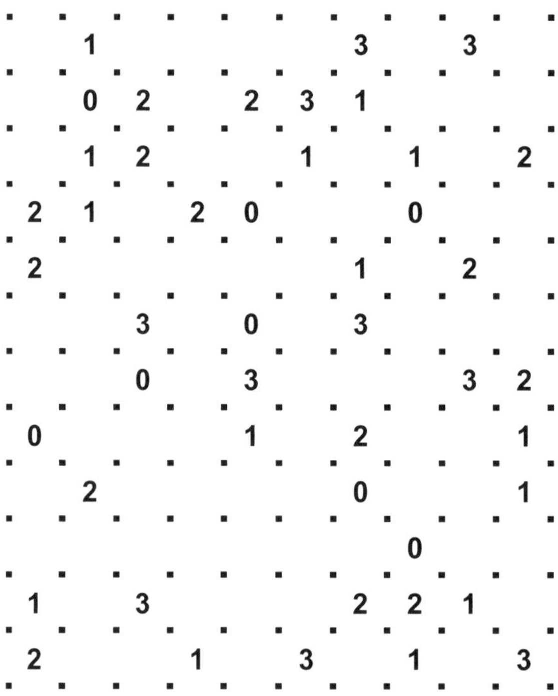

17

Place the eight tiles into the puzzle grid so that all adjacent numbers on each tile match up.

Tiles may be rotated through 360 degrees, but none may be flipped over.

4	1
2	1

2	3
3	1

1	3
2	4

3	1
1	2

1	3
3	1

4	3
1	2

1	3
4	3

3	1
4	1

		3	2		
		3	1		

LEVEL 5

18 Every oval shape in this diagram contains a different letter of the alphabet from A to K inclusive.

Use the clues to determine their locations. Reference in the clues to “due” means in any location along the same horizontal or vertical line.

1 The A is not next to the B, which is next to and south of the E.

2 The C is next to and east of the J, which is due south of both the B and the G.

3 The F is further west than the H, which is further west than the D.

4 The I is next to and east of the G, which is next to and east of the K.

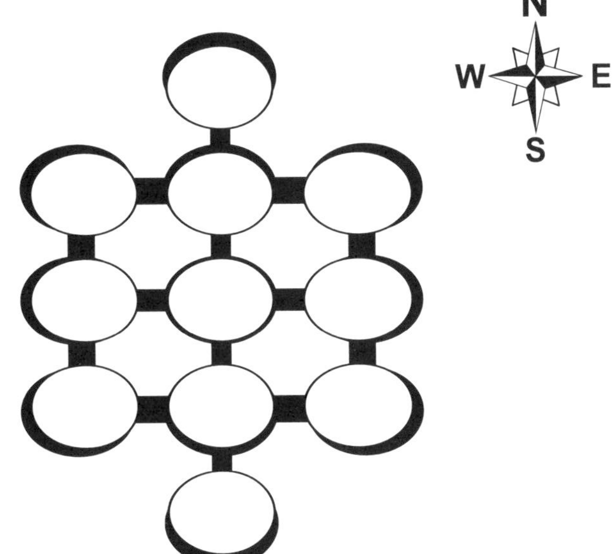

19 Draw walls to partition the grid into areas (some walls are already drawn in for you).

Each area must contain two circles, area sizes must match those numbers shown next to the grid, and each “+” must be linked to at least two walls.

3, 5, 5, 6, 6

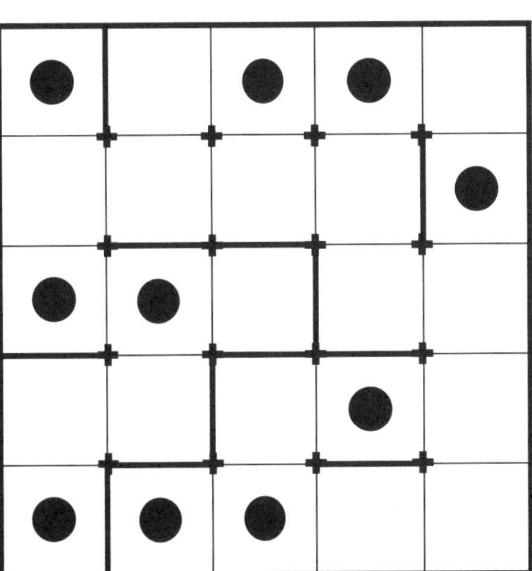

LEVEL 5

20 Twelve L-shapes need to be inserted in the grid, and each L has one hole in it.

There are three pieces of each of the four kinds shown here, and any piece may be turned or flipped over before being put in the grid. No pieces of the same kind touch, even at a corner.

The pieces fit together so well that you cannot see any spaces between them; only the holes show.

Can you tell where the Ls are?

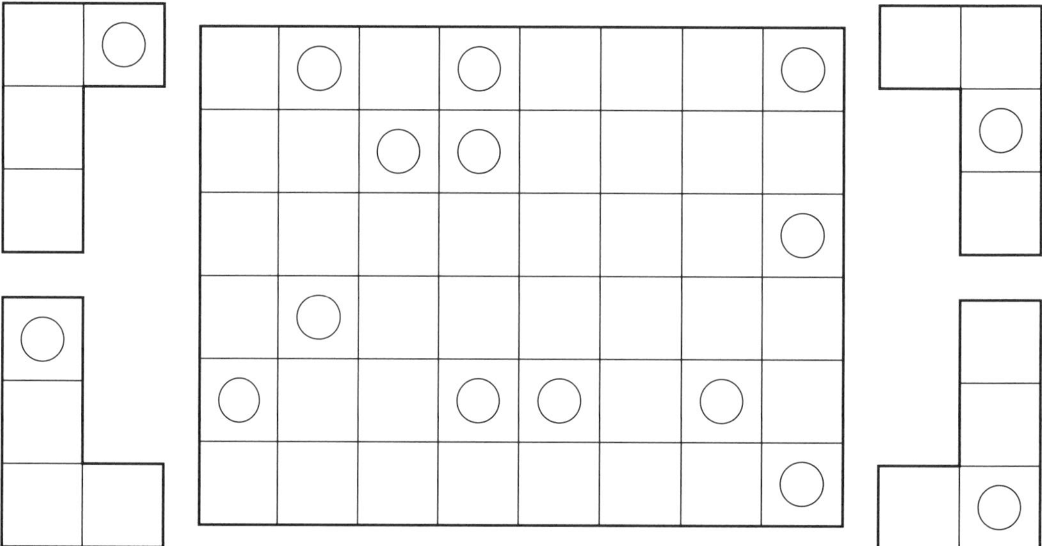

21 Fill the three empty circles with the symbols +, –, and x in some order, to make a sum that totals the central number. Each symbol must be used once, and calculations are made in the direction of travel (clockwise).

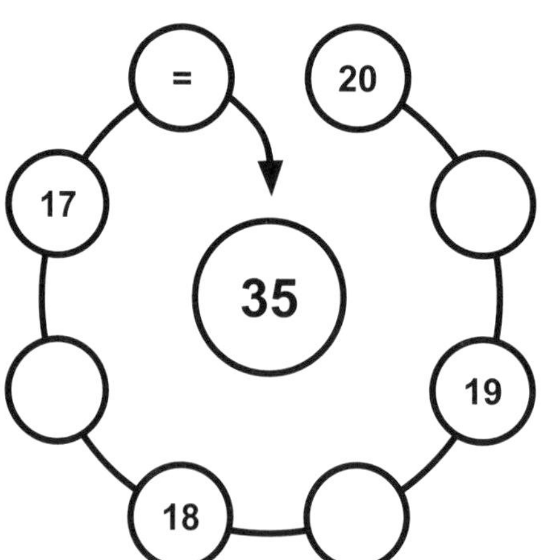

LEVEL 5

22 Each of the small squares in the grid below contains either A, B, or C. Each row, column, and diagonal line of six squares has exactly two of each letter. Can you tell the letter in each square?

Across

1 The Bs are further right than the Cs
2 The As are between the Bs
4 The Bs are between the Cs
5 The Cs are between the As
6 The As are between the Bs

Down

1 No two letters the same are directly next to each other
2 The Cs are next to each other and are higher than the Bs
3 Each A is directly next to and below a C
5 The Bs are higher than the As

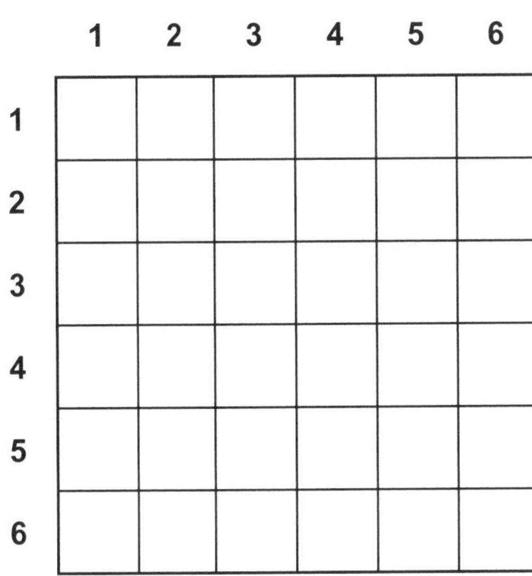

23 Using the numbers below, complete these six equations (three reading across and three reading downwards).

Every number is used once.

1 2 3 4 5 6 7 8 9

	x		+		=	26
x	■	+	■	x		
	–		x		=	6
+	■	–	■	+		
	+		+		=	15
=		=		=		
43		2		25		

LEVEL 5

24 The chart gives directions to a hidden treasure behind the central black square in the grid. Move the indicated number of spaces north, south, east, and west (eg 4N means move four squares north) stopping at every square once only to arrive there. At which square should you start?

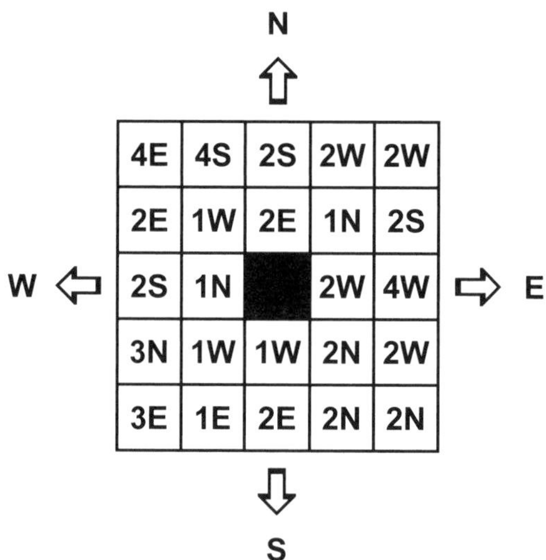

25 The numbers at the top and on the left side show the quantity of single-digit numbers (1-9) used in that row and column. The numbers at the bottom and on the right show the sum of the digits. A number may appear more than once in a row or column, but no numbers are in squares that touch, even at a corner.

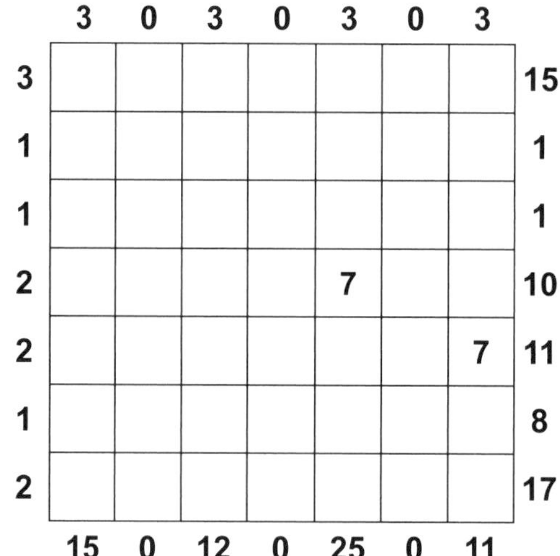

LEVEL 5

26 In the square below, change the positions of six numbers, one per horizontal row, vertical column, and long diagonal line of six smaller squares, in such a way that the numbers in each row, column, and long diagonal line total exactly 277. Any number may appear more than once in a row, column or line.

37	10	64	52	103	37
57	46	44	21	47	52
59	83	46	30	33	42
54	48	47	62	38	45
34	43	55	55	27	42
52	26	47	47	46	31

27 The blank squares below should be filled with whole numbers between 1 and 30 inclusive, any of which may occur more than once, or not at all.

The numbers in every horizontal row add up to the totals on the right, as do the two long diagonal lines; while those in every vertical column add up to the totals along the bottom.

							119
14			3	6	13	19	101
2	1	12		11	24		84
	18	15	7	4		5	107
22	9	13		20	16		114
7	16		18	12	11		110
	12	17	30		5	9	125
10		23	26	6		21	115
112	88	135	134	84	111	92	92

LEVEL 5

28

Can you place the hexagons into the grid, so that where any hexagon touches another along a straight line, the number in both triangles is the same? No rotation of any hexagon is allowed!

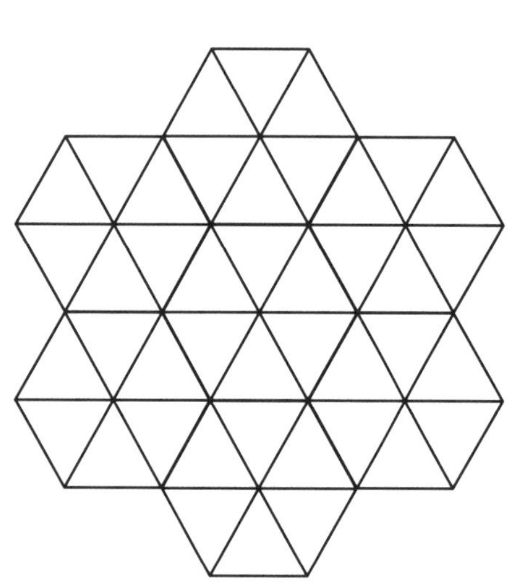

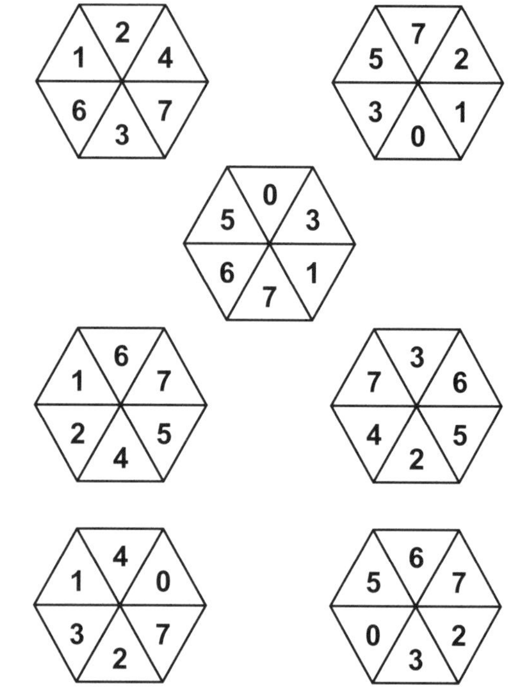

29

Can you place the vessels into the diagram? Some parts of vessels or sea squares have already been filled in. A number to the right or below a row or column refers to the number of occupied squares in that row or column.

Any vessel may be positioned horizontally or vertically, but no part of a vessel touches part of any other vessel, either horizontally, vertically, or diagonally.

Empty Area of Sea: ≈

Aircraft Carrier: ◀■■▶

Battleships: ◀■▶ ◀■▶

Cruisers: ◀▶ ◀▶ ◀▶

Submarines: ● ● ● ●

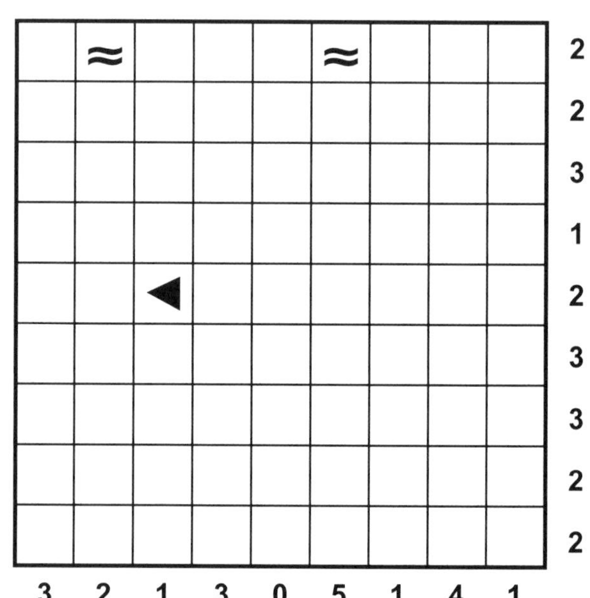

LEVEL 5

30 Each horizontal row and vertical column should contain different shapes and different numbers.

Every square will contain one number and one shape, and no combination may be repeated anywhere else in the puzzle.

				2
	3		2	
			5	
	1			

31 Which of the four lettered alternatives (A, B, C, or D) fits most logically into the empty square?

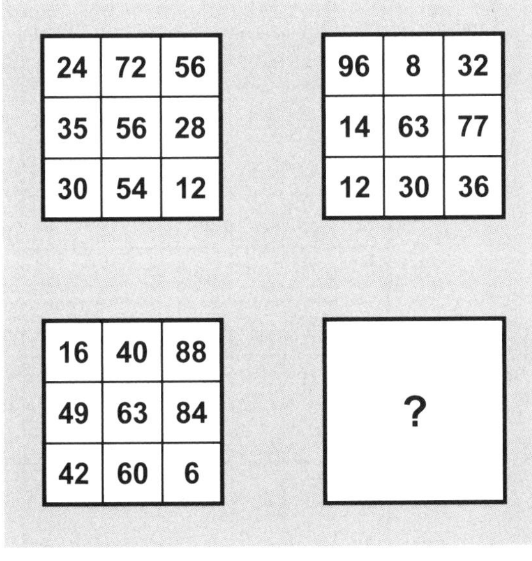

24	72	56
35	56	28
30	54	12

96	8	32
14	63	77
12	30	36

16	40	88
49	63	84
42	60	6

42	16	88
28	36	48
16	35	42

A

16	60	82
36	24	56
26	20	40

B

72	56	64
56	44	28
48	24	18

C

48	64	80
42	70	21
54	18	66

D

LEVEL 5

32

Every brick in this pyramid contains a number which is the sum of the two numbers below it, so that F=A+B, etc.

Just work out the missing numbers!

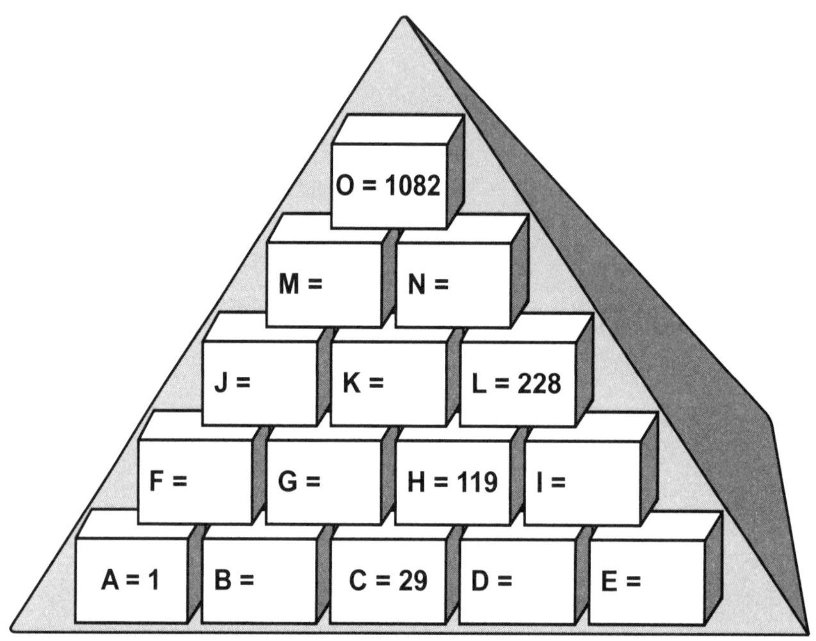

33

In this puzzle, an amateur coin collector has been out with his metal detector, searching for booty. He didn't have time to dig up all the coins he found, so has made a grid map, showing their locations, in the hope that if he loses the map, at least no-one else will understand it…

Those squares containing numbers are empty, but where a number appears in a square, it indicates how many coins are located in the squares (up to a maximum of eight) surrounding the numbered one, touching it at any corner or side. There is only one coin in any individual square.

Place a circle into every square containing a coin.

							4		2
0			4	4		4			
	3					3		2	
1			6					2	
			4	2		1		2	
	1	2				2			
	0		1	2			3		
							3		2
			0					3	
0					2		1		

LEVEL 5

34 Given that the letters are valued 1-26 according to their places in the alphabet, can you crack the mystery code to reveal the missing letter?

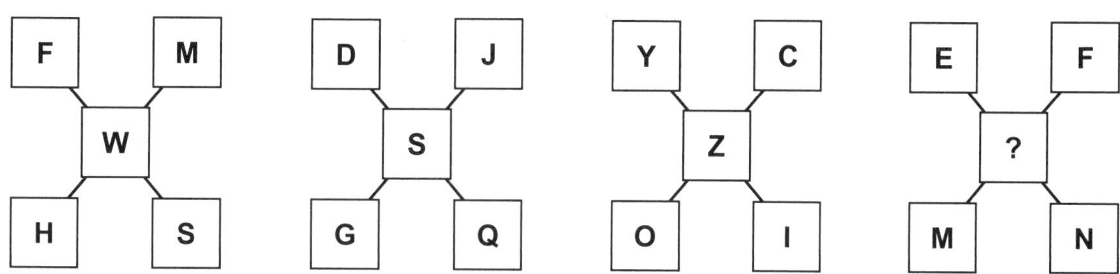

35 Place all twelve of the pieces into the grid. Any may be rotated or flipped over, but none may touch another, not even diagonally. The numbers outside the grid refer to the number of consecutive black squares; and each block is separated from the others by at least one white square. For instance, "3 2" could refer to a row with none, one or more white squares, then three black squares, then at least one white square, then two more black squares, followed by any number of white squares.

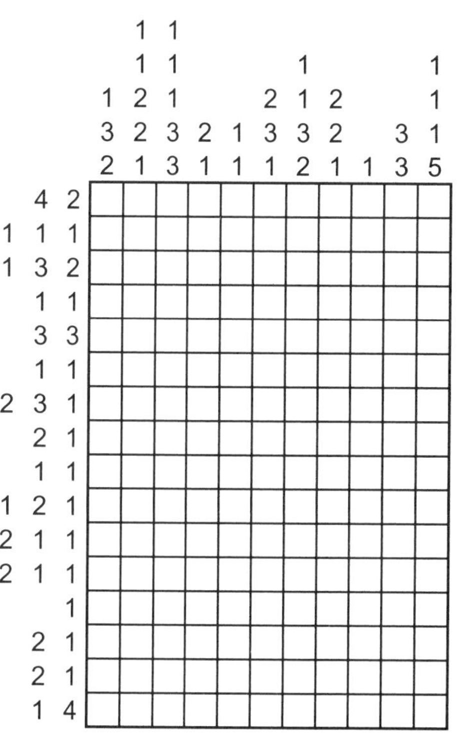

LEVEL 5

36 Each of the eight segments of the spider's web should be filled with a different number from 1 to 8, in such a way that every ring also contains a different number from 1 to 8.

The segments run from the outside of the spider's web to the middle, and the rings run all the way around.

Some numbers are already in place. Can you fill in the rest?

LEVEL 5

37 Every row and column in this grid originally contained one heart, one club, one diamond, one spade, and two blank squares, although not necessarily in that order.

Every symbol with a black arrow refers to the first of the four symbols encountered in the direction of the arrow. Every symbol with a white arrow refers to the second of the four symbols encountered in the direction of the arrow.

Can you complete the original grid?

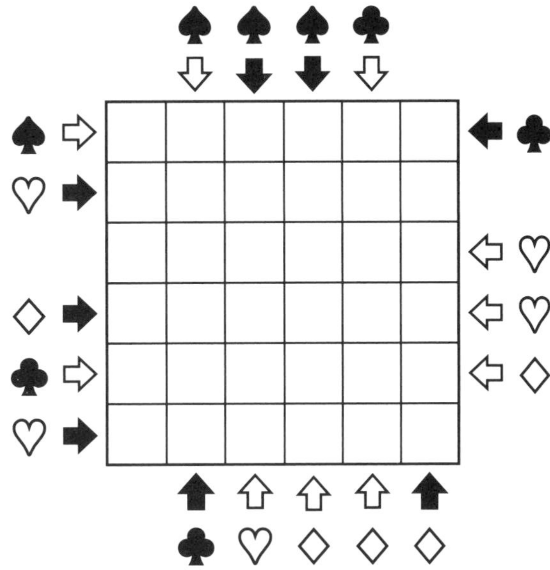

38 Fill the grid so that every horizontal row and vertical column contains the numbers 1-5. Any arrows in the grid always point toward a square that contains a lower number.

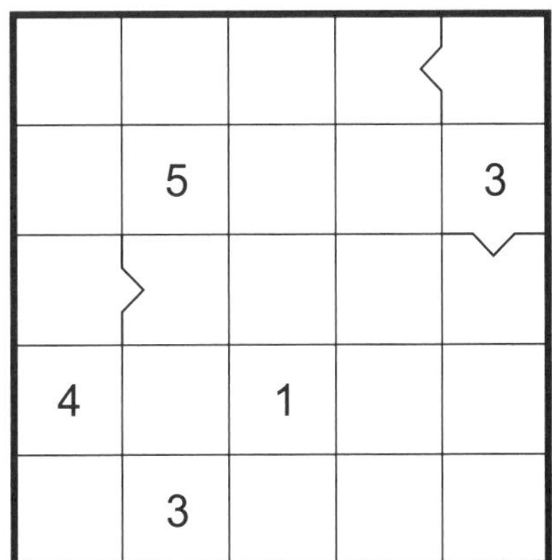

LEVEL 5

39 With the starter already given, can you fit all of the remaining listed numbers into this grid? Take care, this puzzle may not be as easy as it looks!

19	290	691 ✓	2436	69304
23	312	712	4393	74316
34	334	736	5559	92532
58	388	750	5808	93654
61	390	791	17052	116824
90	400	796	18405	122456
93	404	812	21044	216559
99	435	816	27430	225904
179	444	821	39315	565434
182	593	897	41984	572466
222	599	1632	51806	622044
223	682	2211	60453	693637

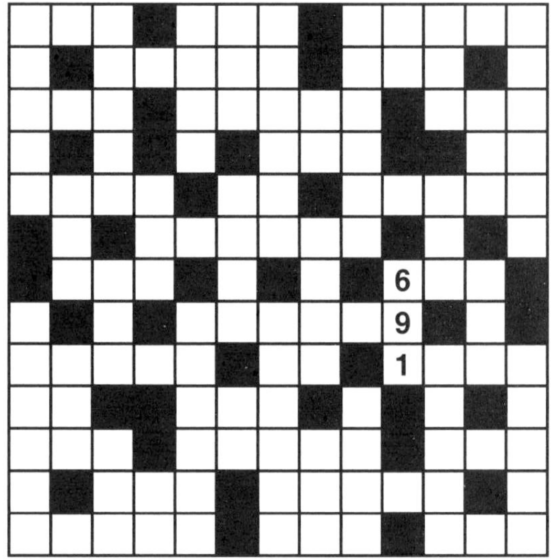

40 The grid should be filled with numbers from 1 to 6, so that each number appears just once in every row and column.

The clues refer to the digit totals in the squares, e.g. A 1 2 3 = 6 means that the numbers in squares A1, A2 and A3 add up to 6.

1 D E 4 = 5
2 E 5 6 = 9
3 D 1 2 = 6
4 A B 1 = 6
5 A B 2 = 8
6 B C D 5 = 10
7 B 3 4 = 7
8 B C 6 = 4
9 C D 3 = 9
10 C 1 2 = 9
11 D E 1 = 7
12 E 3 4 = 3

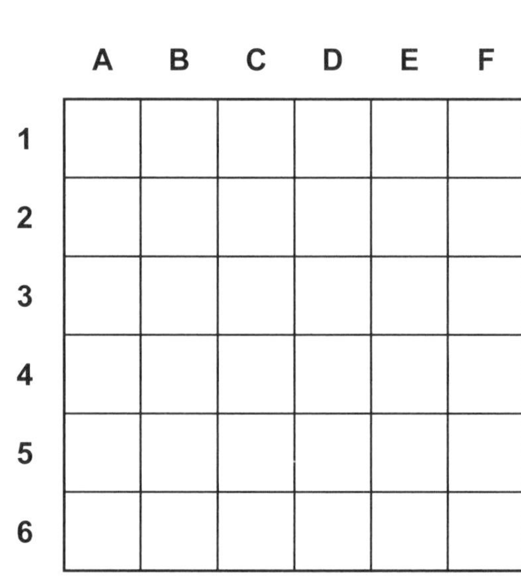

LEVEL 5

41

The object of this puzzle is to trace a single path from the top left corner to the bottom right corner of the grid, moving through all of the cells in either a horizontal, vertical, or diagonal direction.

Every cell must be entered once only, and your path should take you through the numbers in the sequence 1-2-3-4-1-2-3-4, etc.

Can you find the way?

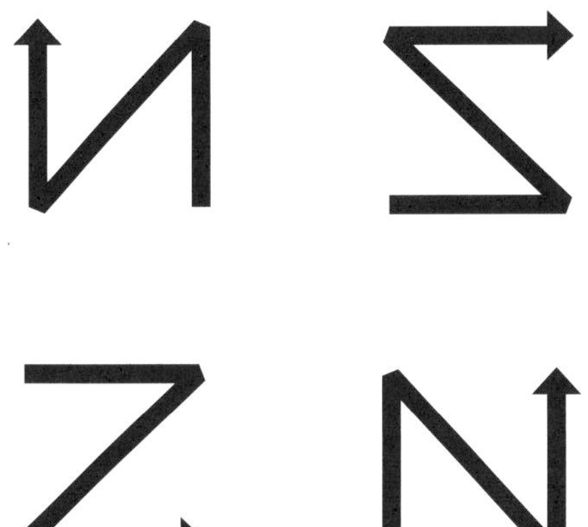

1	1	3	3	2	1	4	4
2	2	4	2	4	3	3	1
3	2	1	3	2	1	2	2
3	4	1	4	1	1	4	3
4	4	3	2	1	2	4	1
3	1	2	4	2	3	3	2
2	3	3	1	3	2	4	3
1	4	4	2	1	4	1	4

42

A standard set of 28 dominoes has been laid out as shown. Can you draw in the edges of them all?

The check-box is provided as an aid and the domino already placed will help.

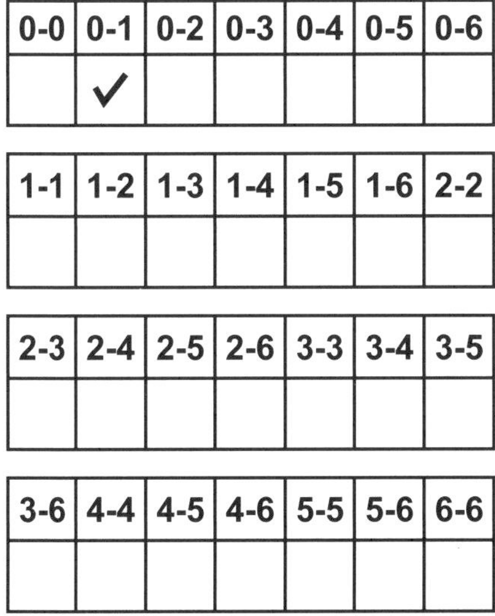

0-0	0-1	0-2	0-3	0-4	0-5	0-6
	✓					

1-1	1-2	1-3	1-4	1-5	1-6	2-2

2-3	2-4	2-5	2-6	3-3	3-4	3-5

3-6	4-4	4-5	4-6	5-5	5-6	6-6

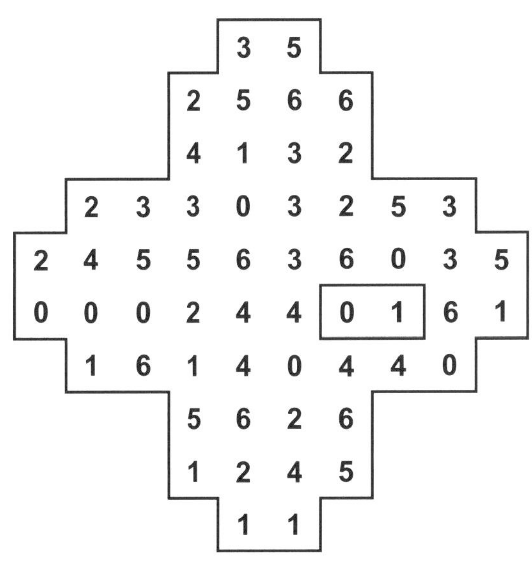

LEVEL 5

43

Draw a single continuous loop, by connecting the dots. No line may cross the path of another.

The figure inside each set of any four surrounding dots indicates the total number of surrounding lines.

	2		1					3	
2	0			3		1		1	
			0	1	1	0		2	
					1			0	
2				1					
2		0			1			3	
2	0		2	2	1		2		1
	1		1			2	2		2
	2			1		3	2	2	
1		3	2		0	1	2		
		3		1			0	2	2
3	1					1	1		

44

Place the eight tiles into the puzzle grid so that all adjacent numbers on each tile match up.

Tiles may be rotated through 360 degrees, but none may be flipped over.

3	4
4	1

2	3
2	4

2	2
3	4

1	4
1	4

4	3
1	3

3	4
4	2

3	2
1	3

4	1
3	2

4	4				
3	1				

LEVEL 5

45 Which of the four lettered alternatives (A, B, C, or D) fits most logically into the empty square?

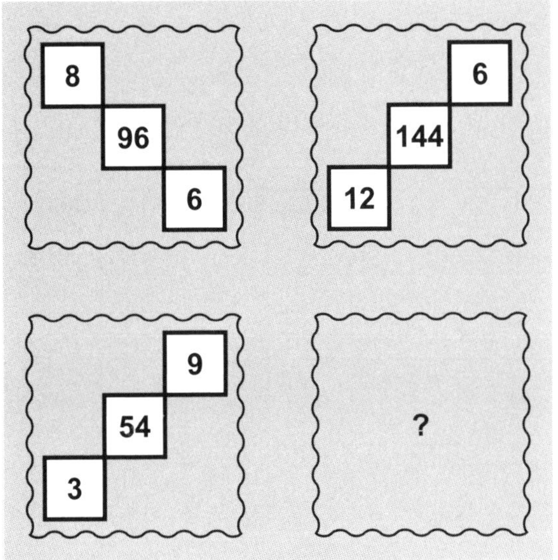

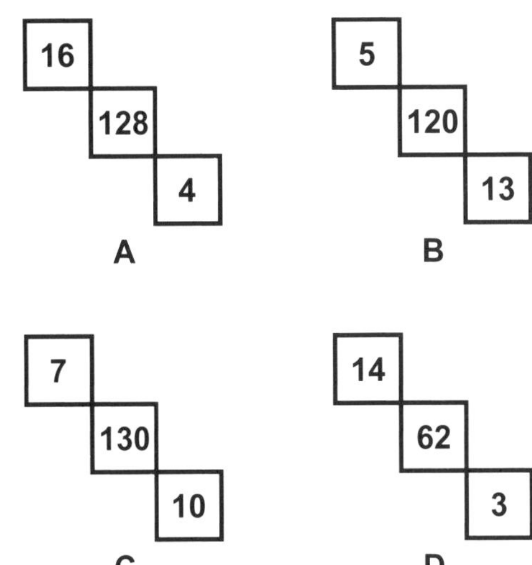

46 Which four pieces can be fitted together to form an exact copy of this shape?

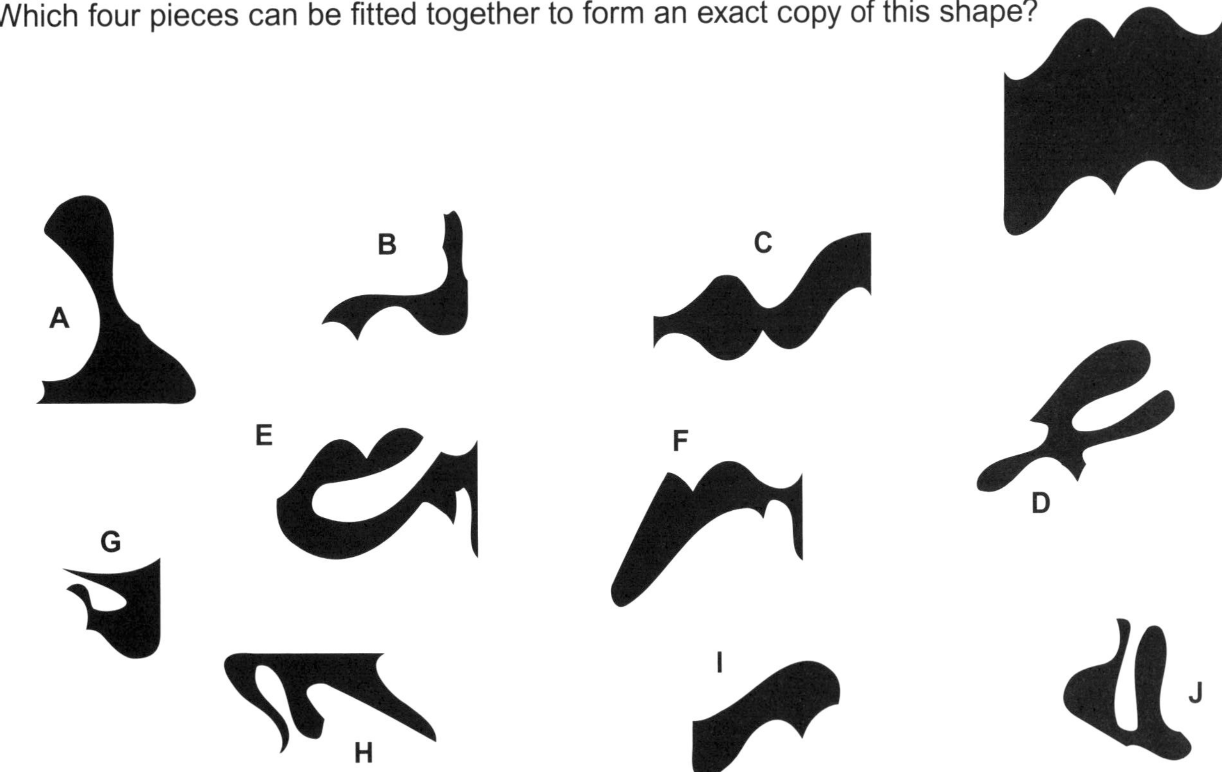

LEVEL 5

47 Twelve L-shapes need to be inserted in the grid, and each L has one hole in it.

There are three pieces of each of the four kinds shown here, and any piece may be turned or flipped over before being put in the grid. No pieces of the same kind touch, even at a corner.

The pieces fit together so well that you cannot see any spaces between them; only the holes show.

Can you tell where the Ls are?

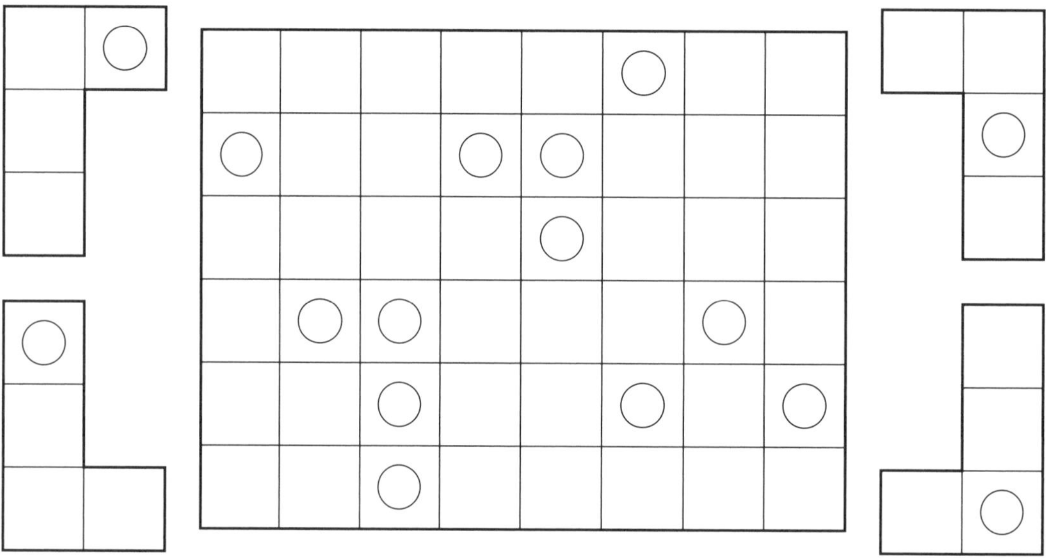

48 Each symbol stands for a different number. In order to reach the correct total at the end of each row and column, what is the value of the circle, cross, pentagon, square and star?

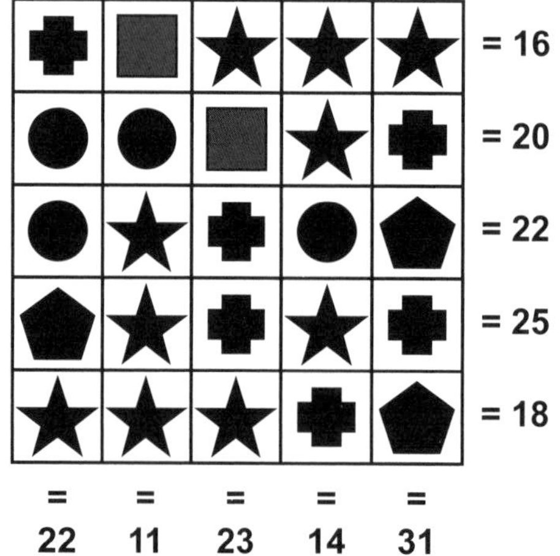

LEVEL 5

49 Each of the small squares in the grid below contains either A, B, or C. Each row, column, and diagonal line of six squares has exactly two of each letter. Can you tell the letter in each square?

Across

1 Any three consecutive squares contain three different letters

3 The Cs are next to each other

4 The Bs are next to each other

5 The As are between the Bs

6 Each A is directly next to and right of a B

Down

1 The As are next to each other and are between the Bs

3 Each B is directly next to and below a C

5 The As are between the Bs

6 The Bs are between the As

	1	2	3	4	5	6
1						
2						
3						
4						
5						
6						

50 Which of the alternatives (A, B, C, or D) comes next in this sequence?

68 K P F L S D

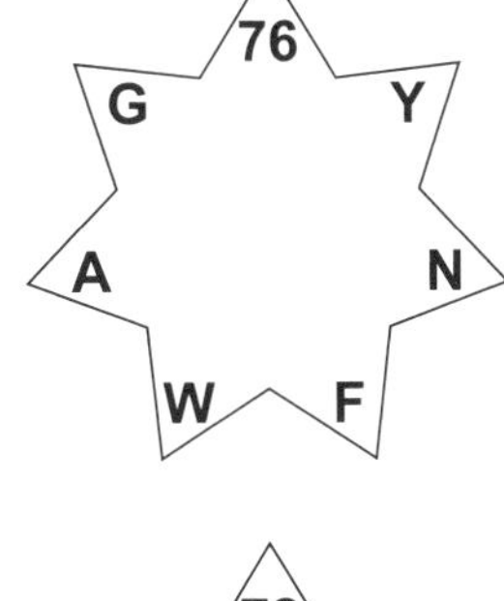

70 T H E R C P

?

72 O L S A D T

A

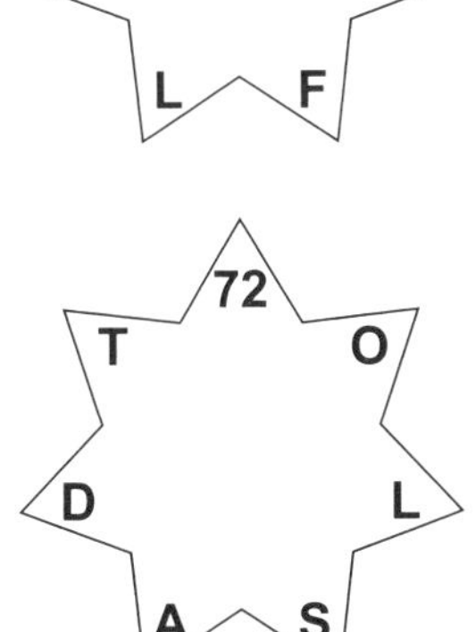

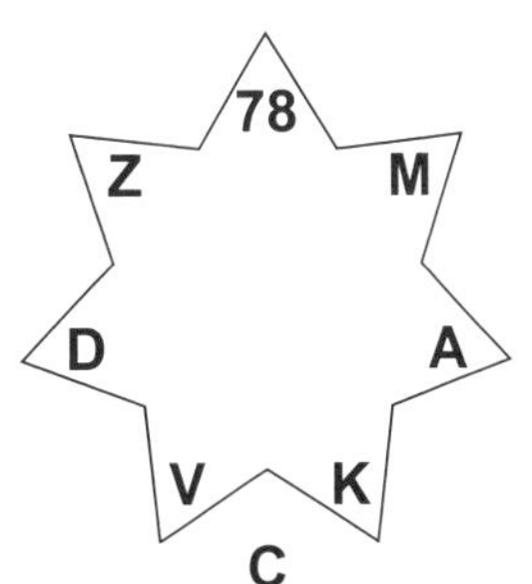

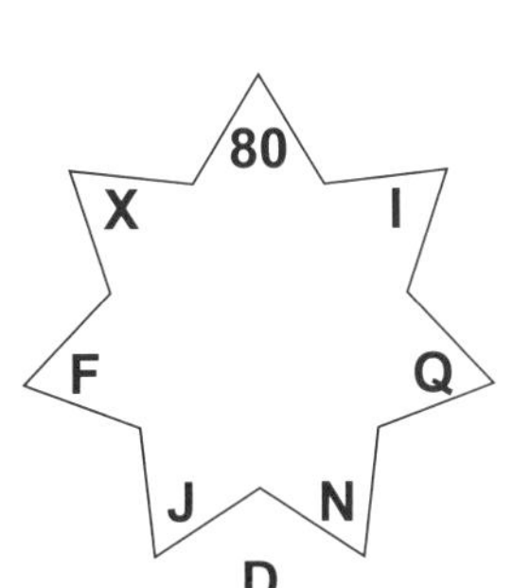

LEVEL 5

51 The chart gives directions to a hidden treasure behind the central black square in the grid. Move the indicated number of spaces north, south, east, and west (eg 4N means move four squares north) stopping at every square once only to arrive there. At which square should you start?

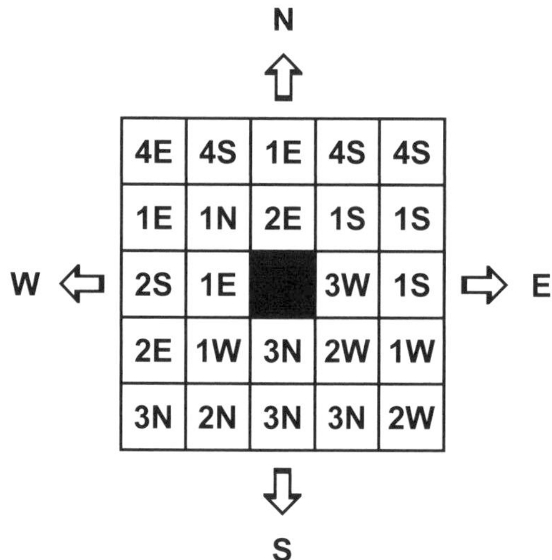

52 What number should replace the question mark?

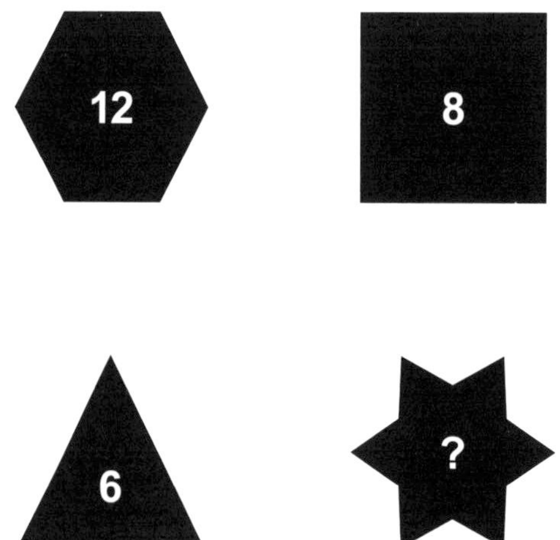

LEVEL 5

53

In the grid below, what number should replace the question mark?

144	141	138	135	132	129	198
147	90	87	84	81	126	195
150	93	60	57	78	123	192
153	96	63	?	75	120	189
156	99	66	69	72	117	186
159	102	105	108	111	114	183
162	165	168	171	174	177	180

54

The blank squares below should be filled with whole numbers between 1 and 30 inclusive, any of which may occur more than once, or not at all.

The numbers in every horizontal row add up to the totals on the right, as do the two long diagonal lines; while those in every vertical column add up to the totals along the bottom.

							90
14	20			30	19	4	127
6	17		11	29		21	108
22	1	5	17	19		15	108
	13	27	22		8		93
18		5		23	6	21	100
19		13	12		23	16	97
	6	26	3		14		88
103	80	101	96	133	114	94	114

LEVEL 5

55 Can you place the hexagons into the grid, so that where any hexagon touches another along a straight line, the number in both triangles is the same? No rotation of any hexagon is allowed!

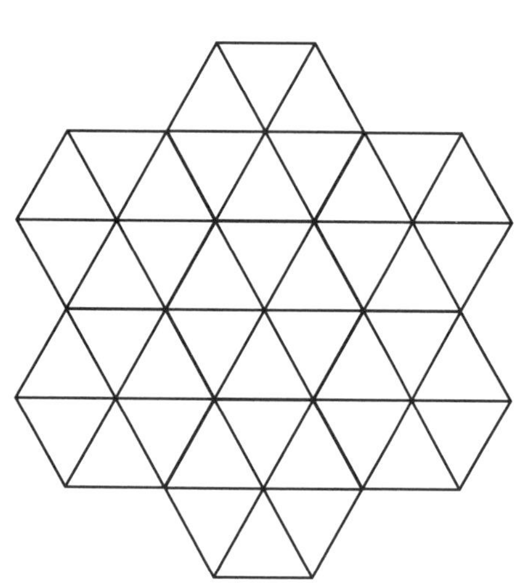

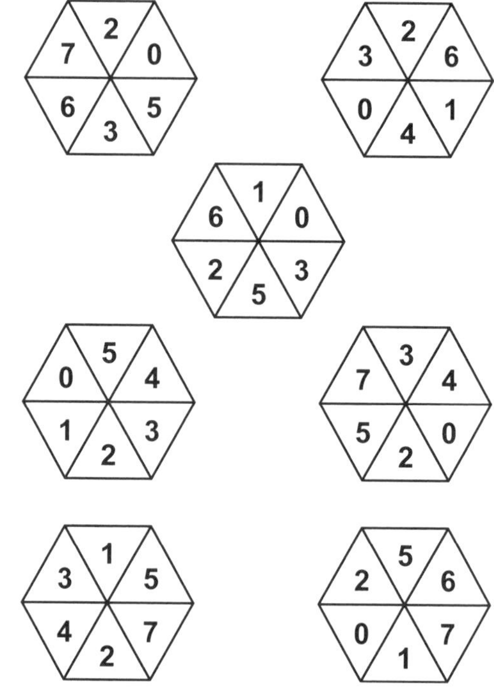

56 Can you place the vessels into the diagram? Some parts of vessels or sea squares have already been filled in. A number to the right or below a row or column refers to the number of occupied squares in that row or column.

Any vessel may be positioned horizontally or vertically, but no part of a vessel touches part of any other vessel, either horizontally, vertically, or diagonally.

Empty Area of Sea: ≈

Aircraft Carrier: ◀■■▶

Battleships: ◀■▶ ◀■▶

Cruisers: ◀▶ ◀▶ ◀▶

Submarines: ● ● ● ●

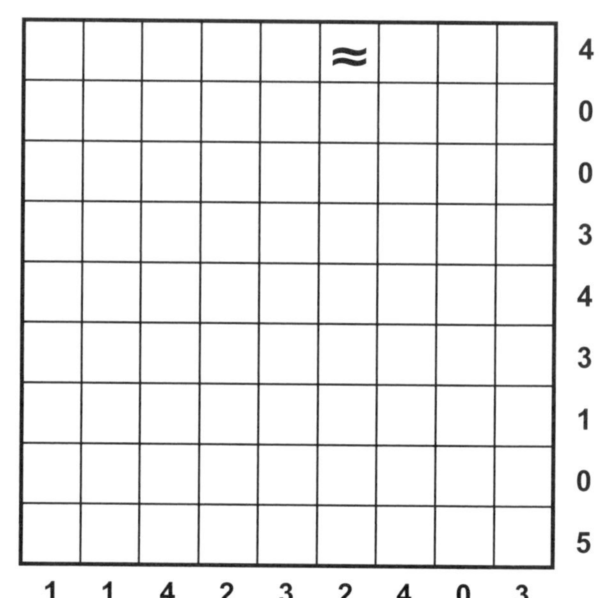

LEVEL 5

57 Each horizontal row and vertical column should contain different shapes and different numbers.

Every square will contain one number and one shape, and no combination may be repeated anywhere else in the puzzle.

1	2	3	4	5

				5
	3	4	2	
	1		4	
	5		1	

58 In the diagram below, what number should replace the question mark?

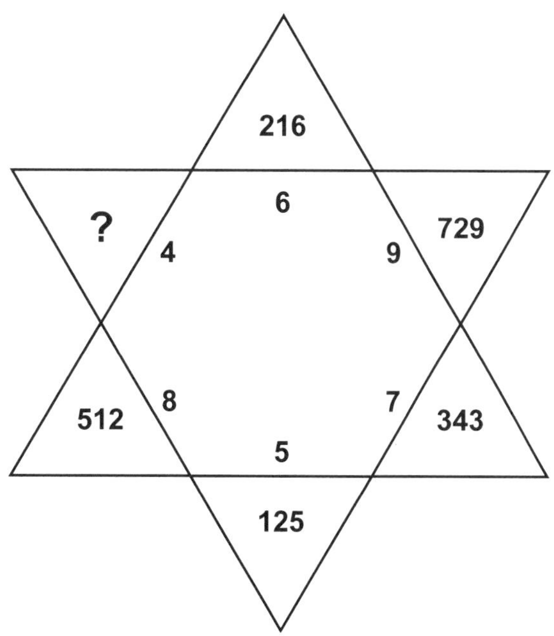

LEVEL 5

59

Every brick in this pyramid contains a number which is the sum of the two numbers below it, so that F=A+B, etc.

Just work out the missing numbers!

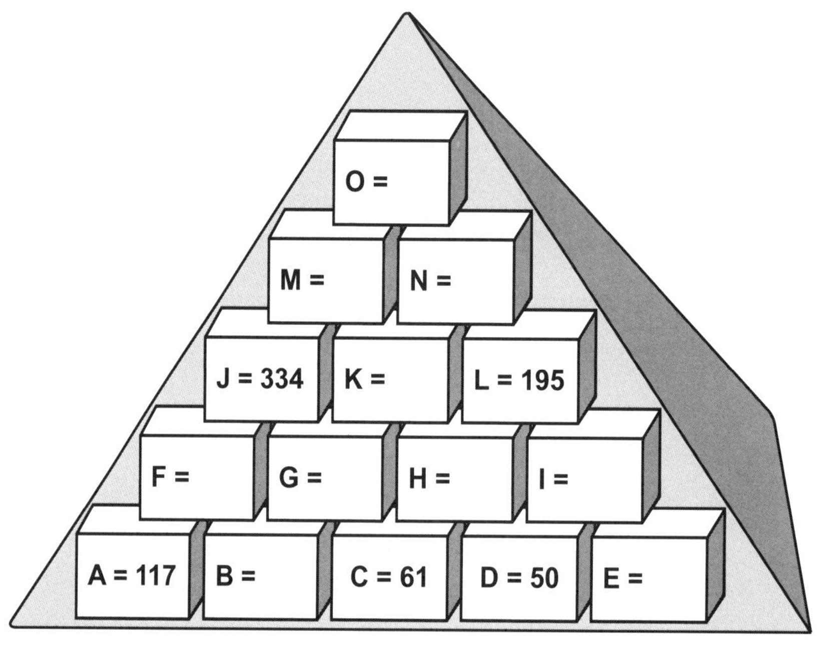

60

In this puzzle, an amateur coin collector has been out with his metal detector, searching for booty. He didn't have time to dig up all the coins he found, so has made a grid map, showing their locations, in the hope that if he loses the map, at least no-one else will understand it…

Those squares containing numbers are empty, but where a number appears in a square, it indicates how many coins are located in the squares (up to a maximum of eight) surrounding the numbered one, touching it at any corner or side. There is only one coin in any individual square.

Place a circle into every square containing a coin.

	0	1				1	2		2
			3				3		
1		2							2
		2		5		3	2	1	0
	4							1	
			3	3					1
3			2	2	4	4	3		
1		2							1
1		2							
	1				2	2		0	

LEVEL 5

61 Given that the letters are valued 1-26 according to their places in the alphabet, can you crack the mystery code to reveal the missing letter?

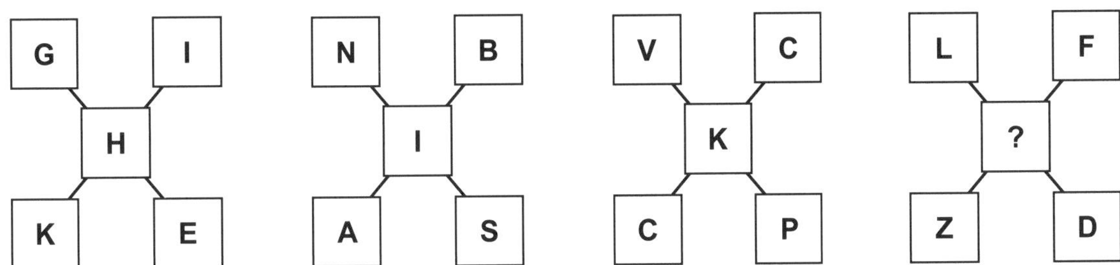

62 Place all twelve of the pieces into the grid. Any may be rotated or flipped over, but none may touch another, not even diagonally. The numbers outside the grid refer to the number of consecutive black squares; and each block is separated from the others by at least one white square. For instance, "3 2" could refer to a row with none, one or more white squares, then three black squares, then at least one white square, then two more black squares, followed by any number of white squares.

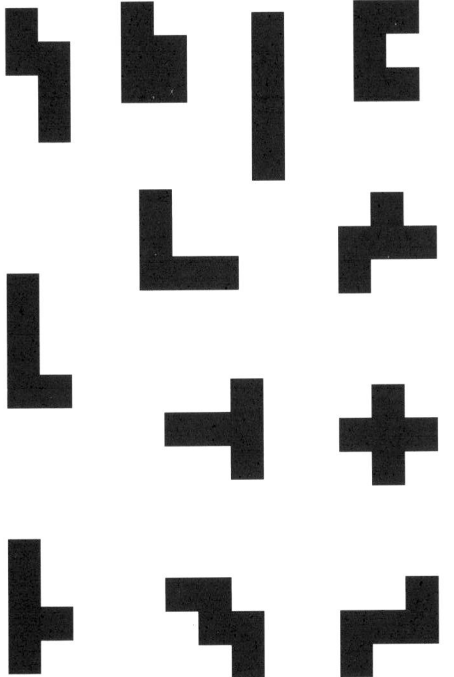

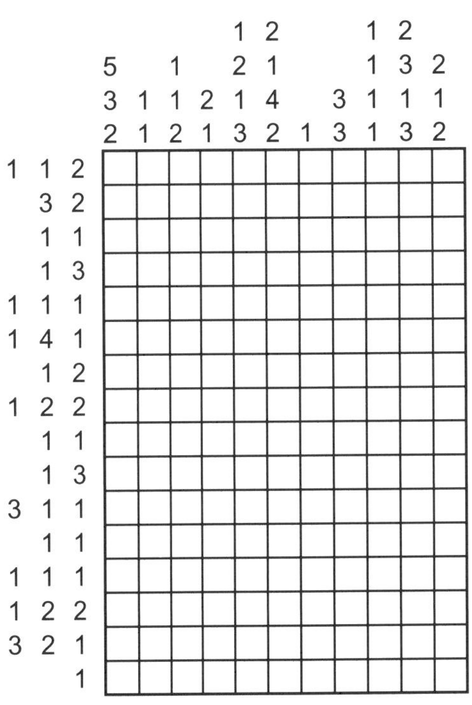

LEVEL 5

63 Each of the eight segments of the spider's web should be filled with a different number from 1 to 8, in such a way that every ring also contains a different number from 1 to 8.

The segments run from the outside of the spider's web to the middle, and the rings run all the way around.

Some numbers are already in place. Can you fill in the rest?

64

Every row and column in this grid originally contained one heart, one club, one diamond, one spade, and two blank squares, although not necessarily in that order.

Every symbol with a black arrow refers to the first of the four symbols encountered in the direction of the arrow. Every symbol with a white arrow refers to the second of the four symbols encountered in the direction of the arrow.

Can you complete the original grid?

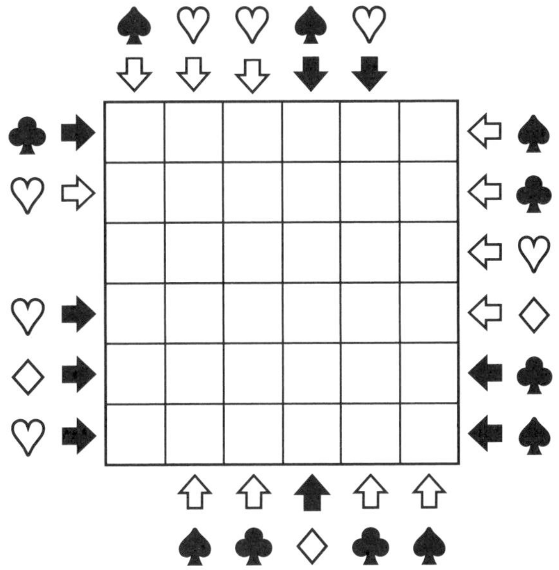

65

Fill the grid so that every horizontal row and vertical column contains the numbers 1-5. Any arrows in the grid always point toward a square that contains a lower number.

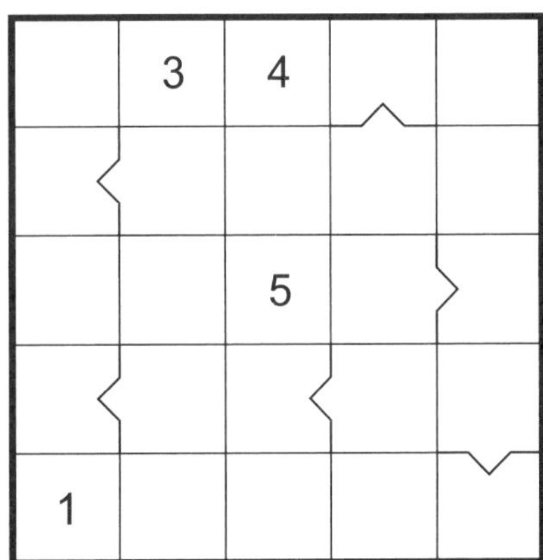

LEVEL 5

66

With the starter already given, can you fit all of the remaining listed numbers into this grid? Take care, this puzzle may not be as easy as it looks!

14	302	4568	29447	59529
30	347	5031	30848	61115
40	451	5322	33173	63150
69	483	8168	34506	64673
74	578	12224	40005	72533
83	608	13566	44349	75542
89	624	16376 ✓	46328	79639
91	707	17678	46517	91658
108	722	18180	49172	299979
179	820	19355	50528	444241
235	827	21635	56437	507683
270	901	24899	56902	610816

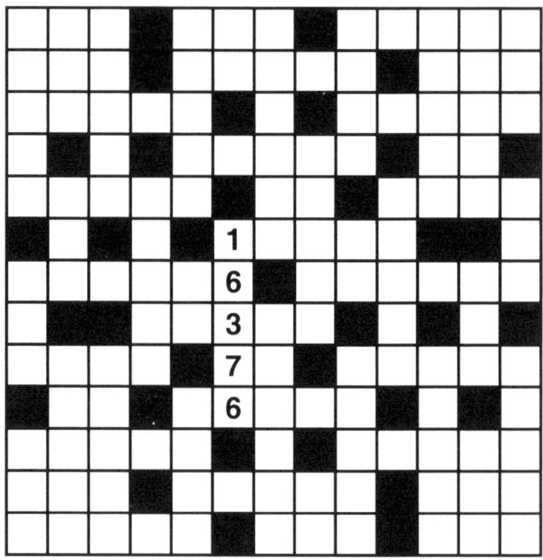

67

The grid should be filled with numbers from 1 to 6, so that each number appears just once in every row and column.

The clues refer to the digit totals in the squares, e.g. A 1 2 3 = 6 means that the numbers in squares A1, A2 and A3 add up to 6.

1 D 1 2 3 = 8
2 E F 1 = 8
3 E F 2 = 6
4 A B 3 = 6
5 B 4 5 = 7
6 A 4 5 = 9
7 D E F 4 = 8
8 A B 6 = 6
9 E 5 6 = 6
10 C D 5 = 10
11 F 5 6 = 11

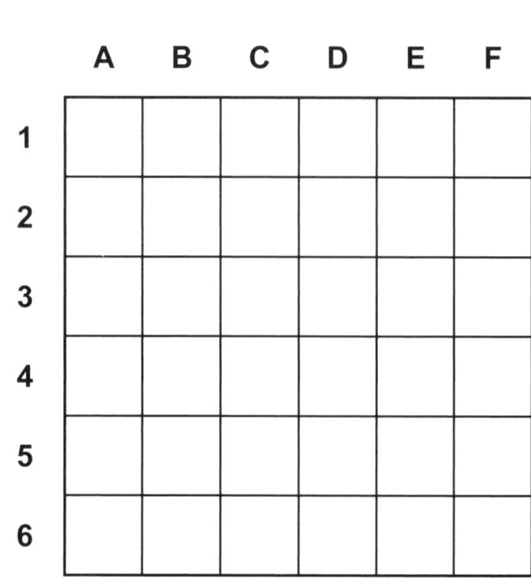

LEVEL 5

68

The object of this puzzle is to trace a single path from the top left corner to the bottom right corner of the grid, moving through all of the cells in either a horizontal, vertical, or diagonal direction.

Every cell must be entered once only, and your path should take you through the numbers in the sequence 1-2-3-4-1-2-3-4, etc.

Can you find the way?

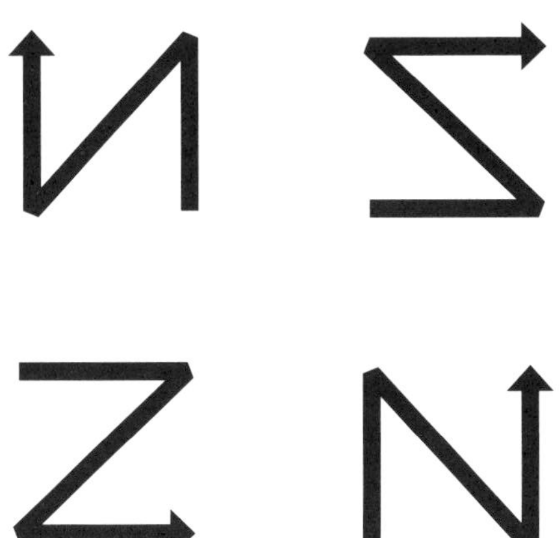

1	3	3	1	2	3	4	3
2	2	4	4	1	1	4	2
1	3	4	3	2	2	2	1
4	2	4	1	3	4	1	3
3	1	1	4	3	1	2	4
2	1	3	2	4	2	3	1
4	2	2	1	1	3	2	4
3	1	4	3	2	4	3	4

69

A standard set of 28 dominoes has been laid out as shown. Can you draw in the edges of them all?

The check-box is provided as an aid and the domino already placed will help.

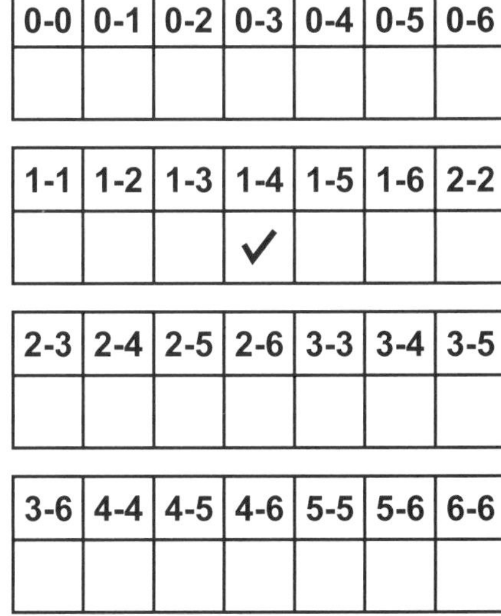

0-0	0-1	0-2	0-3	0-4	0-5	0-6

1-1	1-2	1-3	1-4	1-5	1-6	2-2
			✓			

2-3	2-4	2-5	2-6	3-3	3-4	3-5

3-6	4-4	4-5	4-6	5-5	5-6	6-6

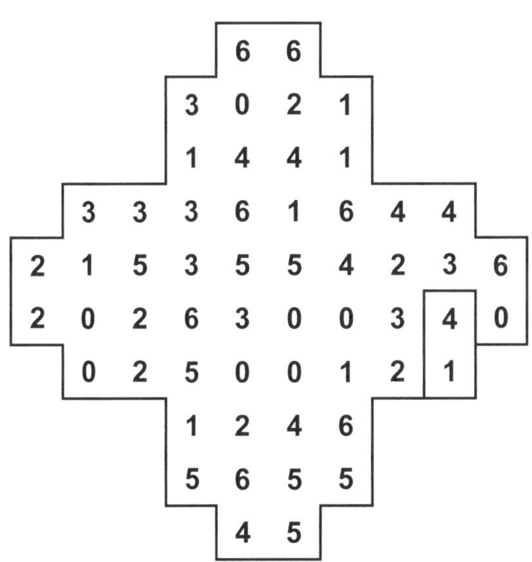

LEVEL 5

70

Draw a single continuous loop, by connecting the dots. No line may cross the path of another.

The figure inside each set of any four surrounding dots indicates the total number of surrounding lines.

1		2		3			1		
2	1	2	2			0			3
2						0	1	2	
	1			1	0				1
				2	2	3			2
1	2		2						
1	1			3				3	
		1	1						
1	2	3	1				2	1	
	0				3	1	0	1	
1					2				1
2		1	1	1	1		3		

71

Place the eight tiles into the puzzle grid so that all adjacent numbers on each tile match up. Tiles may be rotated through 360 degrees, but none may be flipped over.

4	4
1	1

4	3
3	2

1	2
3	1

1	2
4	2

2	2
2	3

1	3
4	3

4	2
1	3

2	1
3	3

		2	2		
		1	1		

LEVEL 5

72

Every oval shape in this diagram contains a different letter of the alphabet from A to K inclusive.

Use the clues to determine their locations. Reference in the clues to "due" means in any location along the same horizontal or vertical line.

1. The A is next to and south of the I, which is due east of both the F and the K.
2. The C is further south than the D, which is next to and east of the G.
3. The E is further east than the B.
4. The K is next to and south of the H, which is next to and south of the J.

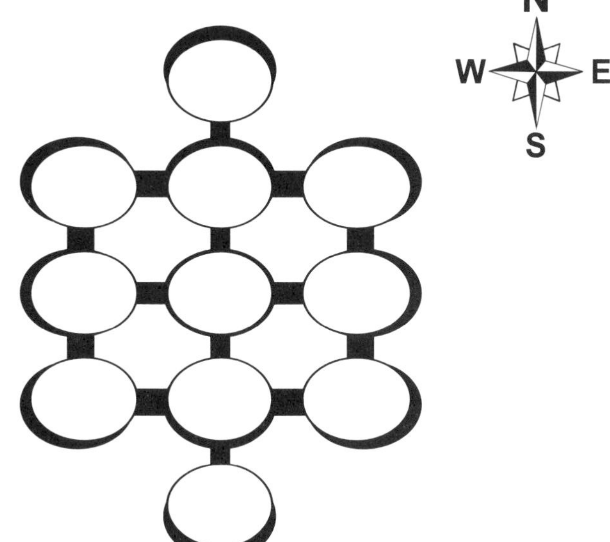

73

Draw walls to partition the grid into areas (some walls are already drawn in for you).

Each area must contain two circles, area sizes must match those numbers shown next to the grid, and each "+" must be linked to at least two walls.

4, 4, 4, 6, 7

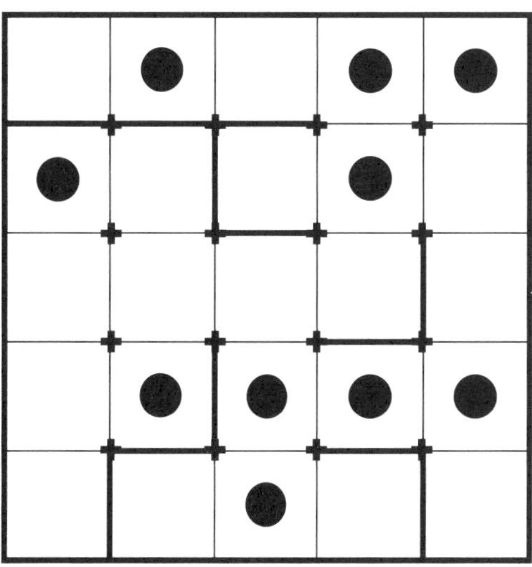

SOLUTIONS : LEVEL 1

1

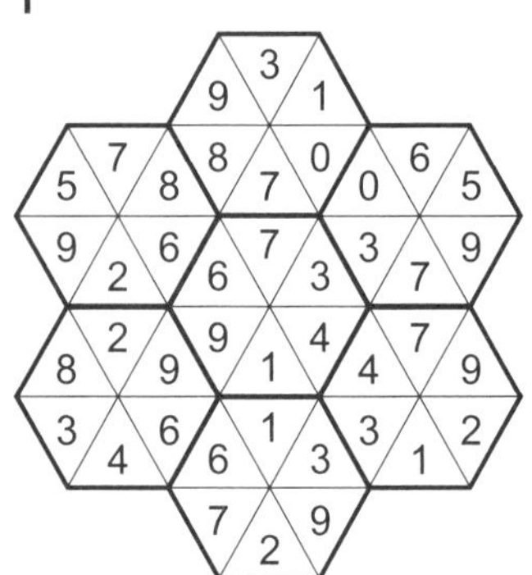

2

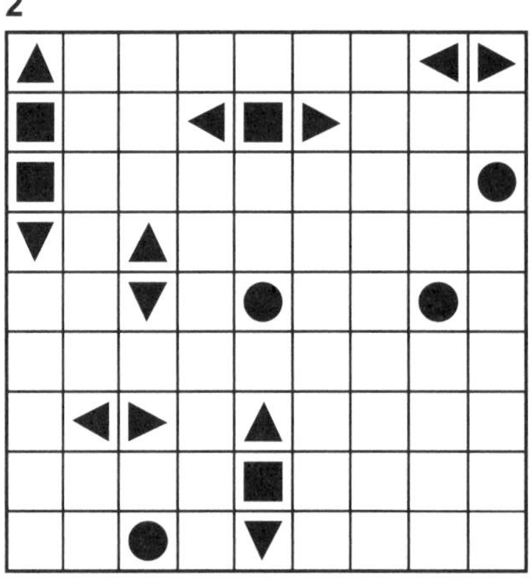

3

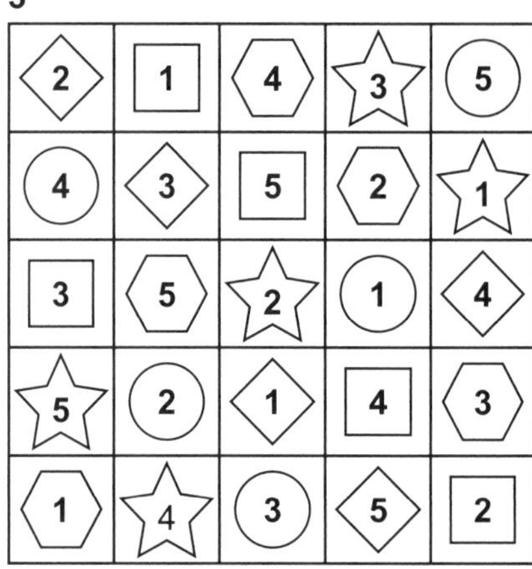

4

369 – Starting at the top, 5–3=2x3=6, 6–3=3x3=9, 9–3=6x3=18, 18–3=15x3=45, 45–3=42x3=126, and 126–3=123x3=369.

5

A=74, B=138, C=55, D=134, E=56, F=212, G=193, H=189, I=190, J=405, K=382, L=379, M=787, N=761, O=1548.

6

	1		0		2		2	●	1
●		0			●	●	2		
●	2	1			3		2	1	●
3	3		●	2		●			
●	●			2	●			0	
		●				1	0	0	
2	●	4	●			3	2	2	
	●	3	1	2	●	●	●		●
2	2	2		3	4	6	●	4	
●			●		●	●	3	●	

7

The value of the letter in the central square is the sum total of the values of the letters in the other squares. Thus the missing value is 22, so the missing letter is V.

8

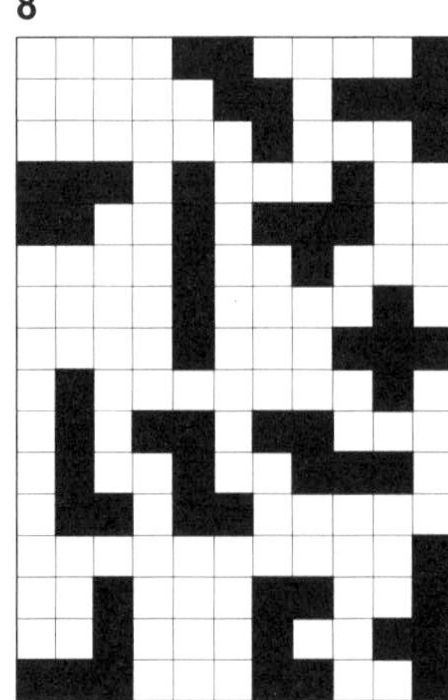

9

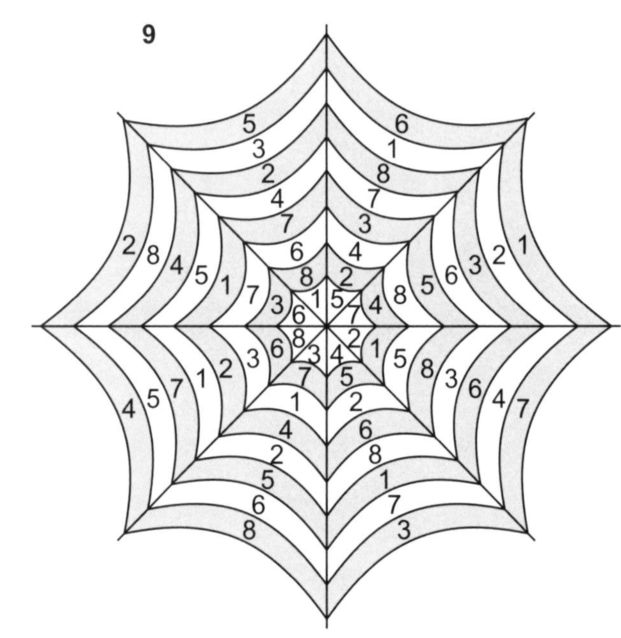

SOLUTIONS : LEVEL 1

10

♣			♡	♢	♠
♠	♢	♣		♡	
♡	♣	♠			♢
♢	♠	♡	♣		
		♢	♠	♣	♡
	♡		♢	♠	♣

11

1	**5**	3	**2**	4
2	**3**	4	5	1
3	4	5 >	1	2
4	1	**2**	3	5
5 >	2	1	4	**3**

12

3	2	6	5	■	6	1	9	■	2	7	3	4
1	■	2	5	■	8	■	3	6	9	7	■	2
4	5	9	■	8	4	9	4	■	1	6	■	2
■	8	7	7	4	5	■	9	9	0	0	5	8
1	3	■	5	■	1	2	3	4	■	■	4	■
3	7	6	6	2	3	■	6	8	7	1	4	8
5	■	8	5	3	■	■	■	4	1	1	■	1
6	5	9	9	9	5	■	1	7	9	0	7	0
■	5	■	■	6	3	4	9	■	0	■	7	2
2	5	3	3	0	0	■	2	7	7	6	9	■
9	■	1	2	■	5	5	4	1	■	7	1	4
9	■	8	9	0	4	■	9	■	9	3	■	2
6	4	9	9	■	8	4	2	■	2	4	6	9

13

6	2	4	1	3	5
3	5	2	6	4	1
1	3	6	4	5	2
4	6	5	2	1	3
2	1	3	5	6	4
5	4	1	3	2	6

14

1	2	2	3	4	5
5	3	4	1	6	6
4	6	1	5	1	2
3	2	1	2	3	3
3	2	6	1	4	4
4	5	6	5	5	6

15

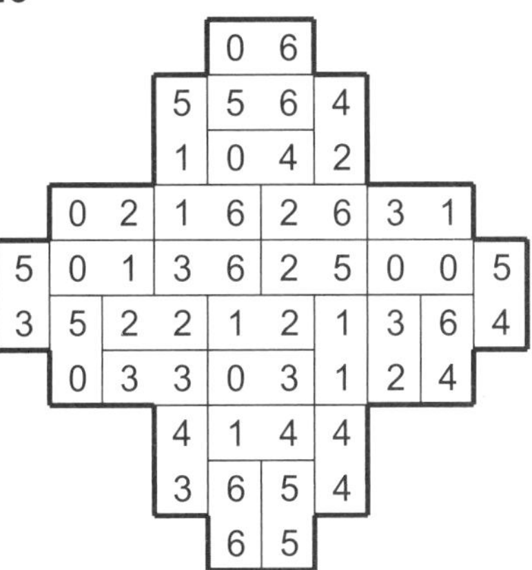

16

3	2		1	3			3		
2		1			2			2	
2	3				1		1	1	
1		1	2			1	2	2	
1					1			1	
				2	1		1	0	
3	2		2	1	0		3	1	
	1	2		1			2	1	
	1	2	2	1	0		1		
	1	1		1	1		2		
	3			0	0			0	
	2	2	1		1		1	1	

17

1	2	2	2	2	1
1	3	3	2	2	1
1	3	3	2	2	1
4	4	4	2	2	4
4	4	4	2	2	4
4	3	3	3	3	1

18

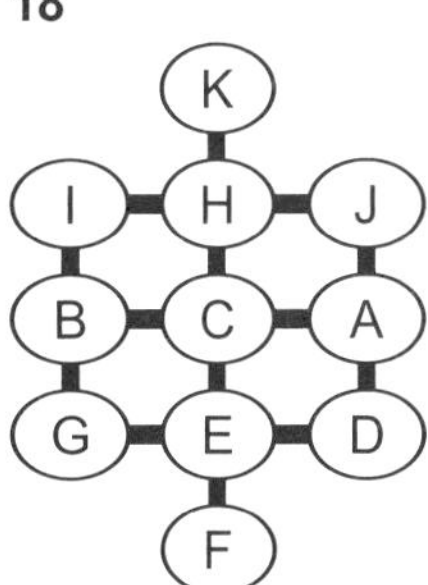

SOLUTIONS : LEVEL 1

19

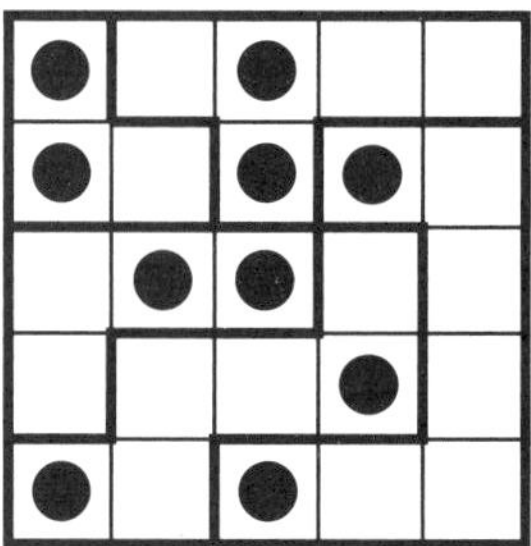

20

O							O
					O		
		O	O	O			
O							
		O	O		O	O	
						O	

21

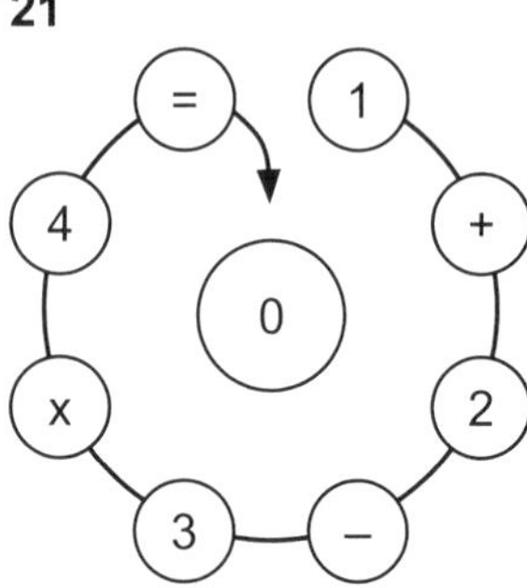

22

B	A	C	B	C	A
A	B	B	C	C	A
C	C	A	A	B	B
A	B	B	C	A	C
C	C	A	B	A	B
B	A	C	A	B	C

23

9	–	6	+	4	=	7
–	■	–	■	+		
8	+	1	x	2	=	18
+	■	+	■	+		
3	x	5	x	7	=	105
=		=		=		
4		10		13		

24

1E	1S	2S	1E	1S
2E	2E	1N	1N	1S
2N	1S	■	2W	2S
2N	1S	2E	1N	1W
1N	1W	1N	1W	1W

25

		4			2	
8						
		1		1		6
	5		6		9	
	9		7			9

26

31	6	11	31	47	**11**
22	22	35	**8**	27	23
23	**31**	22	24	14	23
18	39	27	20	9	24
21	26	16	34	**13**	27
22	13	**26**	20	27	29

27

							93
13	5	27	14	8	6	16	89
9	11	24	20	19	10	4	97
1	7	22	21	17	13	3	84
15	25	20	2	14	29	5	110
30	26	2	4	9	8	28	107
17	19	24	6	5	3	20	94
27	10	2	1	30	14	12	96
112	103	121	68	102	83	88	72

SOLUTIONS : LEVEL 1

28

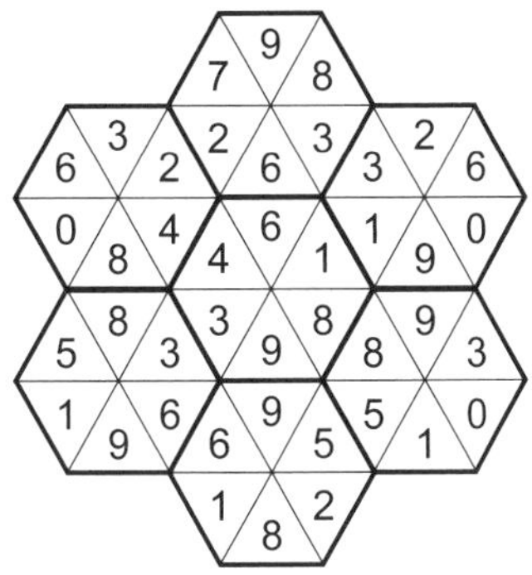

29

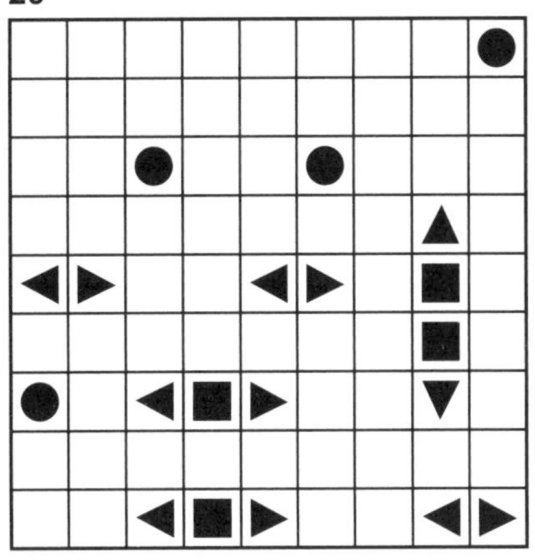

30

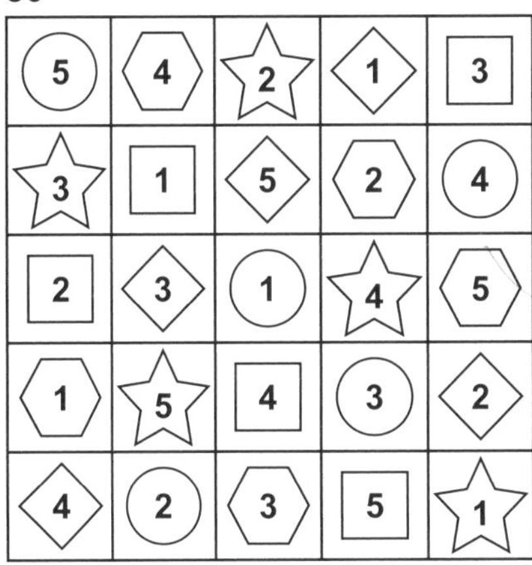

31

C – In the top and bottom row of each grid, add together the numbers in the left and central squares, then deduct the number in the right square, to give the total in the middle.

32

A=121, B=69, C=92, D=122, E=129, F=190, G=161, H=214, I=251, J=351, K=375, L=465, M=726, N=840, O=1566.

33

2	●	●	1	1		●	2	●	●
	●	3		2	●			2	
1		1		●	2		0		0
		2			2	1			
●	●	3	●		●		1		●
●	4	●	3	●			●	3	2
		2	3		3	●		2	●
1	●	2		●	4	3		1	
	2	2	●	3	●	●			0
●	1						1		

34

The sum total of the values of the letters in the bottom squares is subtracted from the sum total of the values of the letters in the top squares. Thus the missing value is 19, so the missing letter is S.

35

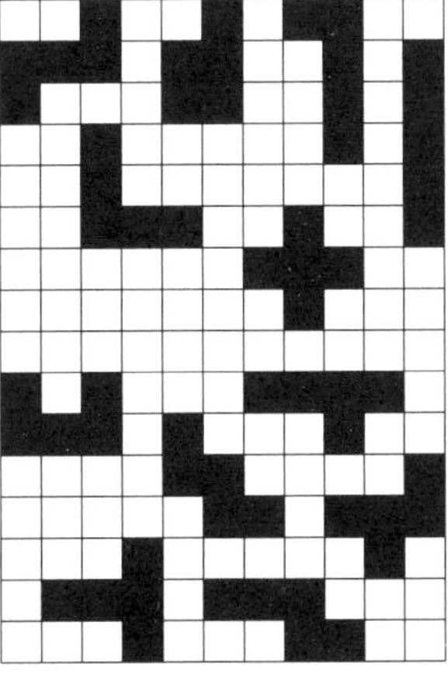

36

SOLUTIONS : LEVEL 1

37

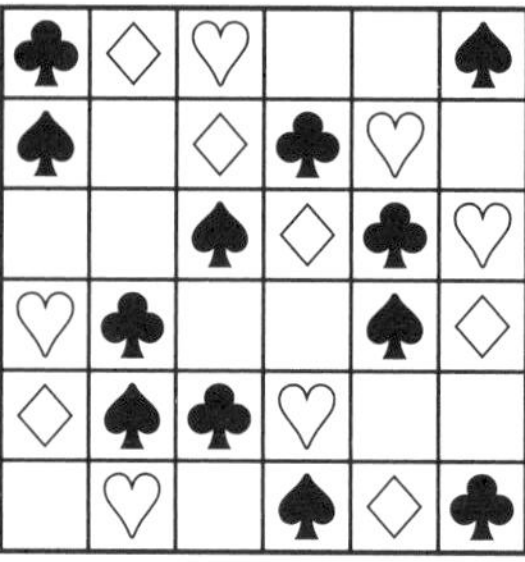

38

5	2	1	**4**	3
3	1	4	5	2
1	3	**5**	**2**	4
4	5	2	3	1
2	4	3	1	5

39

4	2	3		6	2	1		3	1	5	6	6
7		7	3	2	7	6		2	6	8		0
2	9	1		3	5	4	3	1		4	4	0
9		1		4		4	3	3			2	0
4	3	9	7		1	8		4	2	6	9	6
	9		7	3	5	7	6	4		1		6
4	3	6	4		0		5		2	7	3	4
1		1		6	1	8	9	0	0		6	
8	2	4	5	0		4	6		9	2	8	2
8	9			8	4	4		1		4		5
9	4	3		1	5	5	9	0		3	5	3
2		9	7	6		7	2	3	6	0		5
4	7	6	2	3		8	9	9		6	1	2

40

6	3	5	2	1	4
4	1	6	5	2	3
5	2	1	3	4	6
3	5	4	1	6	2
2	6	3	4	5	1
1	4	2	6	3	5

41

1	2	5	4	5	6
3	4	3	6	1	1
2	6	5	3	2	2
1	4	4	4	3	3
6	5	3	5	2	4
1	2	6	1	5	6

42

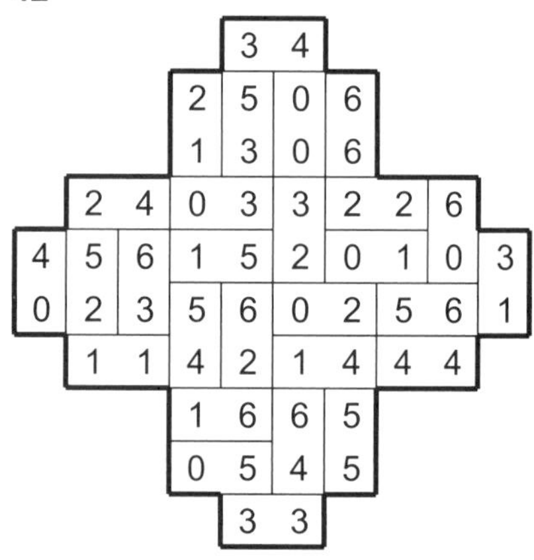

43

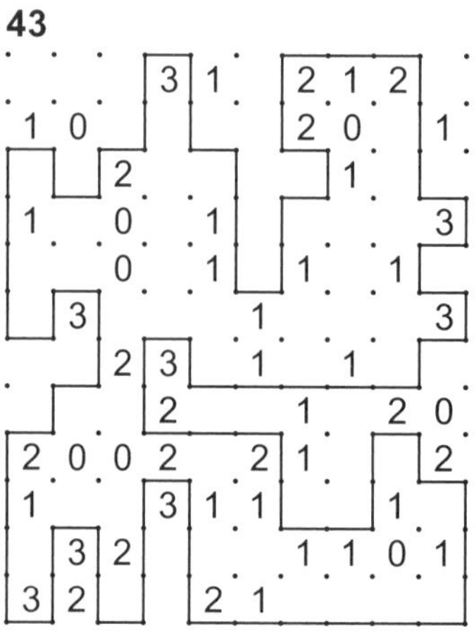

44

1	4	4	1	1	3
1	4	4	3	3	4
1	4	4	3	3	4
3	3	3	2	2	2
3	3	3	2	2	2
1	2	2	1	1	3

45

B – The numbers in each square are all divisible by the central number.

SOLUTIONS : LEVEL 1

46

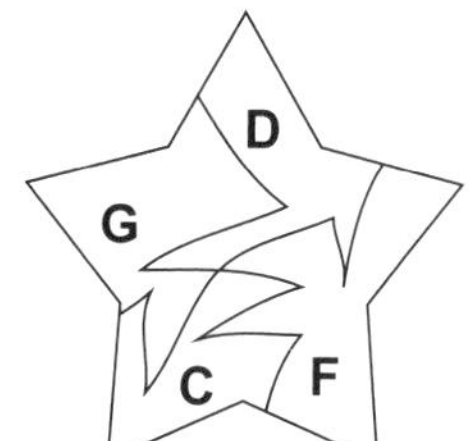

47

○			○				
				○			
○						○	
	○		○		○		
		○					
			○	○		○	

48

Circle = 9, cross = 2, pentagon = 3, square = 7, star = 5.

49

B	C	A	B	A	C
C	B	B	C	A	A
C	C	A	A	B	B
A	A	C	C	B	B
A	B	B	A	C	C
B	A	C	B	C	A

50

D – It has an even number of points.

51

1E	1E	1S	1S	1W
1N	1S	2E	2W	2S
1N	2E	■	2S	2N
1N	1E	1S	2W	1W
1N	1W	2N	2W	**2N**

52

V – The number indicates the position of each letter from the start or end of the alphabet.

53

17 – The totals of the numbers in the vertical columns increases by 6.

54

							132
13	22	16	11	8	20	9	99
12	17	29	15	6	14	23	116
24	30	3	21	26	2	19	125
1	14	15	27	4	7	25	93
13	20	28	10	3	18	17	109
5	11	6	23	20	16	8	89
17	4	14	29	14	15	16	109
85	118	111	136	81	92	117	95

SOLUTIONS : LEVEL 1

55

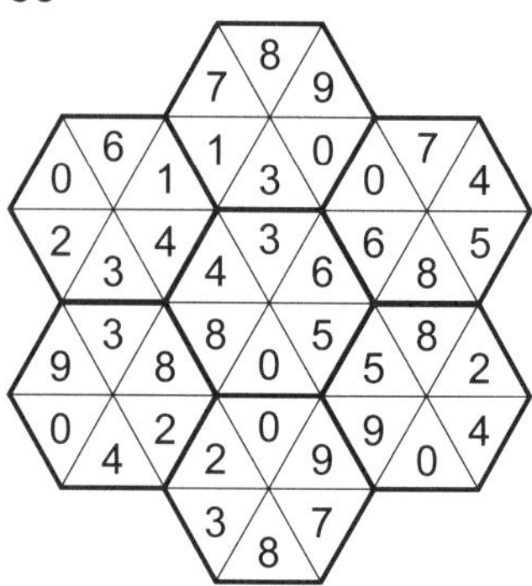

56

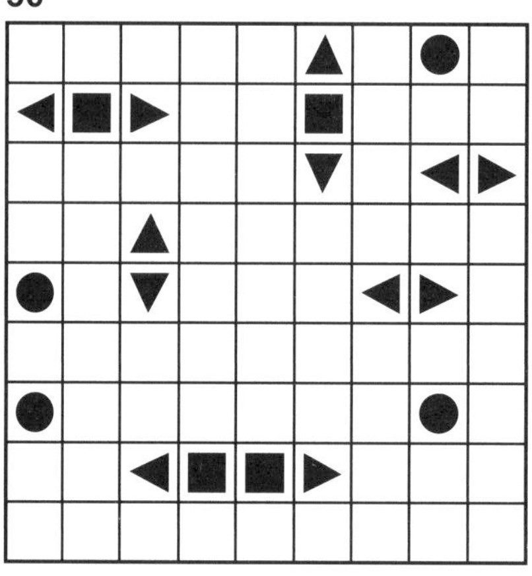

57

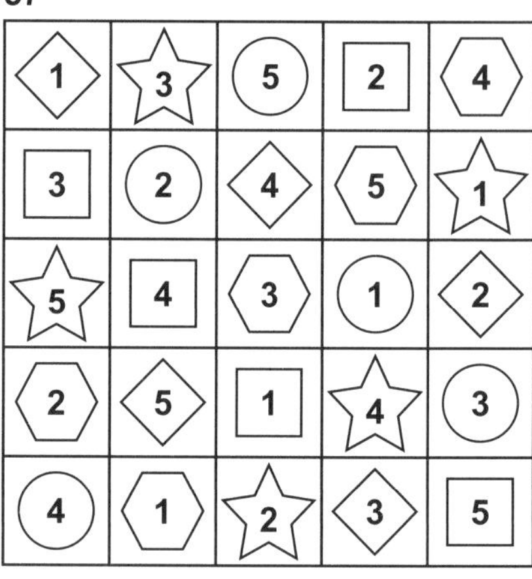

58

12 – The central number is 60 and the lower numbers are 60% of the higher numbers on opposite points of the star.

59

A=24, B=124, C=68, D=35, E=60, F=148, G=192, H=103, I=95, J=340, K=295, L=198, M=635, N=493, O=1128.

60

	1	0		●	●	3	●		●
●					4	●	4		2
1					2	●		●	2
		1	●	1	1		●	3	●
0			3						
	0		●	●	1			1	1
	2			2				●	2
●	3	●	3			3	●	3	●
	4	●	3	●	●	●	4		2
	●	2			3		●	●	

61

The sum total of the values in the top squares equals the value of the central square, as does the sum total of the values in the bottom squares. Thus the missing value is 3, so the missing letter is C.

62

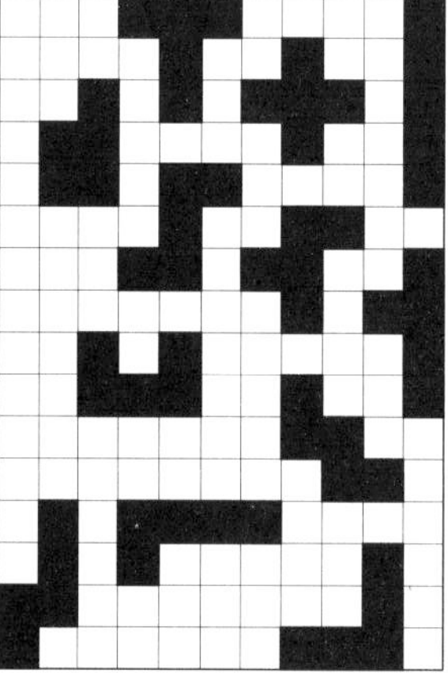

63

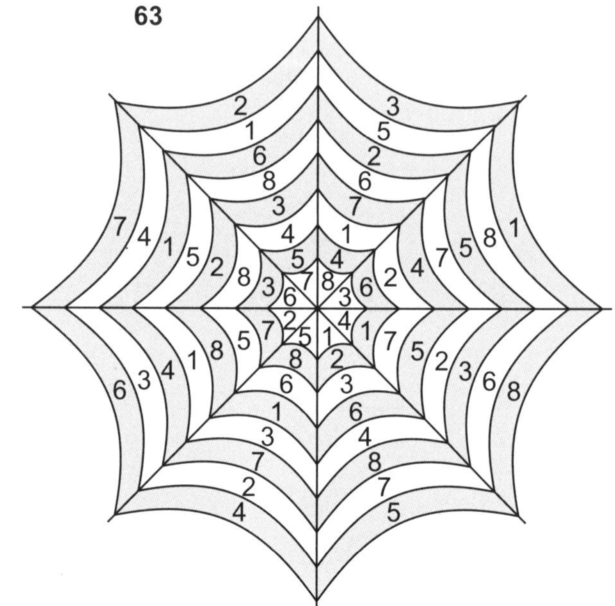

SOLUTIONS : LEVEL 1

64

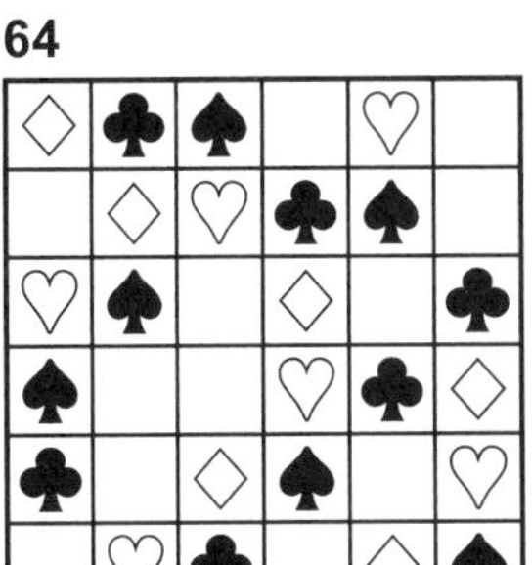

65

1 <	3 <	4	5	2
4	1	5	2	3
2	4	**1**	3 <	5
3	5	2	1 <	4
5	2	3	4	1

66

4	5	9	■	2	4	3	■	8	4	1	■	7
7	0	0	■	3	1	1	0	4	■	3	6	1
2	0	6	1	6	■	3	■	9	4	4	0	8
9	■	6	■	3	0	7	4	2	■	7	1	■
4	9	1	5	8	■	8	1	■	8	1	0	4
■	7	■	7	■	1	3	5	6	6	■	■	8
8	5	0	7	1	6	■	5	6	2	2	4	7
1	■	■	3	2	1	3	5	■	5	■	8	■
2	2	7	8	■	6	0	■	6	7	3	2	6
■	4	0	■	1	8	8	2	7	■	3	■	6
5	1	1	5	8	■	0	■	1	2	1	8	8
8	2	1	■	9	6	2	5	5	■	6	7	2
9	■	9	0	5	■	8	7	6	■	2	8	0

67

5	3	2	1	6	4
3	1	5	6	4	2
1	2	6	4	3	5
2	4	3	5	1	6
6	5	4	3	2	1
4	6	1	2	5	3

68

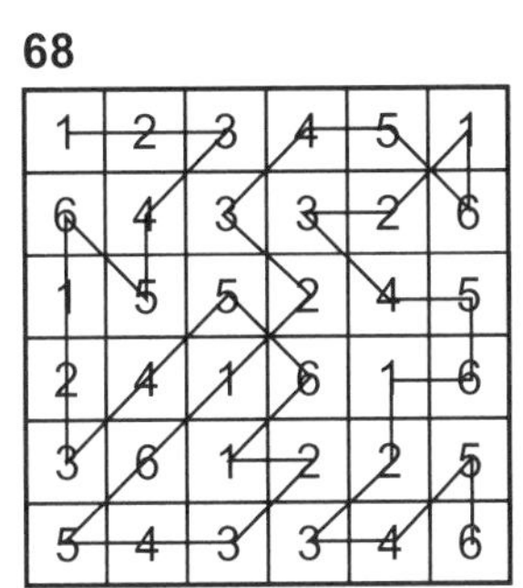

69

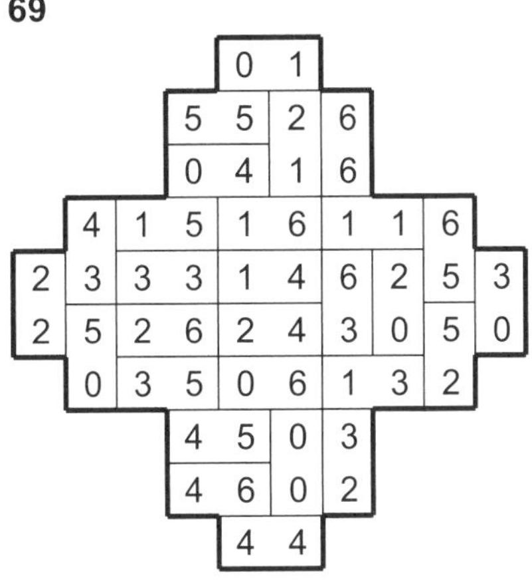

70

71

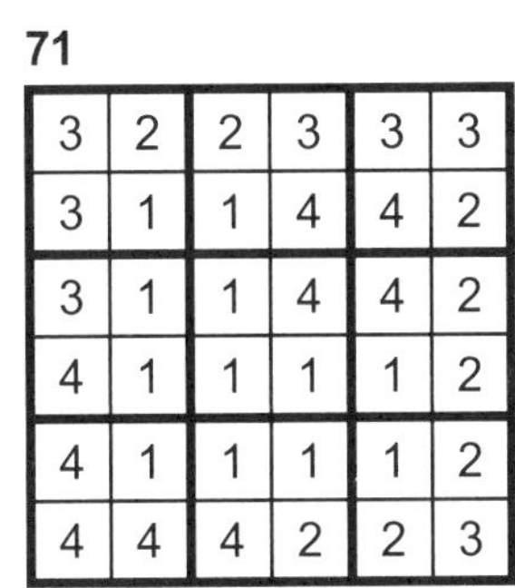

72

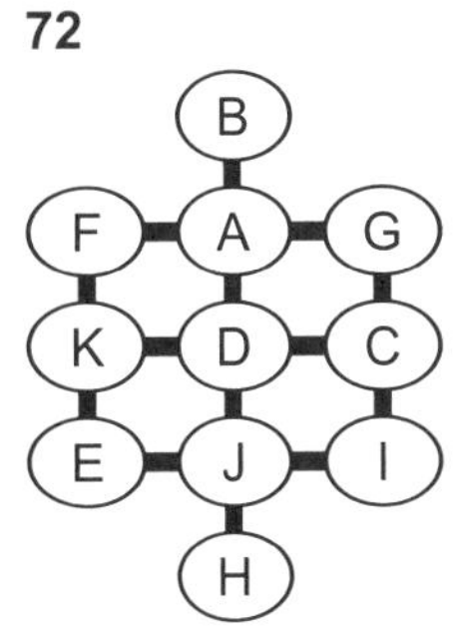

SOLUTIONS : LEVEL 1

73

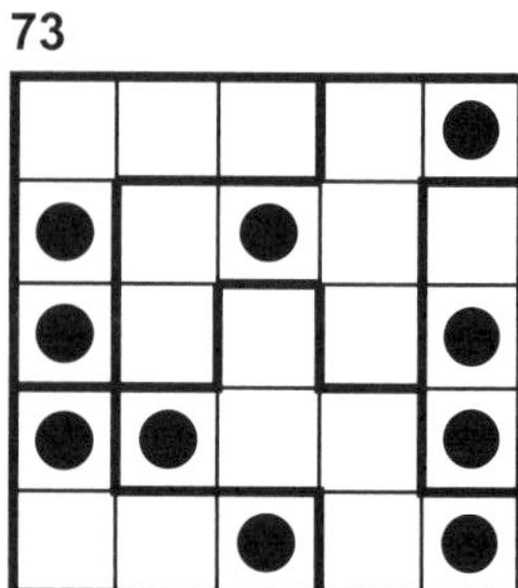

74

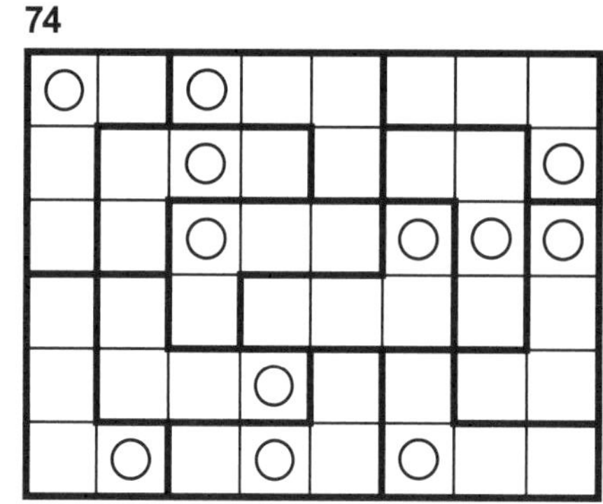

75

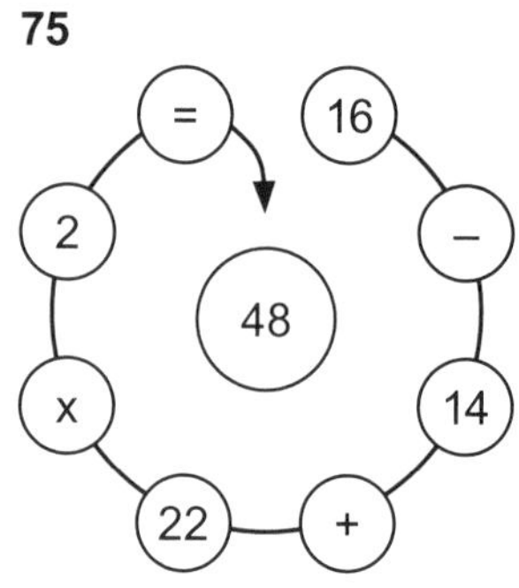

76

B	B	A	C	C	A
A	C	C	B	B	A
B	B	A	A	C	C
C	A	B	C	A	B
A	C	B	B	A	C
C	A	C	A	B	B

77

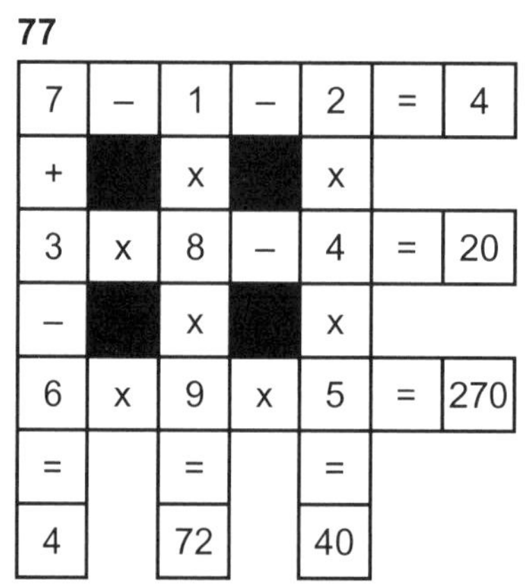

78

1E	2E	2E	1W	2S
2S	**2E**	2W	1S	2W
2N	2S		2W	2W
1S	2E	1W	1S	2N
2N	1E	1N	1E	1N

79

		9		1		1
3						
					1	
3		1				
				9		9
	1					
				8		6

80

44	17	24	30	38	**18**
32	28	31	**23**	31	26
15	40	28	50	15	23
35	**45**	31	6	15	39
26	22	19	42	**31**	31
19	19	**38**	20	41	34

81

							103
21	28	14	27	4	17	5	116
11	13	6	20	2	30	9	91
19	24	12	1	3	27	7	93
8	14	29	22	15	26	16	130
18	5	17	13	24	8	23	108
7	6	21	18	15	6	19	92
20	10	13	16	9	4	11	83
104	100	112	117	72	118	90	109

SOLUTIONS : LEVEL 2

1

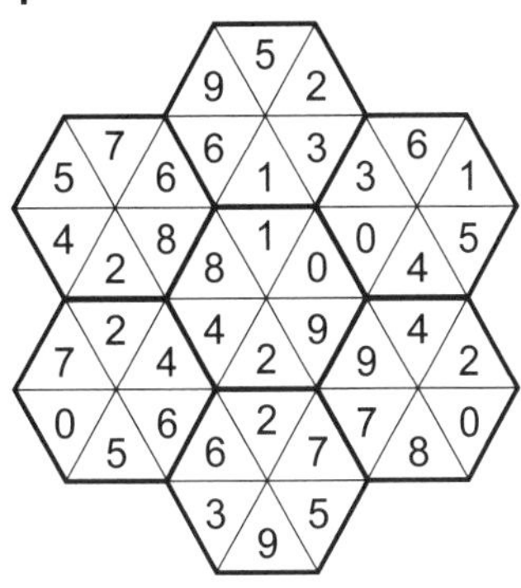

2

	◀	▶		●		▲		
						▼		
	◀	■	■	▶				
	●				●		●	
			▲		▲		▲	
			■		▼		■	
			▼				▼	

3

◇ 3	⬡ 1	○ 5	□ 4	☆ 2
⬡ 5	○ 2	☆ 4	◇ 1	□ 3
☆ 1	□ 5	◇ 2	○ 3	⬡ 4
□ 2	◇ 4	⬡ 3	☆ 5	○ 1
○ 4	☆ 3	□ 1	⬡ 2	◇ 5

4

P – Assign a number to each letter according to its place in the alphabet. Working clockwise from the top, add the two together, so A+B(1+2)=3, A+E(1+5)=6, C+F(3+6)=9, etc. E=5, so P(16) is needed to make the final figure to 21, and E+P=21.

5

A=22, B=58, C=99, D=75, E=119, F=80, G=157, H=174, I=194, J=237, K=331, L=368, M=568, N=699, O=1267.

6

	1	2	●	2	●			1	●
1	●						3		2
	3	4			1	●	●	●	
	●	●	●		1		5		
●	3	3			1		●	●	1
	2	1		2	●	2	2		
0		●		●				2	●
0		●			1	2	●		
2		●	3	1		3	●		0
●	●	●	2	1	●				

7

The sum total of the values of the letters in each diagonal line of three are all equal. Thus the missing value is 16, so the missing letter is P.

8

9

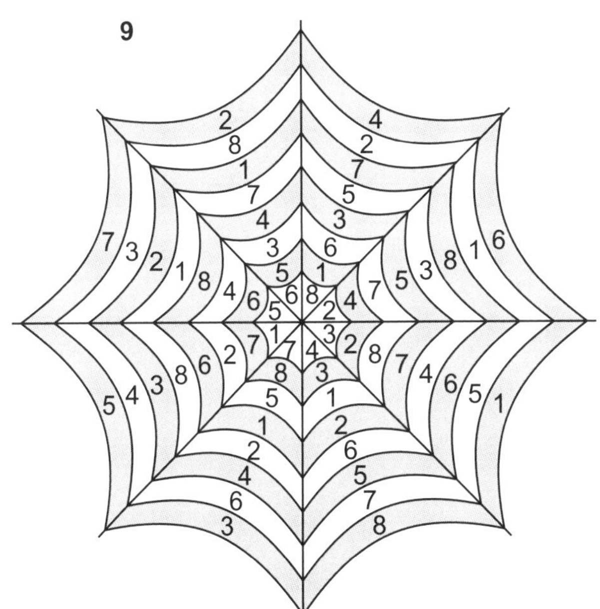

SOLUTIONS : LEVEL 2

10

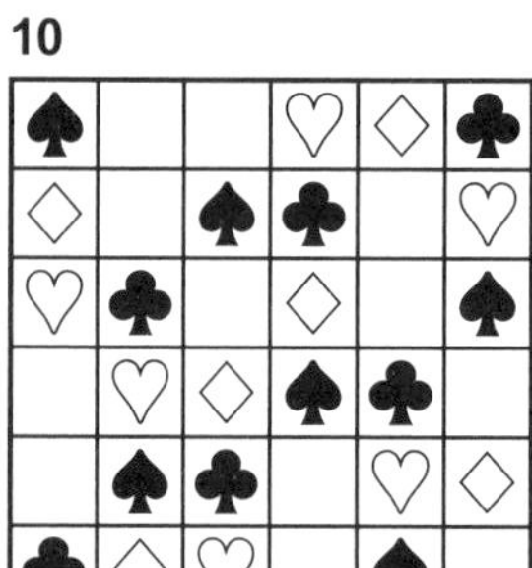

11

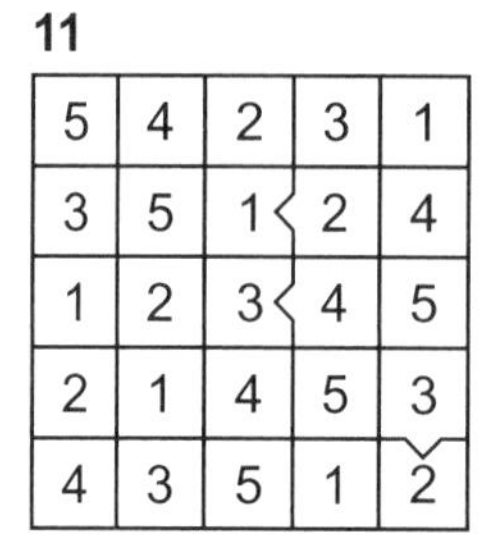

12

4	0	2	0		2	5	7	6		3	2	4
5		8		4	9	6		7		6	9	
2	7	0	6	8		5		1	8	0	1	3
3	5		9	4	6	0	9	9		4	0	0
5	6	3	3		2		3		1	4	7	7
		4		3	9	8	7	5	9			5
1	8	4	3	0				7	9	4	9	6
9			1	0	8	3	6	1		2		
4	1	3	3		9		0		4	4	1	2
6	7	8		4	5	1	3	8	0		7	8
8	5	5	6	7		8		2	3	5	5	0
	2	3		6		7	4	9		0		3
6	7	7		7	0	8	5		2	9	9	9

13

2	5	3	1	4	6
6	3	4	5	2	1
4	2	1	6	5	3
3	6	2	4	1	5
5	1	6	2	3	4
1	4	5	3	6	2

14

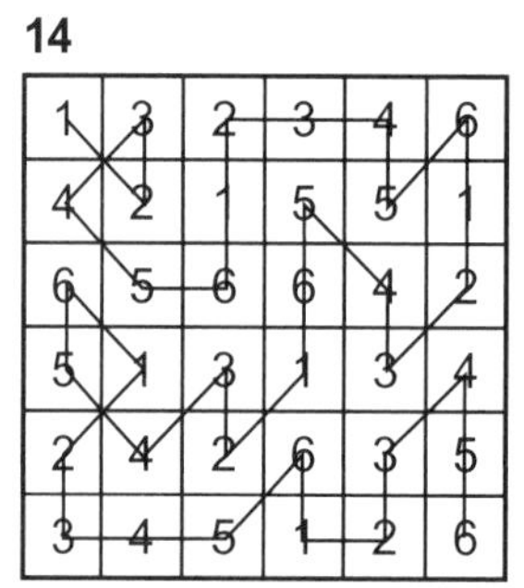

15

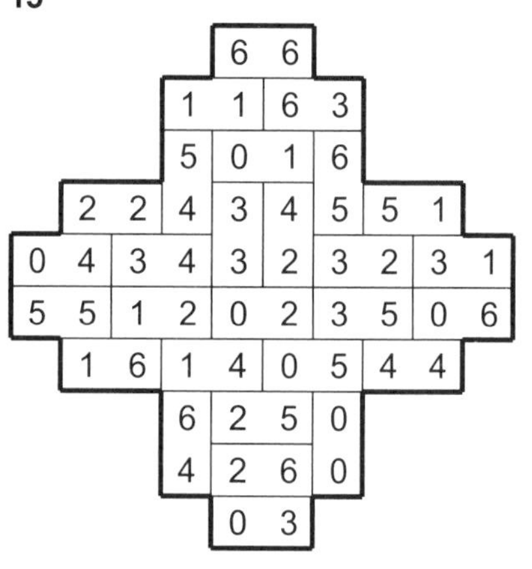

16

2	1	2		2	2	3	3		
				3		1		0	2
			1				3	1	
2		1		3		2		1	
2	2	1		1		2	2	1	1
			1						
2	2			2		0		2	2
		2		0			0	1	
	0	0			3				3
	1			2	1			1	
	1	3	2		3	2		3	
2	2						1		1

17

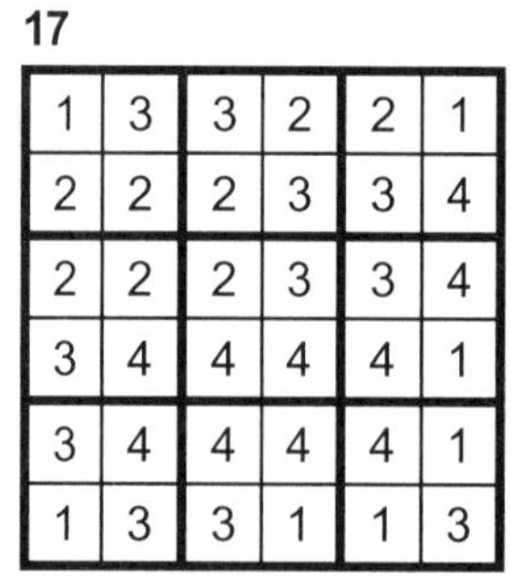

18

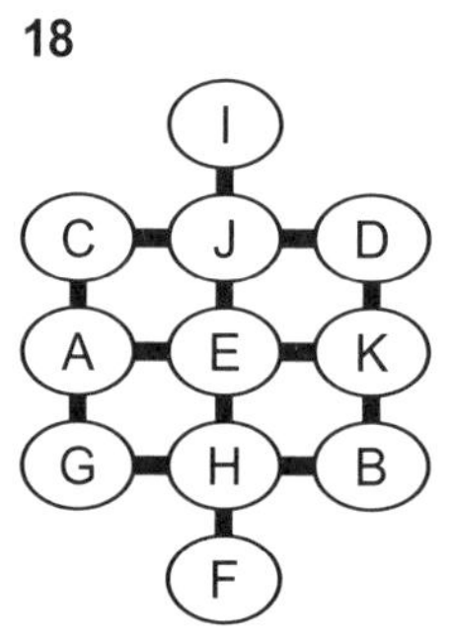

SOLUTIONS : LEVEL 2

19

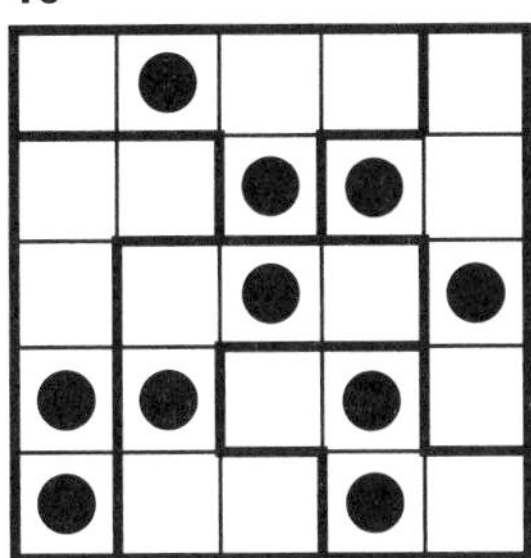

20

21

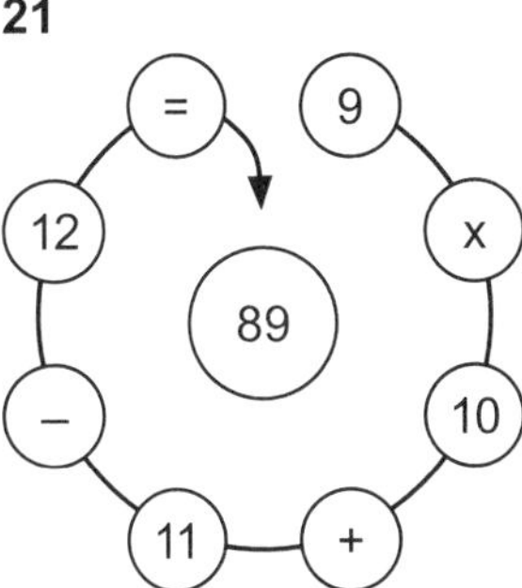

22

B	C	A	C	A	B
C	A	B	C	B	A
A	C	B	A	C	B
A	B	C	A	B	C
B	A	C	B	C	A
C	B	A	B	A	C

23

9	–	6	x	5	=	15
+		–		+		
8	x	2	–	7	=	9
+		x		x		
3	+	4	x	1	=	7
=		=		=		
20		16		12		

24

1S	1E	2S	1E	1S
2E	1N	1W	2S	1W
2N	**2E**		2N	1S
1N	1S	1W	1S	2W
1N	1E	2W	1E	2N

25

8		1			1	
1		9				
					5	
9		1				
				9		6
3		5				

26

14	16	13	30	34	30
31	22	24	**9**	27	24
26	35	22	18	20	**16**
23	33	27	26	**5**	23
18	**10**	29	31	29	20
25	21	**22**	23	22	24

27

							121
10	14	3	27	29	16	9	108
18	20	4	1	15	17	11	86
26	13	19	24	30	16	12	140
4	7	20	29	12	13	2	87
8	25	18	6	27	21	5	110
14	17	19	16	12	9	22	109
1	18	4	10	20	23	28	104
81	114	87	113	145	115	89	142

SOLUTIONS : LEVEL 2

28

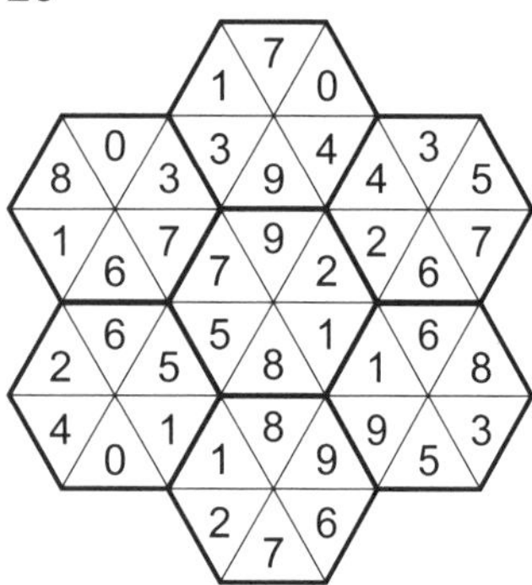

29

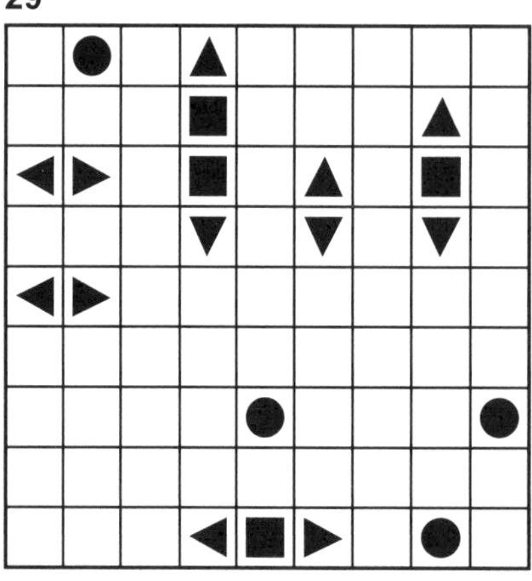

30

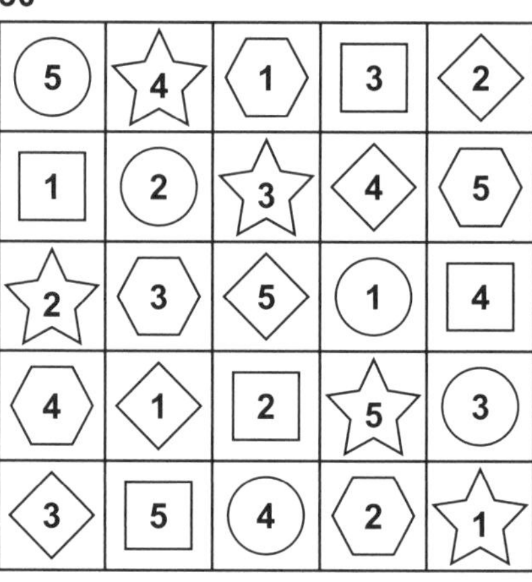

31

D – From top to bottom, the sum of the numbers in the horizontal rows is 44, 40 and 36.

32

A=84, B=77, C=21, D=53, E=6, F=161, G=98, H=74, I=59, J=259, K=172, L=133, M=431, N=305, O=736.

33

			0		●	●	●		1
	1	1			5	●	4	3	●
	●			1	●	●	4		●
1				3		●		●	
		2	●	●	2		2	2	2
	0		●				0		●
	1		2	2				3	●
3	●			●	3		●		
●	●	●	4	●	●		1		0
2		●	3	2					

34

The sum total of the letters in all five boxes is 60. Thus the missing value is 14, so the missing letter is N.

35

36

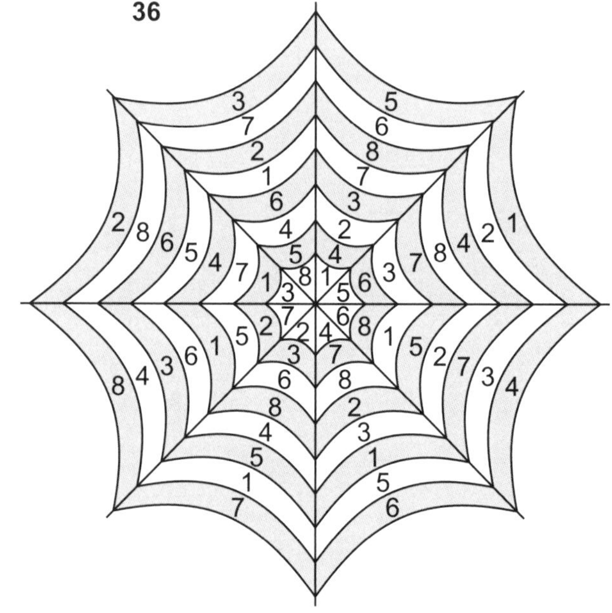

SOLUTIONS : LEVEL 2

37

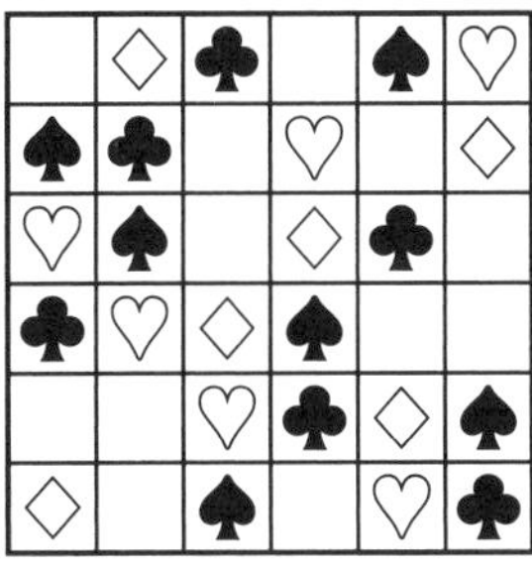

38

5	**4**	2	3	1
3	**1**	**5**	4	2
1	2	4	5	**3**
2	5	**3**	1	**4**
4	3	1	2	5

39

5	7	6	0	2	8		3	6	6	4	4	9
8	8	3		4	9	5	3	7		9	7	
6	0	0	0	6		7		6	3	8	0	1
9		0		3	3	0	2	9		4		6
6	2	0		7	0	3	4		2	3	8	0
2	9	0	1		3	0	5	7	4		6	5
	9		1	5	6		6	6	0		9	
1	5		8	5	3	4	0		8	4	3	1
5	3	4	3		8	5	5	2		7	5	5
9		9		3	9	5	3	5		3		5
7	4	9	0	5		5		5	0	4	2	9
	7	3		3	6	9	9	3		9	2	7
8	4	0	4	4	7		1	4	5	7	0	7

40

1	2	3	6	5	4
5	1	2	4	6	3
2	4	6	1	3	5
6	5	4	3	2	1
4	3	5	2	1	6
3	6	1	5	4	2

41

1	2	6	5	3	2
3	3	1	4	6	1
4	2	4	5	1	3
5	5	1	6	4	2
6	6	4	2	5	5
1	2	3	3	4	6

42

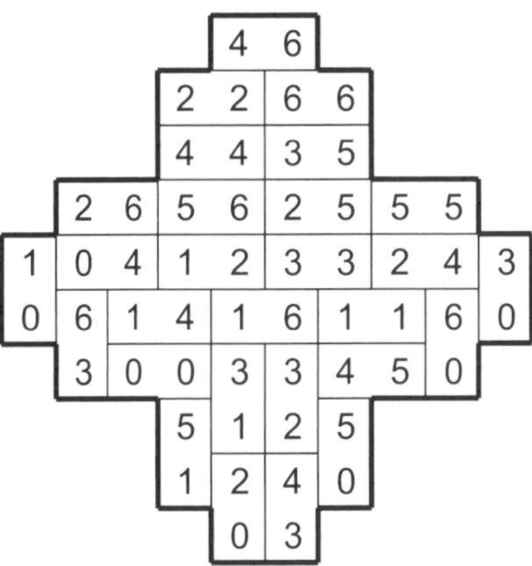

43

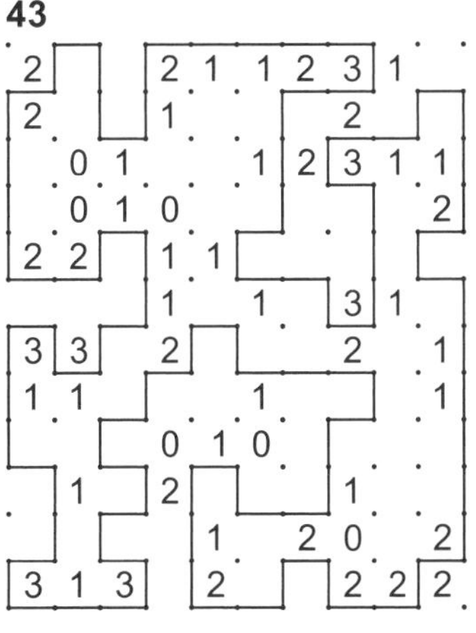

44

1	4	4	3	3	3
4	2	2	4	4	1
4	2	2	4	4	1
1	1	1	4	4	1
1	1	1	4	4	1
2	3	3	2	2	3

45

C – Starting top left, all odd numbers increase by two and even numbers decrease by two from set to set.

SOLUTIONS : LEVEL 2

46

47

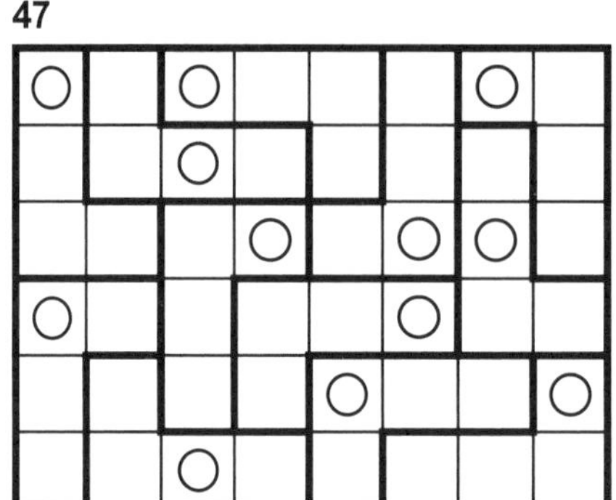

48

Circle = 5, cross = 1, pentagon = 6, square = 8, star = 7.

49

C	A	B	B	C	A
B	A	C	C	A	B
C	C	B	B	A	A
A	B	C	A	B	C
A	C	A	C	B	B
B	B	A	A	C	C

50

B – The shape at the bottom moves to the top and all others therefore move down one place in the pile.

51

3S	3S	1W	3W	2W
3E	1S	2W	3S	1N
2S	1E		1S	1W
1N	2N	2N	3N	**1N**
1E	1E	1N	1E	3N

52

8 – Add the top and bottom left numbers and divide by the bottom right number to get the central number.

53

28 – The numbers in each vertical column increase by 3, 5, 7, 8, 6 and 4.

54

							125
16	27	13	9	4	17	14	100
7	11	15	24	26	30	2	115
1	14	8	29	21	13	11	97
5	3	12	20	10	6	25	81
18	23	4	19	28	14	13	119
2	16	12	11	17	22	30	110
20	17	4	5	18	14	13	91
69	111	68	117	124	116	108	118

SOLUTIONS : LEVEL 2

55

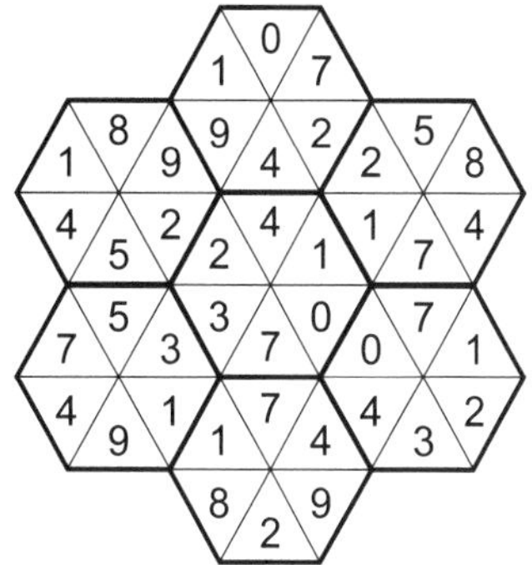

56

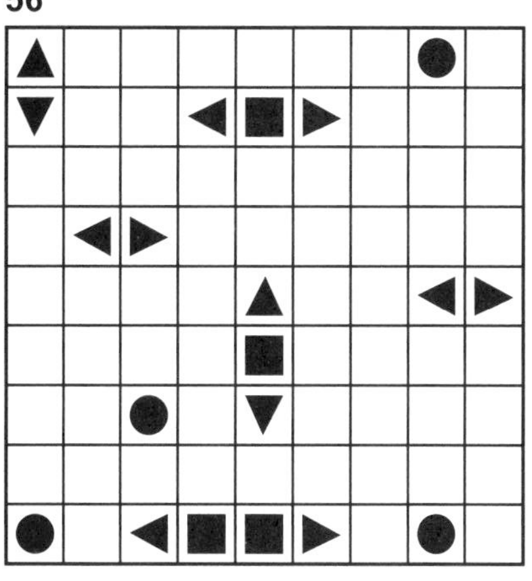

57

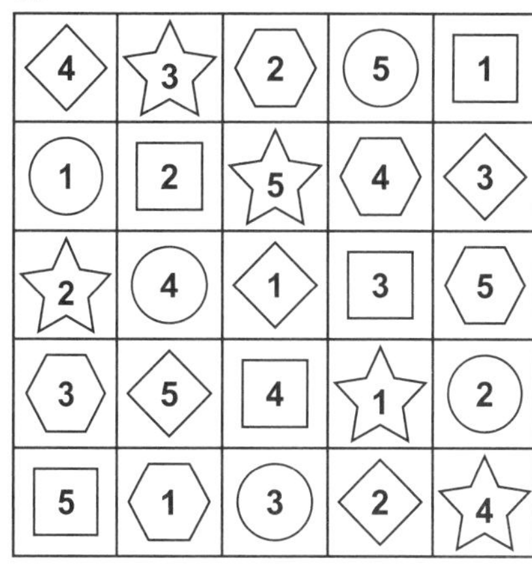

58

7 – The numbers in the outer points of the star all add up to the central figure.

59

A=121, B=25, C=96, D=67, E=126, F=146, G=121, H=163, I=193, J=267, K=284, L=356, M=551, N=640, O=1191.

60

●		●		2		2	2	2	●
1	3	2		●	●	●		●	
		●	4	●	●	4		1	
1		3	●			●			
●	3	●		1					1
2	●				0		2	●	1
						2	●		3
0		0	1	●	2	●	4	●	●
1		2		2			3	●	
	●	●			●	1		1	

61

The value of the letter in the central square is the sum total of the values of the letters in the other squares. Thus the missing value is 24, so the missing letter is X.

62

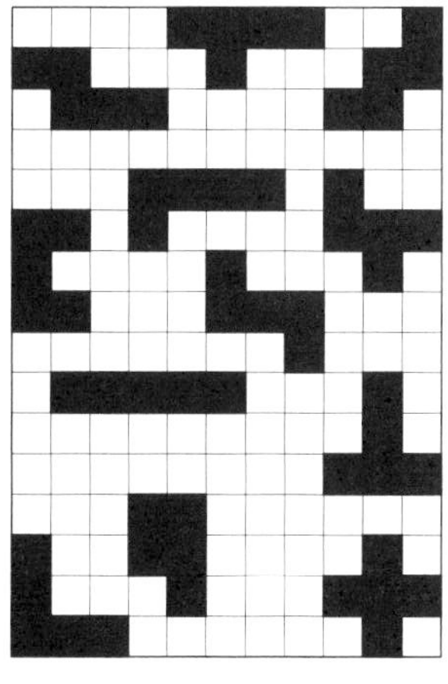

63

SOLUTIONS : LEVEL 2

64

♣		♠		♡	♢
♡	♣		♢		♠
	♠	♣	♡	♢	
		♢	♠	♣	♡
♠	♢	♡	♣		
♢	♡			♠	♣

65

2	5	1	4	3
3	1	4	2	5
1	**4**	3	**5**	**2**
4	2	5	3	1
5	3	2	1	4

66

2	0	5	7	■	7	2	5	4	■	2	6	6
3	■	5	4	3	5	5	■	7	2	3	■	7
1	1	5	1	0	5	■	9	2	■	3	7	0
7	8	2	■	4	■	6	0	5	5	0	4	■
9	9	8	3	■	1	0	5	0	0	2	■	3
■	0	■	3	8	4	1	0	9	■	1	2	9
4	8	6	8	■	0	■	1	■	6	0	2	4
9	8	0	■	2	3	4	1	0	9	■	4	■
3	■	4	4	3	3	1	8	■	3	2	2	3
■	1	8	9	9	3	7	■	1	■	9	9	9
4	2	5	■	4	1	■	5	4	4	4	1	9
8	■	8	8	7	■	2	5	7	1	3	■	0
8	6	9	■	7	3	1	5	■	8	0	0	4

67

5	4	6	1	3	2
3	5	2	4	6	1
6	3	1	5	2	4
2	6	4	3	1	5
1	2	5	6	4	3
4	1	3	2	5	6

68

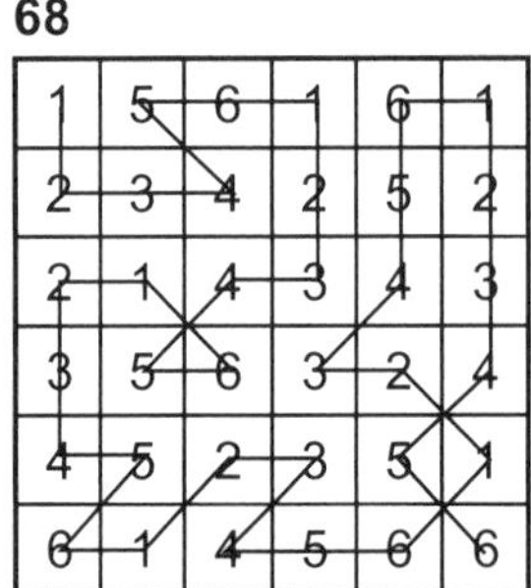

69

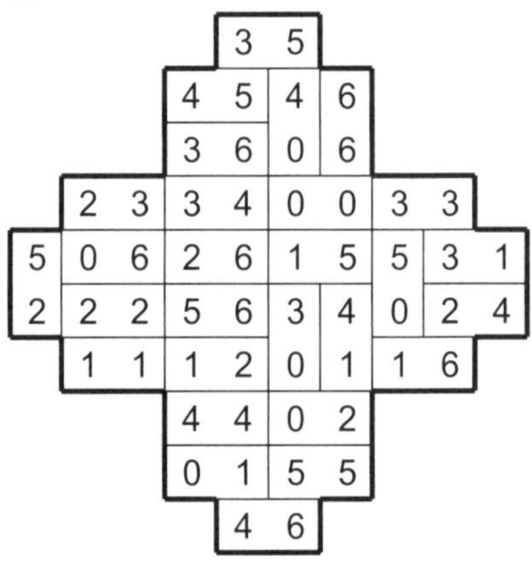

70

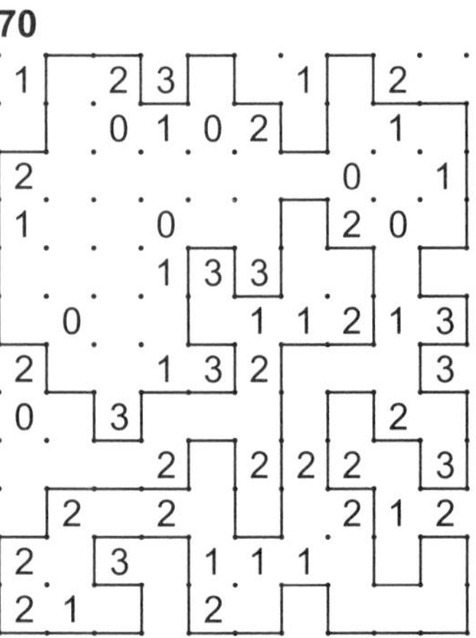

71

1	2	2	4	4	1
1	3	3	3	3	1
1	3	3	3	3	1
2	2	2	1	1	2
2	2	2	1	1	2
2	2	2	4	4	3

72

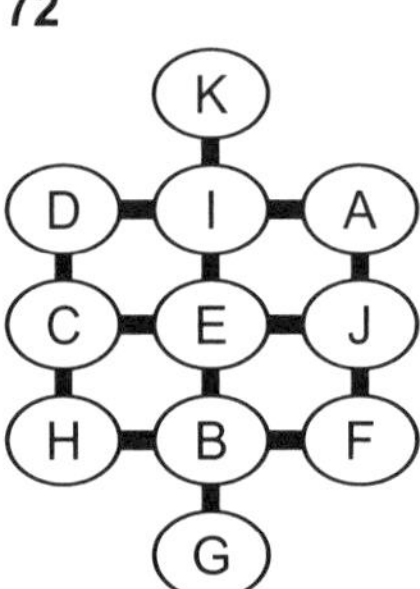

SOLUTIONS : LEVEL 2

73

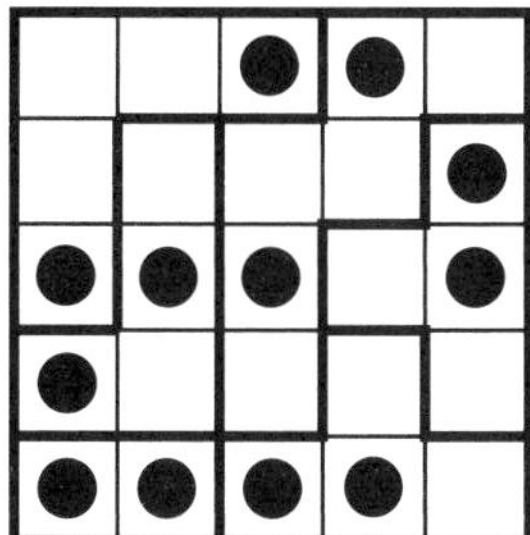

74

○							
	○		○			○	○
○			○				○
	○			○			○
	○						

75

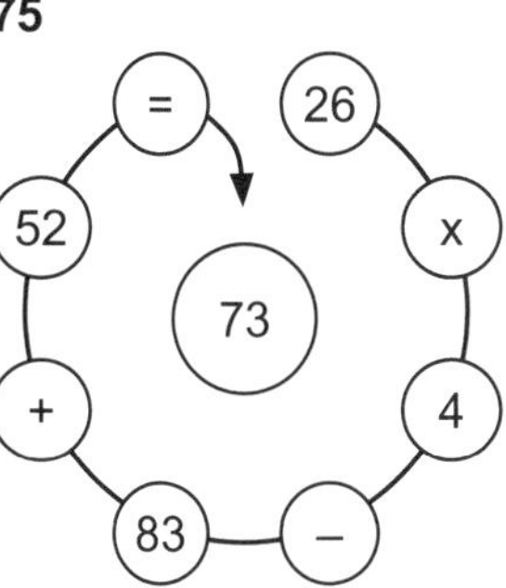

76

A	C	B	B	A	C
C	B	C	A	A	B
B	A	A	C	C	B
A	B	B	C	C	A
C	A	C	B	B	A
B	C	A	A	B	C

77

1	x	7	–	4	=	3
x	■	x	■	+		
8	x	6	–	5	=	43
+	■	+	■	x		
2	x	3	x	9	=	54
=		=		=		
10		45		81		

78

3S	1S	2W	1E	3W
3S	1W	1N	1S	2W
1E	3E	■	2N	1S
1E	1E	1N	2N	1W
3E	1E	2E	2W	3N

79

	5			9		7
2		5				2
				8		
	1					8
			8			
	9				8	

80

54	8	**42**	20	59	36
38	36	29	**30**	39	47
32	65	36	34	**20**	32
33	45	39	38	17	47
29	**38**	45	43	31	33
33	27	28	54	53	**24**

81

							82
11	27	19	24	30	4	16	131
17	29	14	5	7	18	15	105
12	21	25	20	6	1	3	88
13	11	28	26	14	17	8	117
2	9	12	11	10	19	21	84
23	2	14	25	20	30	15	129
2	6	29	16	24	8	6	91
80	105	141	127	111	97	84	137

SOLUTIONS : LEVEL 3

1

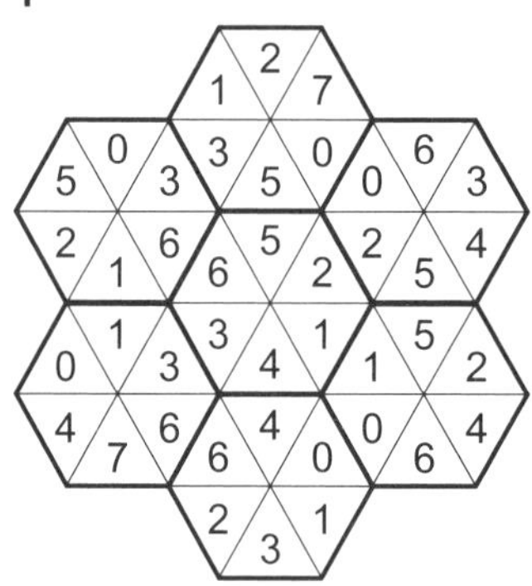

2

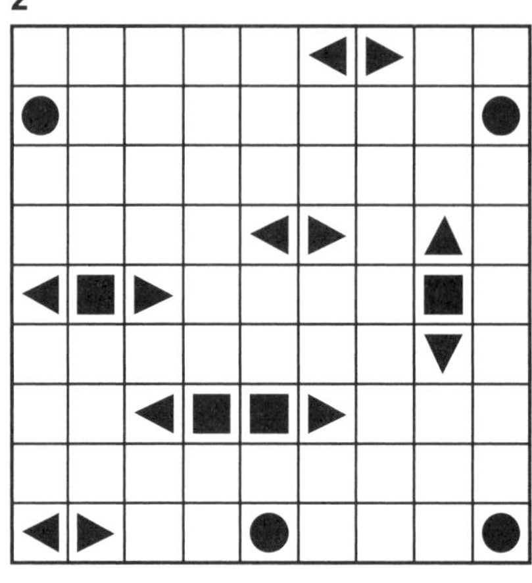

3

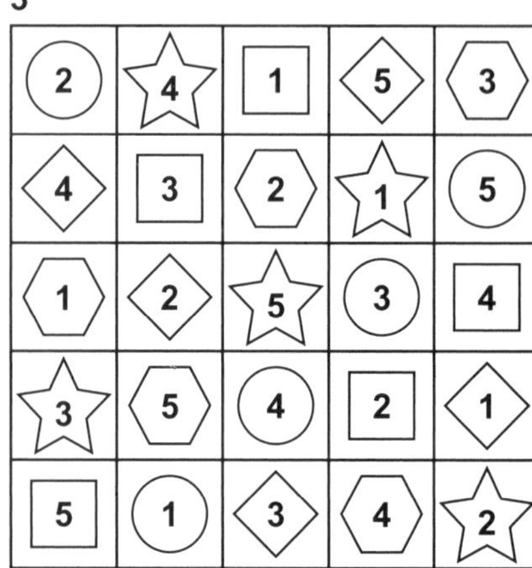

4

K – Assign a number to each letter according to its place in the alphabet, so A=1, B=2, C=3, etc. Adding together the values of the two letters in each point of the star results in the central figure, 17. F=6, so the missing letter is K(=11).

5

A=45, B=57, C=143, D=36, E=4, F=102, G=200, H=179, I=40, J=302, K=379, L=219, M=681, N=598, O=1279.

6

3	●	4		2		●	2		0
●	●	●	●		●	4	●		
			4	●	2	3	●		
	1	●			1			1	
		3		1					1
0		●	●			●	2	●	1
		3				2		2	
		●	3	1		2	●	3	
	2	●	●	4		●	3	●	●
			●	●	●				2

7

The sum total of the values of the letters in the two left squares minus the sum total of the values of the letters in the two right squares equals that of the central square. Thus the missing value is 9, so the missing letter is I.

8

9

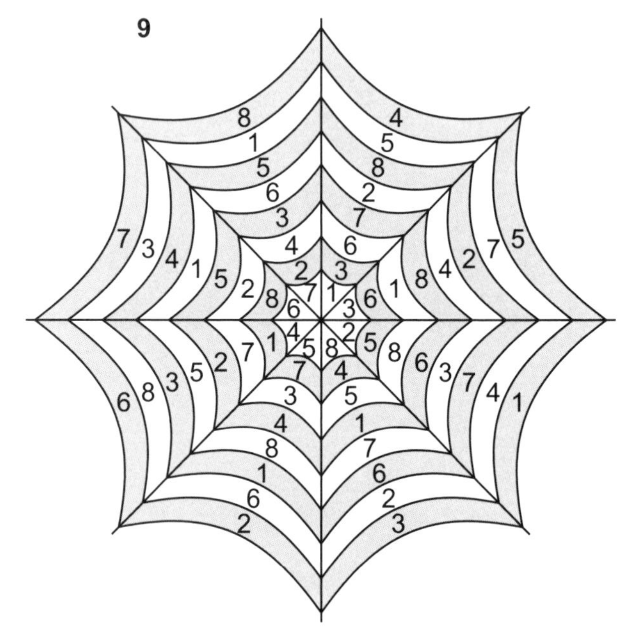

SOLUTIONS : LEVEL 3

10

	♡	◇	♠		♣
♡	♠		♣	◇	
♣	◇	♡			♠
♠			◇	♣	♡
	♣	♠		♡	◇
◇		♣	♡	♠	

11

3	1	4	2	5
5	3	**2**	4	1
1	4	5	**3**	2
2	**5**	3	1	4
4	2	1	**5**	3

12

5	9	6	■	3	5	9	2	■	3	1	1	6
2	■	7	9	2	1	■	6	3	3	5	■	0
1	4	0	0	■	1	7	0	■	2	8	4	2
8	4	■	6	7	7	7	5	■	2	0	9	8
■	■	2	1	■	1	9	9	■	7	■	9	■
7	8	6	4	9	9	■	4	7	4	5	1	1
6	■	4	■	5	■	■	■	4	■	5	■	5
4	5	3	1	8	6	■	2	2	3	2	5	0
■	0	■	0	■	7	2	0	■	9	4	■	■
3	9	3	9	■	3	6	0	7	2	■	5	1
3	6	8	0	■	7	6	0	■	9	7	2	0
8	■	8	2	8	8	■	9	1	1	1	■	8
9	6	3	5	■	4	8	3	5	■	9	3	8

13

1	2	5	6	4	3
6	3	1	4	5	2
2	1	4	3	6	5
4	5	3	1	2	6
3	6	2	5	1	4
5	4	6	2	3	1

14

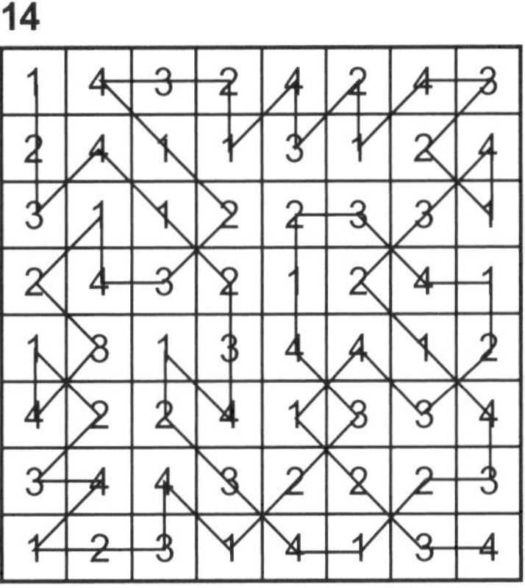

15

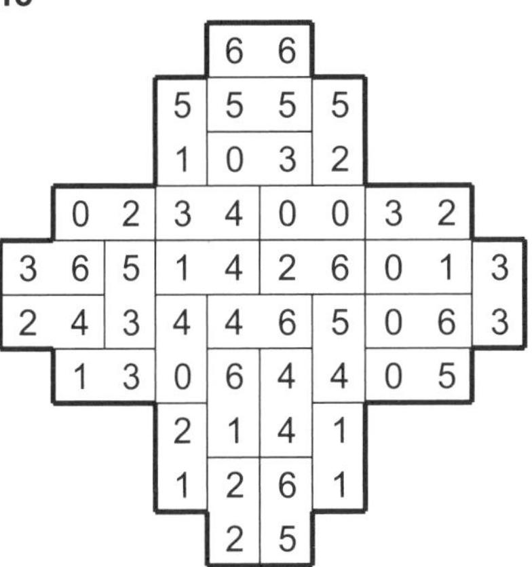

16

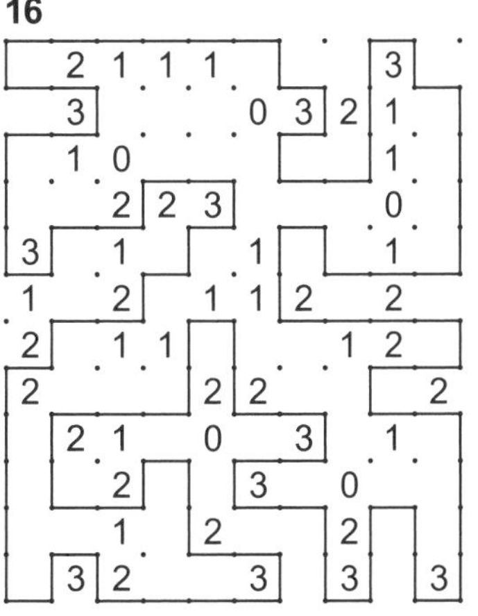

17

3	2	2	2	2	2
1	4	4	4	4	1
1	4	4	4	4	1
2	1	1	3	3	3
2	1	1	3	3	3
3	1	1	1	1	2

18

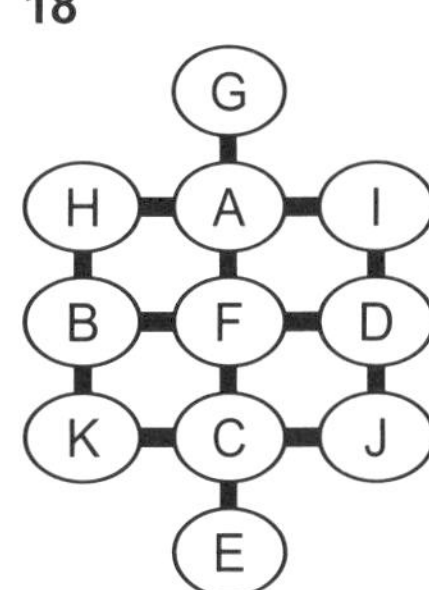

SOLUTIONS : LEVEL 3

19

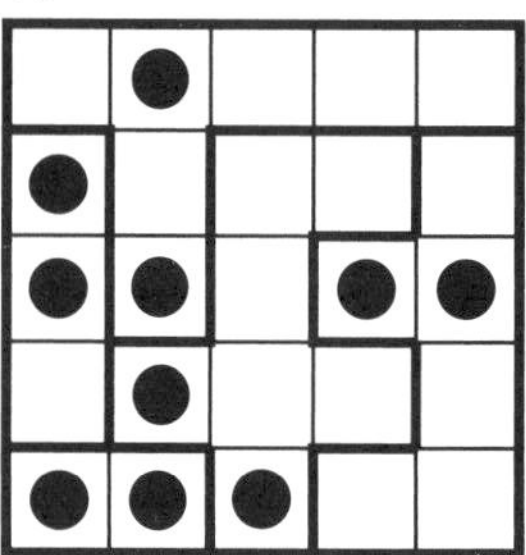

20

	O		O		O		
		O		O	O		
O			O				
							O
O			O	O			

21

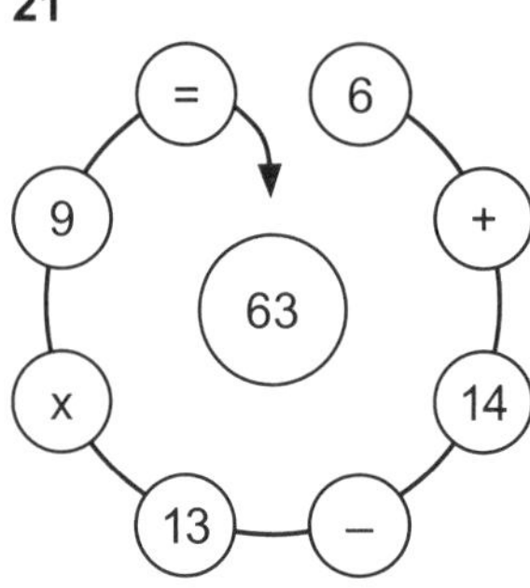

22

B	A	C	A	B	C
B	C	A	C	B	A
A	C	B	B	C	A
C	B	C	A	A	B
C	A	B	C	A	B
A	B	A	B	C	C

23

7	+	4	–	8	=	3
+	■	+	■	x		
9	x	1	–	3	=	6
x	■	–	■	x		
6	x	2	–	5	=	7
=		=		=		
96		3		120		

24

2E	1W	1S	2W	3S
1S	2S	3S	**1E**	1N
2E	2S	■	2W	1W
3E	1E	2W	3N	1S
3N	3N	1E	3W	2N

25

	7		9			
					5	
6		9				
8			5			6
1		2		2		8

26

25	**29**	12	38	15	25
36	44	24	26	**8**	6
37	21	8	38	19	21
12	8	44	**4**	54	22
9	4	16	32	38	**45**
25	38	**40**	6	10	25

27

							113
16	4	10	12	27	29	2	100
14	24	4	5	17	18	25	107
3	6	11	13	20	21	19	93
1	12	21	26	15	13	8	96
30	10	14	22	7	9	14	106
28	16	13	5	8	6	15	91
17	4	30	25	23	2	7	108
109	76	103	108	117	98	90	97

SOLUTIONS : LEVEL 3

28

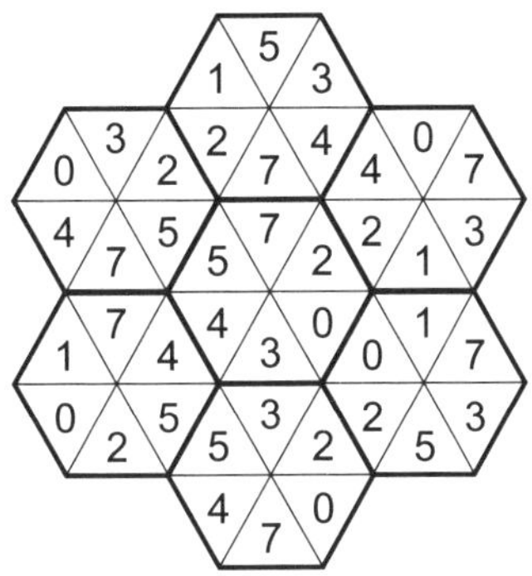

29

▲								▲
▼		●			●			▼
					●			●
	▲							
	▼		◀	■	▶		▲	
							■	
							■	
		◀	■	▶			▼	

30

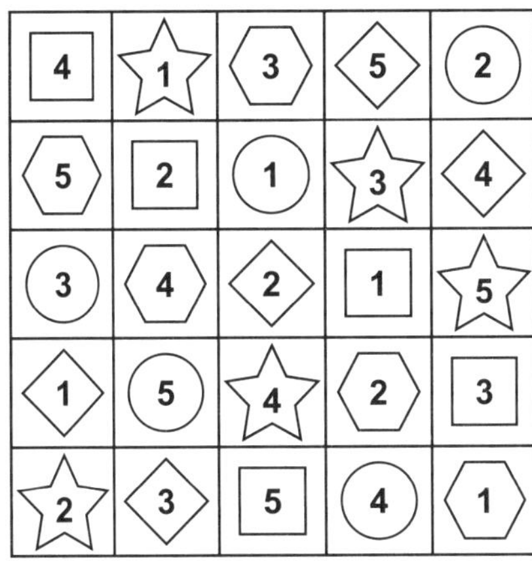

31

A – Starting top left and moving clockwise towards the middle, the letters in each square move forward two places in the alphabet.

32

A=50, B=104, C=53, D=111, E=146, F=154, G=157, H=164, I=257, J=311, K=321, L=421, M=632, N=742, O=1374.

33

2	●	2	●		1			0	
●	2			3	●				
			●	4	3	2		●	
●	5	●		●	●		1		1
●	●	●		●			1		
3	●	3	2		2	●		0	
	3	2		1		3			1
●		●	2		●	●		2	●
		2	●			●	●		2
	0				1	2	3	●	

34

The value of the letter in each top square is added to the value of the letter in the central square to give the value of the letter in the bottom square diagonally opposite. Thus the missing value is 8, so the missing letter is H.

35

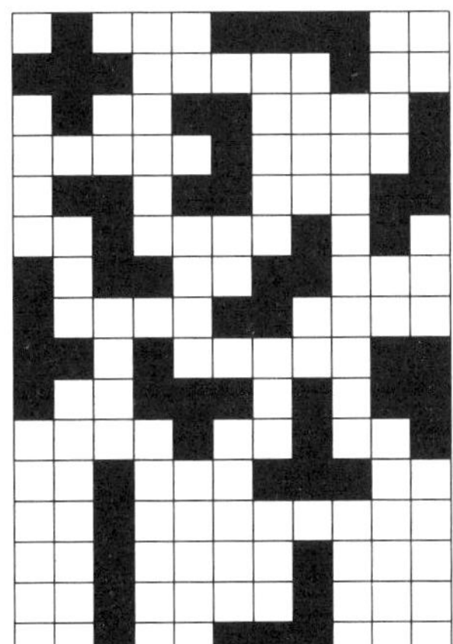

36

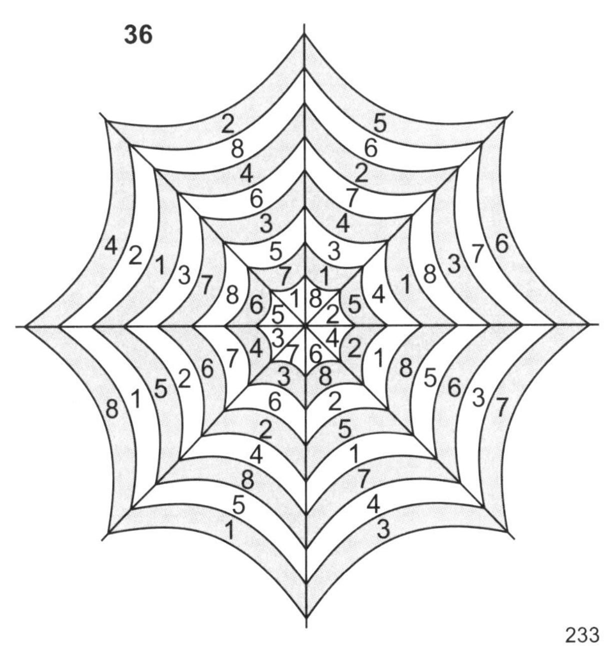

SOLUTIONS : LEVEL 3

37

38

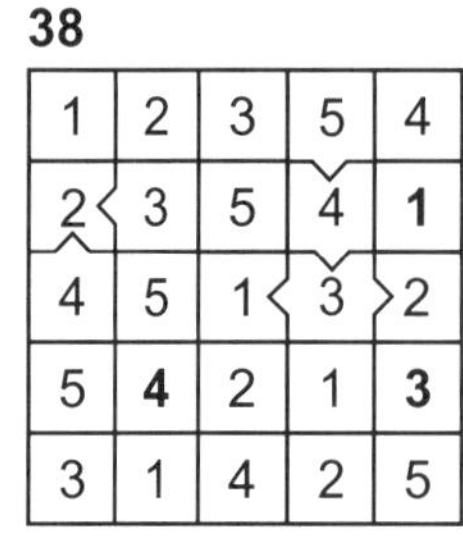

1	2	3	5	4
2	3	5	4	1
4	5	1	3	2
5	4	2	1	3
3	1	4	2	5

39

5	4	7	8	2		4	1	7	1	5	6	3
4		6		8	1	2		9	2	9		8
2	2	1	7	3		4	6	8	8	6	5	1
	7		5	7	8	0		0			2	1
6	0	3	0		5		3	1	7	4	6	3
2	3	0		1	2	2	2		7	9		
9	9	1	3	1	5		1	6	9	0	2	1
		9	2		4	5	5	9		4	9	9
1	3	0	6	8	4		0		4	9	3	7
4	4			5		5	6	8	3		0	
6	7	7	2	4	0	3		1	3	2	7	3
7		4	5	6		6	0	9		0		2
9	4	7	8	2	7	3		9	0	6	0	5

40

4	2	3	5	1	6
3	6	1	2	5	4
2	5	4	1	6	3
1	4	2	6	3	5
6	1	5	3	4	2
5	3	6	4	2	1

41

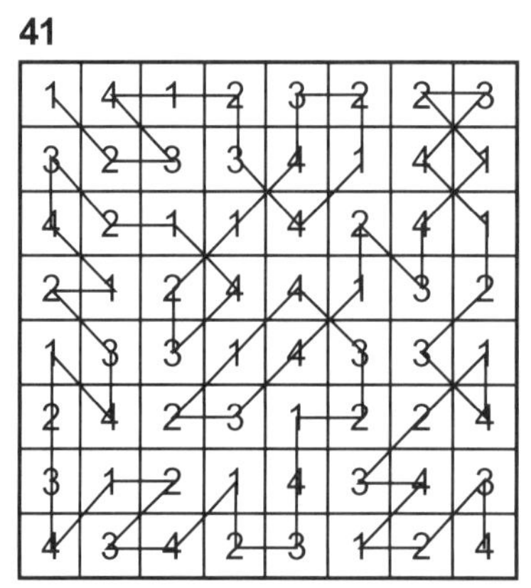

42

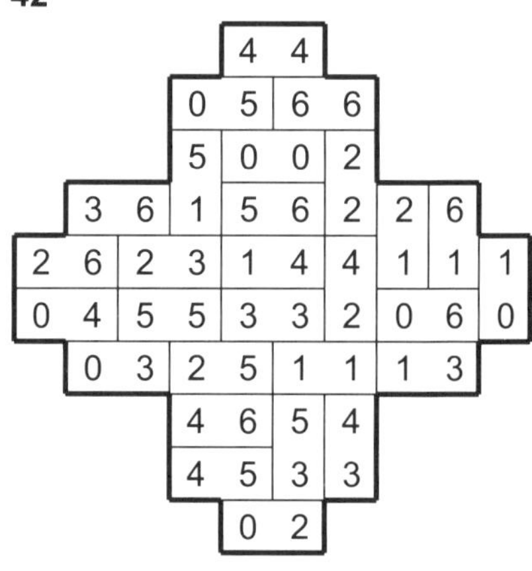

43

3 1 1 1 3
1 0 1 3 2
2 1 3 2
0 3 1
2 1 2 1 1 1 2
3 1
3 2 1 0 3
3 1 1 0 1 2
1 1 2 3
1 0 2
3 1 1
3 1 3 1 0

44

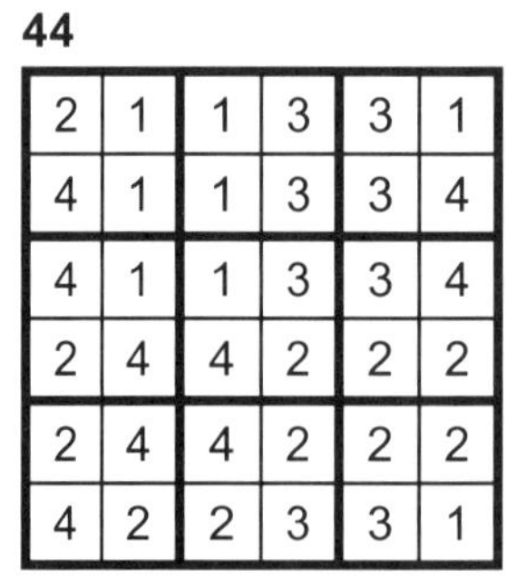

2	1	1	3	3	1
4	1	1	3	3	4
4	1	1	3	3	4
2	4	4	2	2	2
2	4	4	2	2	2
4	2	2	3	3	1

45

B – Assign a value to each letter according to its place in the alphabet. The corner squares increase by two, and all other letters increase by three from set to set.

SOLUTIONS : LEVEL 3

46

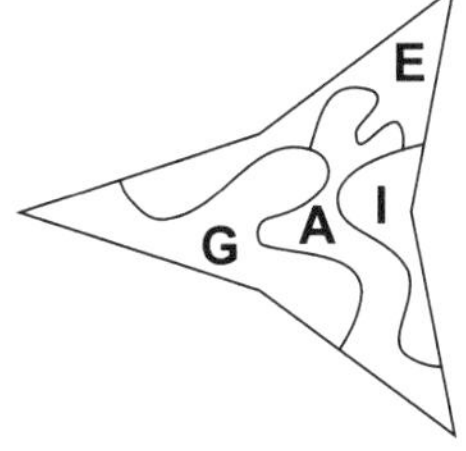

47

	O	O				O	
			O		O	O	
O		O					
			O			O	
			O	O			

48

Circle = 3, cross = 9, pentagon = 2, square = 1, star = 7.

49

B	B	C	A	C	A
A	C	B	C	A	B
A	A	B	B	C	C
C	B	C	A	B	A
C	C	A	B	A	B
B	A	A	C	B	C

50

1 – It has made a 90 degree turn clockwise, whereas the others have made a 90 degree turn anticlockwise.

51

3E	2S	2S	1W	3S
1E	1N	2W	1E	2W
2N	2E	■	1E	2N
1N	**2E**	1S	1S	2W
1N	1W	2E	3N	3W

52

2 – The numbers in the bottom boxes are multiplied together to get the sum total of the numbers in the top boxes.

53

20 – Reading along each row from left to right, the sequence of numbers is the first number plus 2 equals the second number minus 3 equals the third number plus 4 equals the fourth number minus 5 equals the fifth number plus 6 equals the sixth number minus 7 equals the seventh number.

54

							117
15	28	8	14	6	20	13	104
10	17	24	30	1	22	18	122
2	7	15	19	12	16	27	98
25	5	21	26	14	3	29	123
4	9	17	23	19	5	11	88
20	15	13	27	3	9	12	99
12	17	30	28	18	1	20	126
88	98	128	167	73	76	130	121

SOLUTIONS : LEVEL 3

55

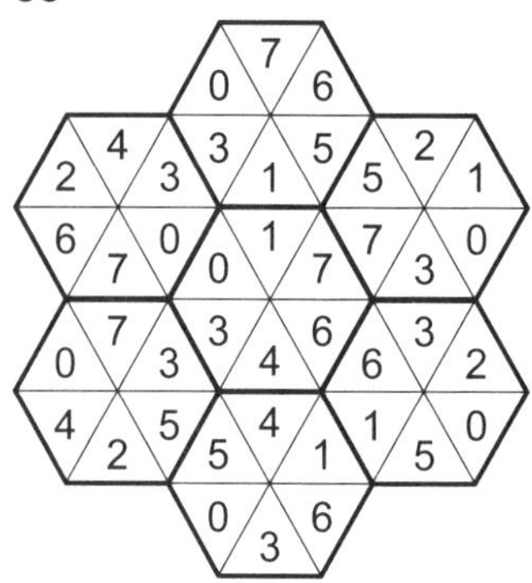

56

	▲			●				▲
	▼							▼
			◀	■	■	▶		
			▲					
	●		■					
			▼			◀	■	▶
▲								
▼				●			●	

57

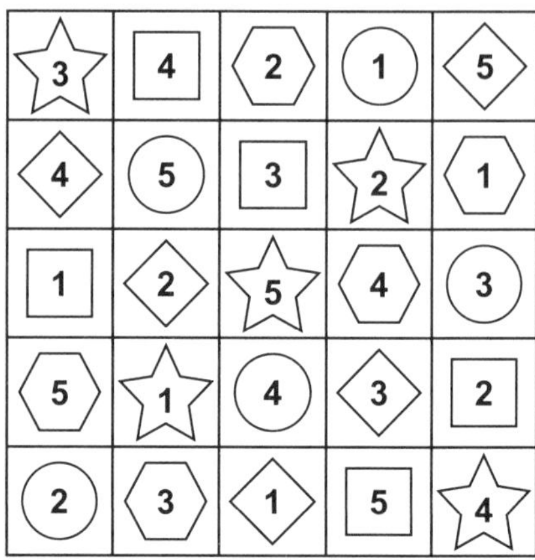

58

N – Clockwise from the top, move 3 places forwards in the alphabet, then 2 back, 5 forwards, 2 back, 7 forwards (N), then 2 back, to L in the middle.

59

A=135, B=119, C=147, D=58, E=97, F=254, G=266, H=205, I=155, J=520, K=471, L=360, M=991, N=831, O=1822.

60

	0	1	●		1	2	●		
					2	●		●	1
●	3	2		●		2		2	1
●		●	●				●		
2	●	4		1	0	2	●		1
	3	●	3		2			3	●
0		●	3	●	●		●	3	2
					●	4	1	3	●
2	●				●	3		2	●
	●	2	0			●	1		

61

The sum total of the values of the letters in the top squares and central square is equal to the sum total of the values in the bottom squares. Thus the missing value is 17, so the missing letter is Q.

62

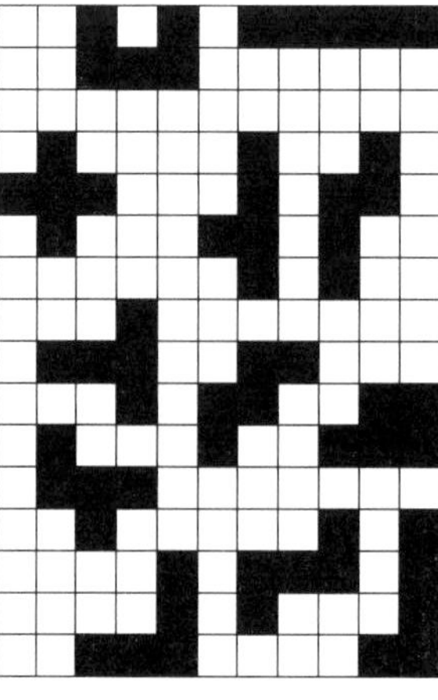

63

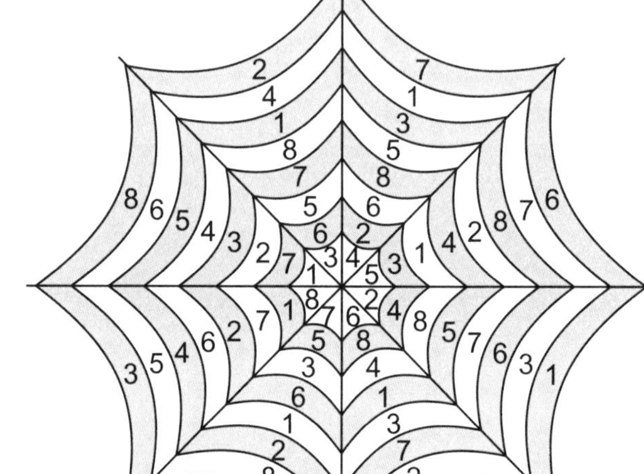

SOLUTIONS : LEVEL 3

64

	◇	♡	♠	♣	
♠	♣		♡		◇
◇	♡		♣	♠	
♡	♠	◇			♣
♣		♠		◇	♡
		♣	◇	♡	♠

65

5	1	4	**3**	2
1	4	2	5	3
4	5	3	2	1
3	2	**5**	1	4
2	**3**	**1**	4	5

66

2	7	4	6	5	■	1	6	4	■	3	1	6
9	1	5	■	8	1	1	■	8	2	1	3	■
3	2	5	5	0	■	1	■	5	7	8	0	2
2	■	8	■	3	5	5	6	5	■	6	■	2
2	1	2	5	0	■	9	0	■	6	3	5	4
9	9	■	9	■	3	1	0	6	1	■	8	■
7	8	8	7	5	2	■	1	0	6	7	7	2
■	0	■	8	0	6	6	9	■	7	■	1	8
1	5	4	4	■	7	6	■	2	3	1	0	4
7	■	0	■	6	2	9	8	1	■	6	■	6
9	4	0	8	0	■	8	■	7	2	8	3	0
■	7	0	2	3	■	4	5	4	■	8	4	9
9	4	0	■	1	3	9	■	7	6	2	4	9

67

4	2	1	6	3	5
1	6	4	3	5	2
2	5	3	1	4	6
5	3	6	4	2	1
3	1	5	2	6	4
6	4	2	5	1	3

68

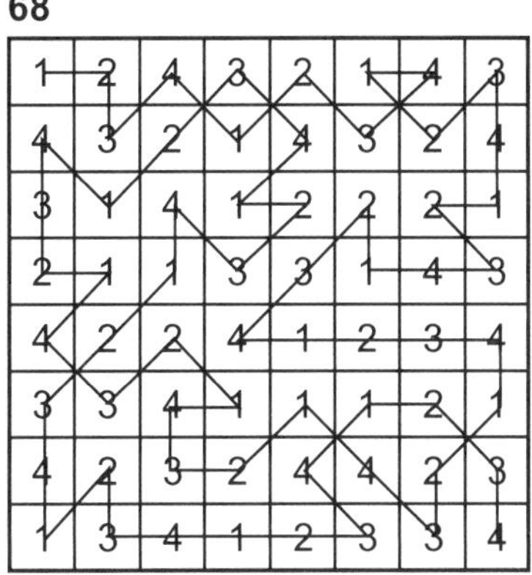

69

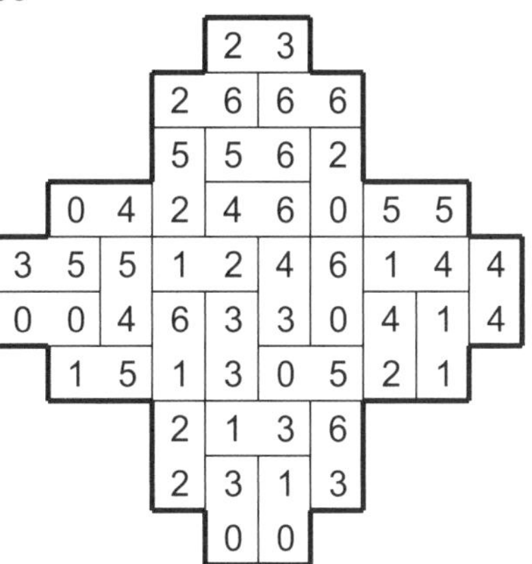

70

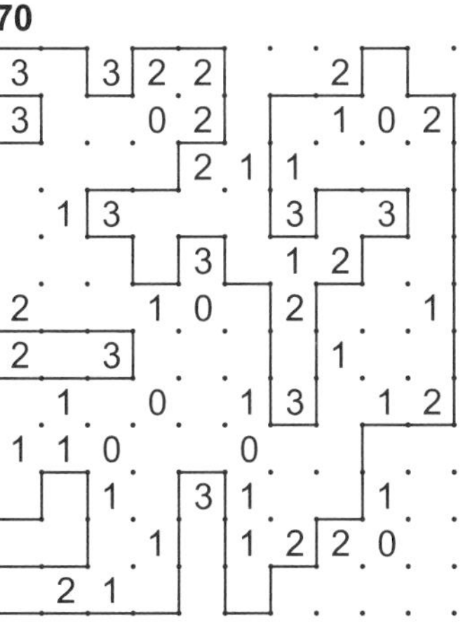

71

1	2	2	3	3	4
2	1	1	2	2	1
2	1	1	2	2	1
3	3	3	4	4	4
3	3	3	4	4	4
4	1	1	4	4	3

72

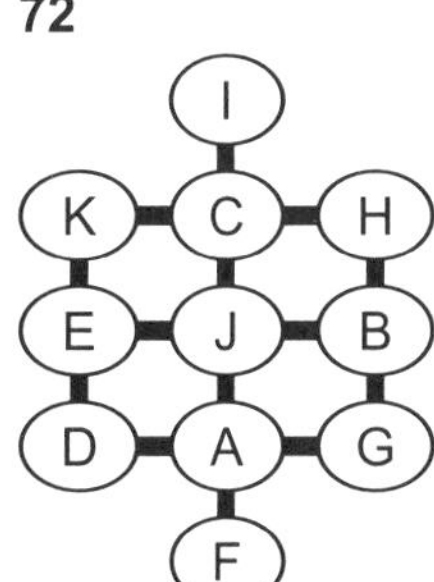

SOLUTIONS : LEVEL 3

73

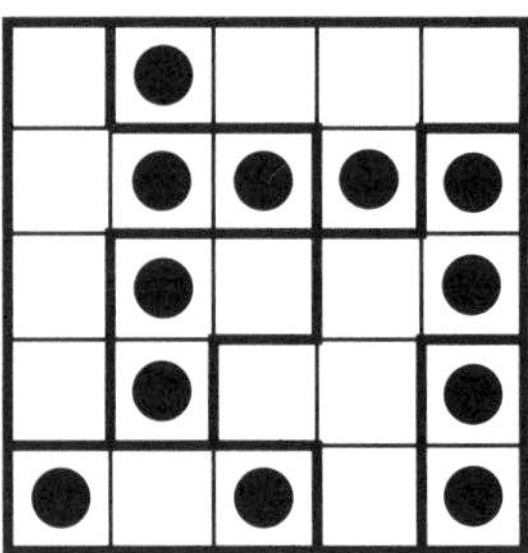

74

	○		○				○
						○	
	○					○	
				○		○	
	○						
	○		○		○		

75

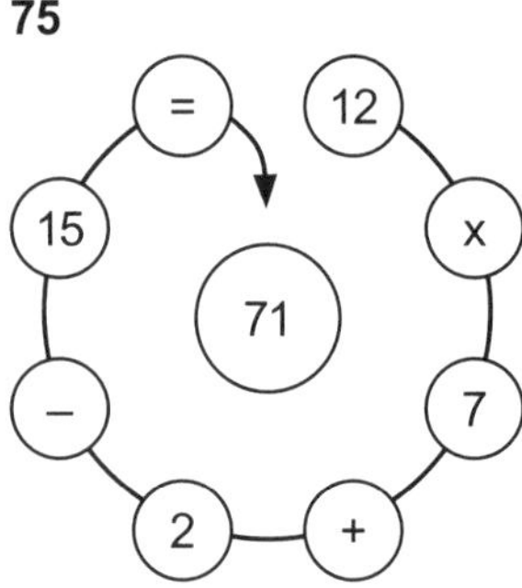

76

C	B	B	C	A	A
A	C	B	B	C	A
A	C	A	B	B	C
C	B	C	A	A	B
B	A	C	A	B	C
B	A	A	C	C	B

77

6	x	1	x	5	=	30
–		x		+		
2	x	8	–	9	=	7
x		+		x		
7	x	3	x	4	=	84
=		=		=		
28		11		56		

78

2S	3S	1W	3W	**1W**
1E	2E	1N	1E	2S
1N	2E		2S	3W
2E	1S	2N	3W	1S
2E	1W	2N	1N	2N

79

3		4				4
				5		
	3					5
				9		
	2					
						9
3		7		7		

80

58	**13**	23	32	62	40
51	38	30	26	**38**	45
29	59	38	44	20	38
41	55	38	**32**	18	44
19	38	53	43	38	**37**
30	25	**46**	51	52	24

81

							107
14	17	29	2	6	15	10	93
13	28	16	9	27	18	28	139
30	21	26	17	12	11	25	142
24	20	14	23	8	7	22	118
1	11	27	15	19	2	13	88
4	15	9	26	22	14	17	107
2	30	29	12	6	5	18	102
88	142	150	104	100	72	133	142

SOLUTIONS : LEVEL 4

1

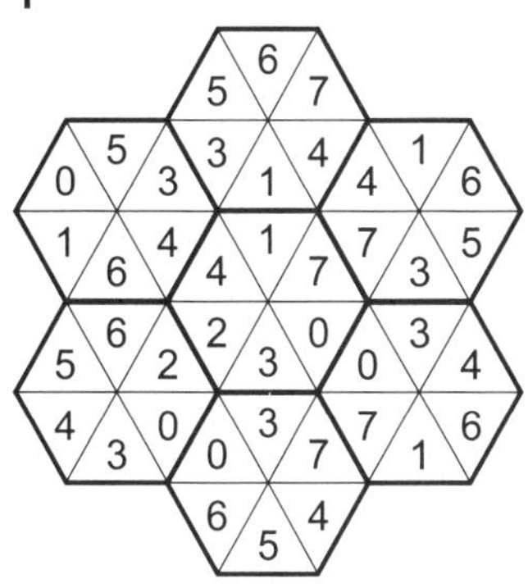

2

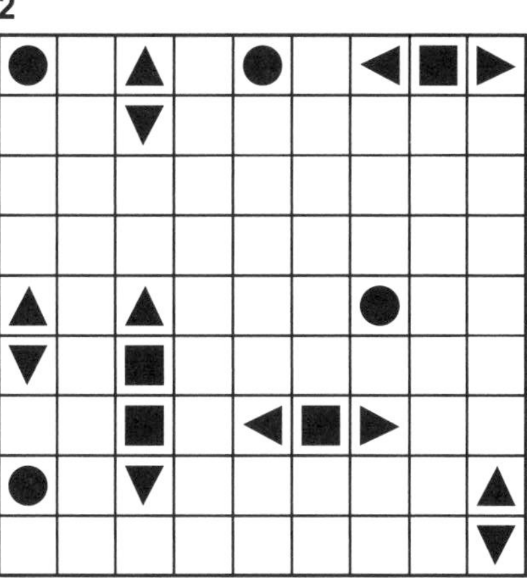

3

5	3	2	4	1
1	4	3	5	2
3	1	5	2	4
4	2	1	3	5
2	5	4	1	3

4

F – Start from the top and move clockwise, going back four letters in the alphabet each time, finally moving from J to F, then from F to B.

5

A=138, B=17, C=148, D=13, E=131, F=155, G=165, H=161, I=144, J=320, K=326, L=305, M=646, N=631, O=1277.

6

1		2	●					2	●
●		●	3		0	1		●	4
1	4	●					●	●	●
1		●		1			●		●
●				●		2	2	4	●
●		0		1		1	●	3	2
	1			1				●	
	0		●		1	0	2	●	
			●	●		2			1
	0		●	4	●	●		0	

7

The sum total of the values of the letters in the top left and bottom right squares is subtracted from the sum total of the values of the letters in the top right and bottom left squares, giving the value of the letter in the central square. Thus the missing value is 15, so the missing letter is O.

8

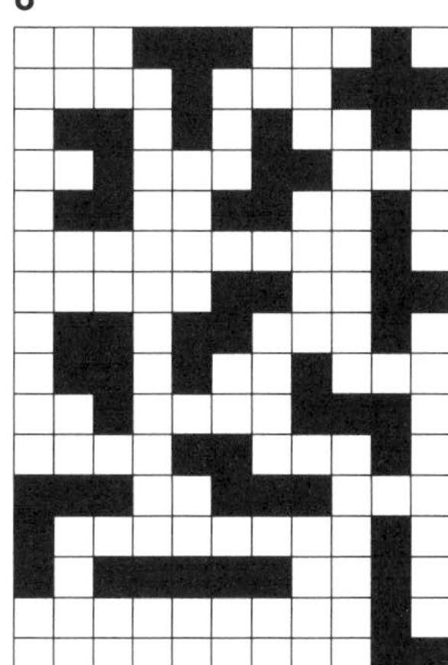

9

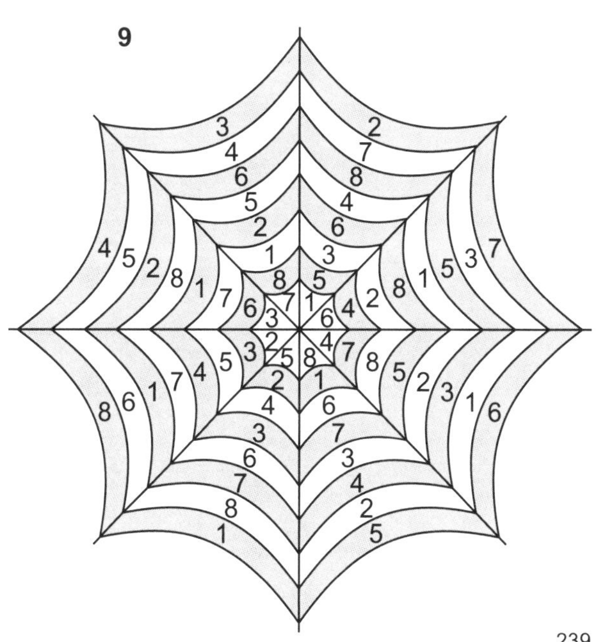

SOLUTIONS : LEVEL 4

10

♡		♠		♢	♣
	♣	♡	♠		♢
♣	♡		♢		♠
♢	♠		♡	♣	
	♢	♣		♠	♡
♠		♢	♣	♡	

11

2	5	4	**3**	1
5	3	**2**	1	4
4	1	5	2	3
3	**4**	1	5	2
1	**2**	3	4	5

12

3	7	6	6	6		5	2	3	7	6		7
4		5	0	7		3		2	7	8	1	5
7	8	0		8	3	2		7	1	6	4	3
5		8	5	9		9	1	4		9		
	3	5	2		3	1	7		2	0	0	6
4	5		6	7	4		4	5	7			1
1	4	0	9		3		4		6	0	1	5
9			9	5	5		8	9	7		9	3
6	1	1	0		9	2	6		7	3	8	
		4		2	6	0		4	2	1		3
4	2	6	5	6		2	8	6		9	0	6
3	8	9	1	1		0		9	5	0		8
8		9	0	8	7	4		4	6	6	0	3

13

1	5	6	3	2	4
4	6	2	1	3	5
2	1	3	4	5	6
5	4	1	2	6	3
6	3	4	5	1	2
3	2	5	6	4	1

14

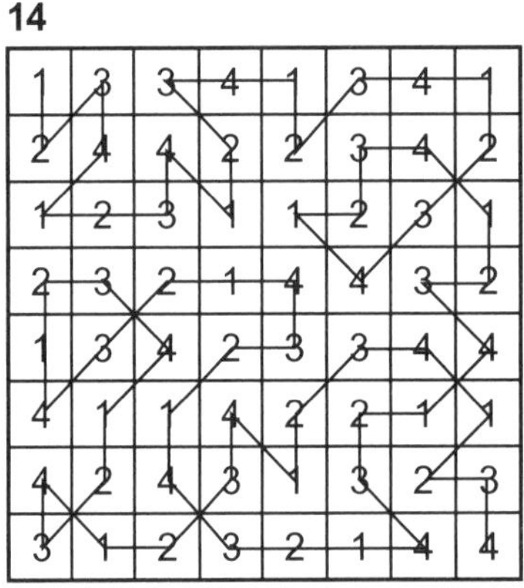

15

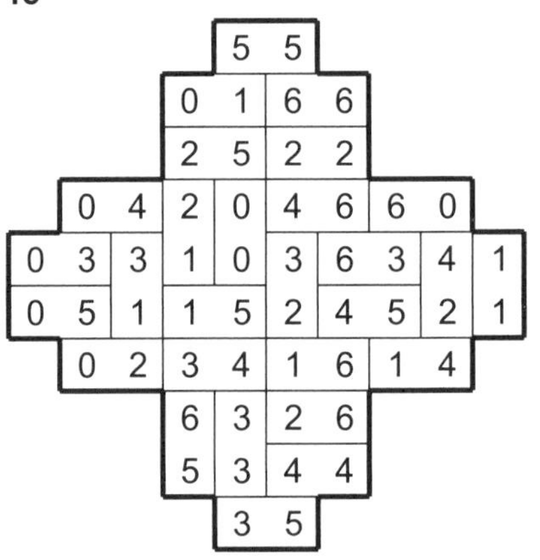

16

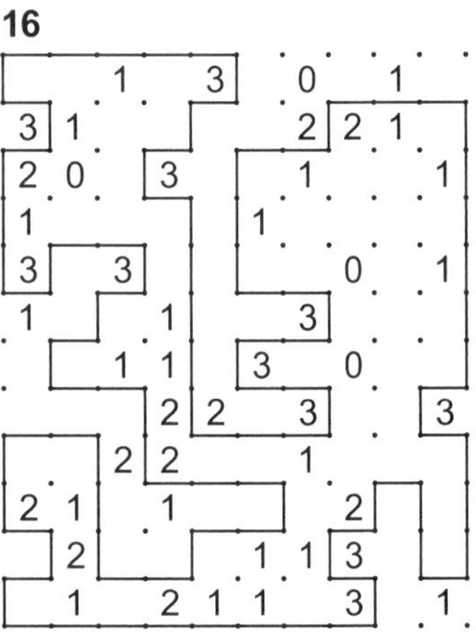

17

3	3	3	1	1	3
2	4	4	2	2	2
2	4	4	2	2	2
4	1	1	1	1	2
4	1	1	1	1	2
4	1	1	3	3	3

18

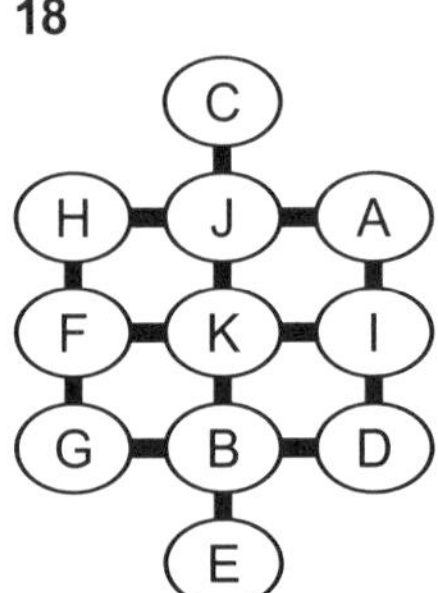

SOLUTIONS : LEVEL 4

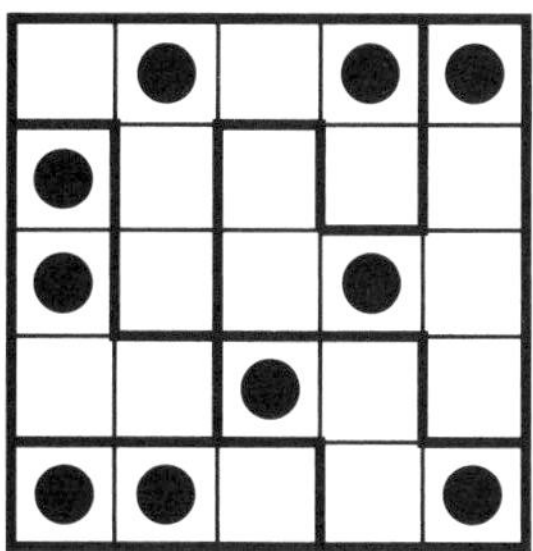

○			○			○	
	○						
		○		○		○	
○		○			○		○
	○						

21

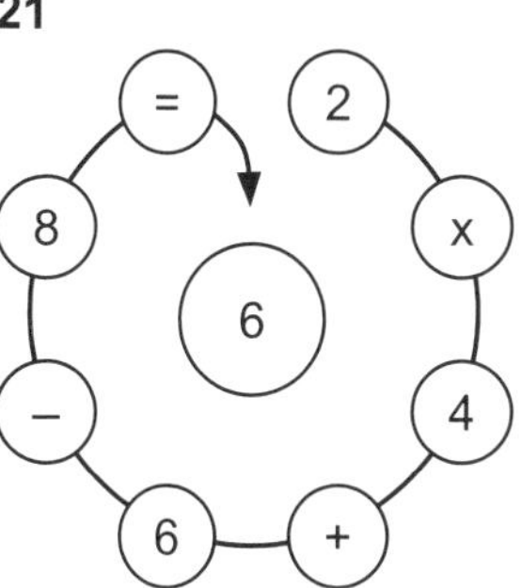

22

C	A	B	B	C	A
B	B	C	C	A	A
A	B	A	C	B	C
C	A	B	A	C	B
A	C	C	A	B	B
B	C	A	B	A	C

23

5	+	7	+	3	=	15
x		x		+		
4	x	6	x	8	=	192
–		x		–		
1	+	9	x	2	=	20
=		=		=		
19		378		9		

24

3E	2S	**2E**	2W	2S
2E	3E	2S	1S	3S
2N	1N		3W	1S
3E	1W	1S	2N	3W
3N	1W	2N	2W	1W

25

	9			2		
						6
	3			8		
						1
4		9				
				5		9
9		6				

26

29	30	33	44	51	47
33	39	**47**	33	39	43
40	61	39	27	**22**	45
29	53	39	51	20	**42**
36	**15**	36	40	63	44
67	36	40	**39**	39	13

27

							126
15	8	28	30	6	5	21	113
19	13	27	24	7	12	11	113
16	29	8	3	26	30	22	134
9	15	17	14	12	10	20	97
18	25	6	11	10	27	21	118
6	28	13	3	14	22	18	104
19	20	10	16	4	15	1	85
102	138	109	101	79	121	114	83

SOLUTIONS : LEVEL 4

28

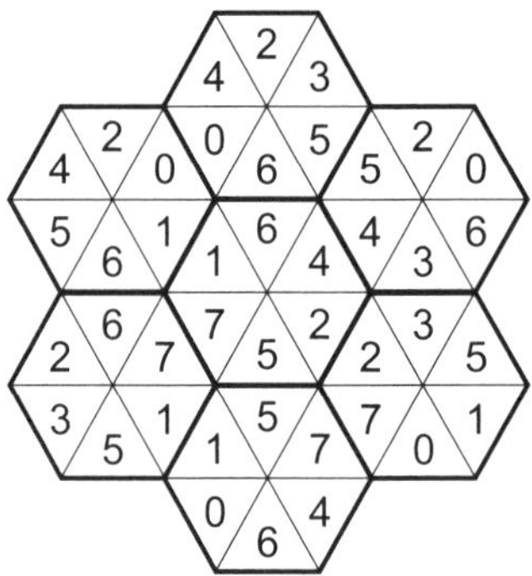

29

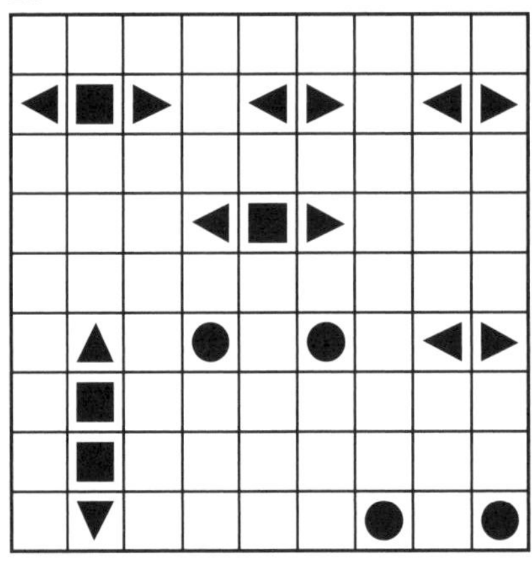

30

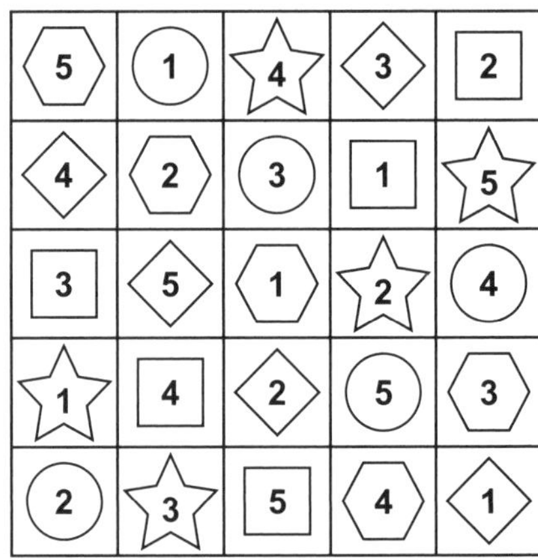

31

B – The numbers in all four corners total the same (91) as the numbers in the other five squares.

32

A=102, B=97, C=70, D=18, E=21, F=199, G=167, H=88, I=39, J=366, K=255, L=127, M=621, N=382, O=1003.

33

●	3	1	2	●	2			2	●
●		●	3	3	●		1	●	
	3			●			1	1	
●			●	2	2	2			
	1	1			1	●	●		0
	1		0				●	3	
●		1	2		2	3	●	2	
2		●		●	●		3		2
●	3		●	4	4	●		●	●
●	2		1		●			2	

34

The value of the letter in the bottom right is subtracted from the value in the bottom left; this total is subtracted from the sum total of the values in the two top squares, to give the value in the central square. Thus the missing value is 2, so the missing letter is B.

35

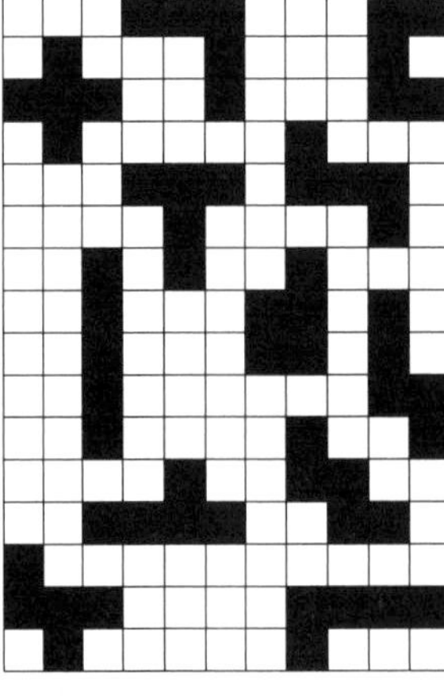

36

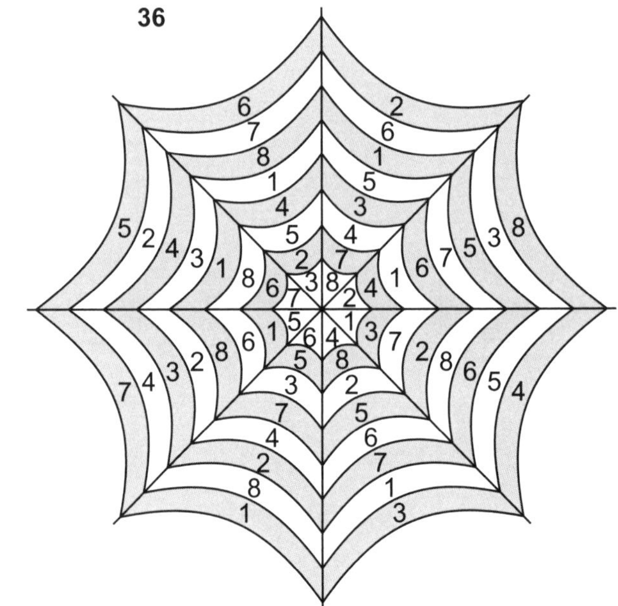

SOLUTIONS : LEVEL 4

37

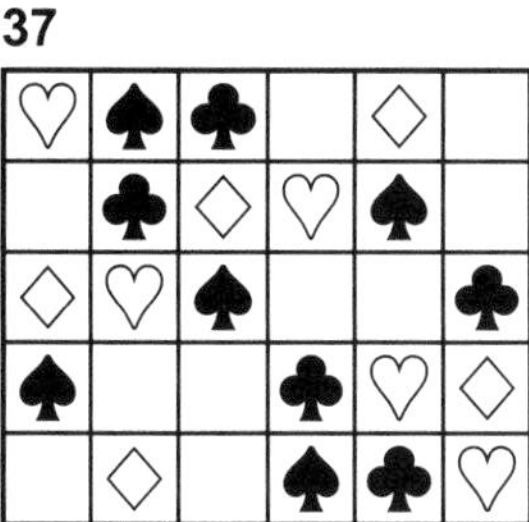

38

1	2	5	**4**	3
3	1	2	5	4
5	**3**	4	1	2
2	**4**	1	**3**	5
4	5	3	**2**	1

39

3		1	7	5			1	2	0	3		1
4	2	5		9	4	0	9	1		5	3	4
6	7	9	8	8	4			6	0	9	8	9
0		9			8	7	4	3		0		9
7	2	0	2	5		8	3		4	2	6	3
9	5			5	3	9	1	6	0		5	2
	9	0	8	2	5		9	5	2	4	6	
3	3		1	0	3	8	5	6			2	1
8	1	3	5		4	1		1	1	4	3	0
0		9		1	5	2	2			0		4
5	6	4	0	1			4	2	0	2	3	1
9	7	3		7	8	6	0	9		6	2	1
5		2	0	3	8			5	9	6		6

40

5	1	2	6	3	4
6	5	4	3	2	1
4	6	1	2	5	3
2	3	5	4	1	6
1	4	3	5	6	2
3	2	6	1	4	5

41

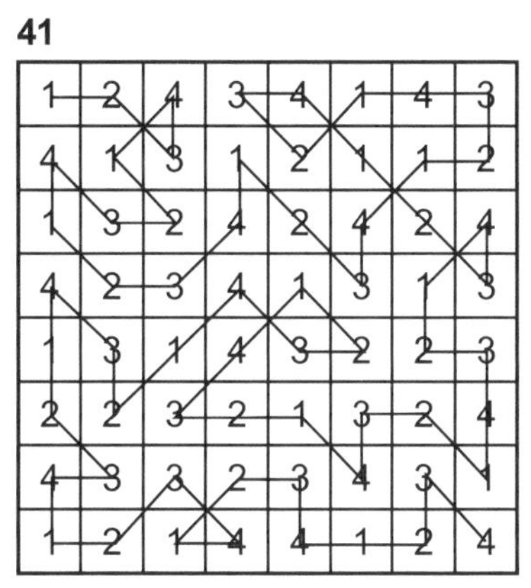

42

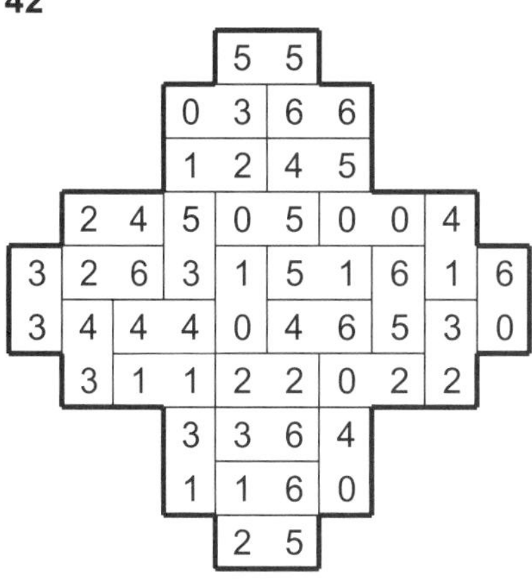

43

	1		1	1		2		1	
	1	0			1		2	2	3
	0				0				1
	1		1					0	
1		2	2	2		1			3
2			1			3	1		
		1						3	
1	3	2	2		2	2		1	
3	2		3			2	0	2	
2		0			3	1			
		3				3	1		
	2							3	

44

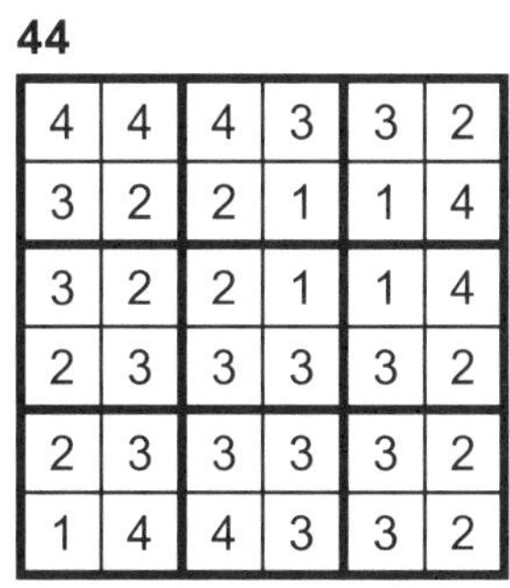

45

8 – In each case, the sum total of the outer numbers minus the sum total of the inner numbers equals five.

SOLUTIONS : LEVEL 4

46

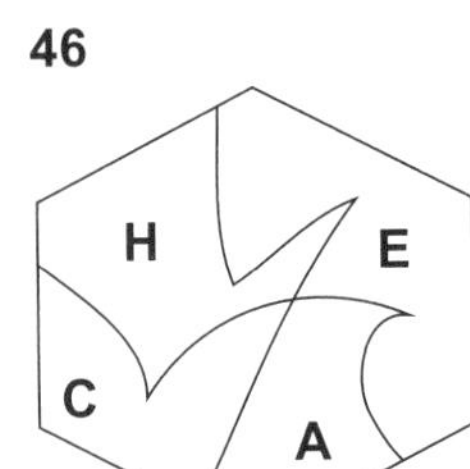

47

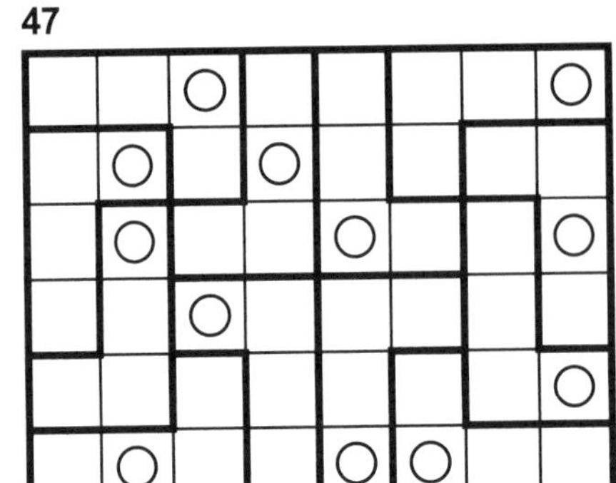

48

Circle = 6, cross = 3, pentagon = 7, square = 5, star = 2.

49

B	B	C	C	A	A
A	C	A	B	C	B
B	C	A	C	A	B
C	A	B	A	B	C
C	B	C	A	B	A
A	A	B	B	C	C

50

C – Numbers in black squares total an even number and those in shaded squares total an odd number.

51

3E	1E	1S	1E	3W
1N	3S	1E	1E	3W
2S	**1W**		2S	1S
1E	2E	2W	1N	2W
3N	3E	2N	1W	2N

52

9 – Start at the top and add the next number down, then subtract the next number, then add the next, then subtract the next, to arrive at the total shown.

53

74 – Reading down each column, add each number to the preceding number.

54

							133
11	16	26	22	6	3	30	114
7	14	9	28	25	23	2	108
1	10	14	13	26	29	4	97
20	2	11	10	14	27	24	108
8	12	19	30	26	21	4	120
5	23	13	15	17	14	29	116
2	12	4	16	27	11	5	77
54	89	96	134	141	128	98	94

SOLUTIONS : LEVEL 4

55

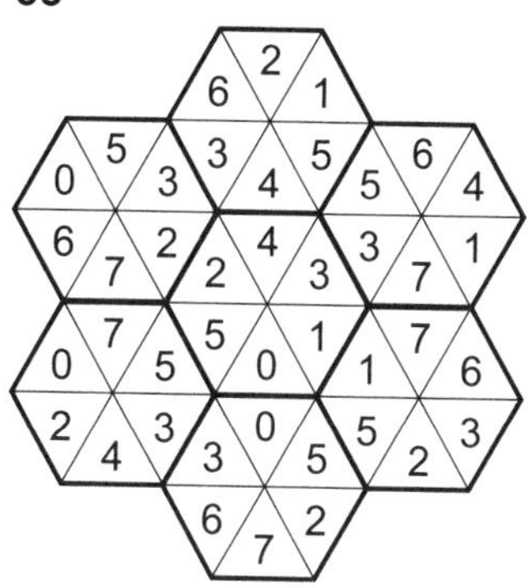

56

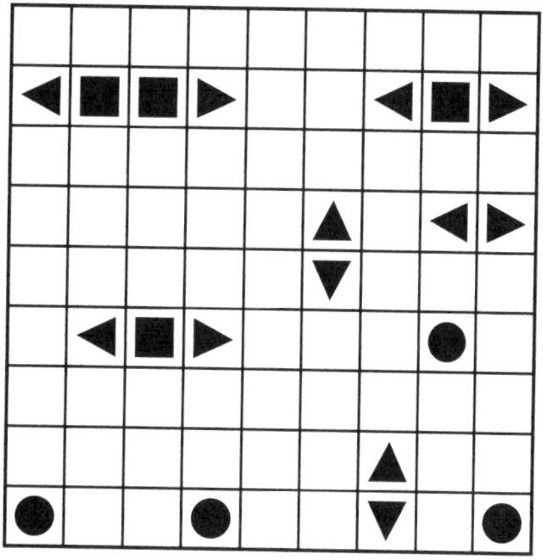

57

58

7 – Each of the lower numbers is the square root of the higher number in the opposite point of the star.

59

A=66, B=61, C=67, D=100, E=135, F=127, G=128, H=167, I=235, J=255, K=295, L=402, M=550, N=697, O=1247.

60

●	●		2	●		2	2		0
4	●		●	2		●	●		
2	●			2		2			
			1	●	3		1	1	●
0					●	●		2	
	2	2				●	3	2	●
2	●	●		2	3	3		●	
●	5	●	●	2	●	●		1	
●	4					3			
1	2	●		1	●		0	0	

61

The sum total of the values of the top two squares is equal to the square of the value of the central square, as is the sum total of the values of the bottom two squares. Thus the missing value is 3, so the missing letter is C.

62

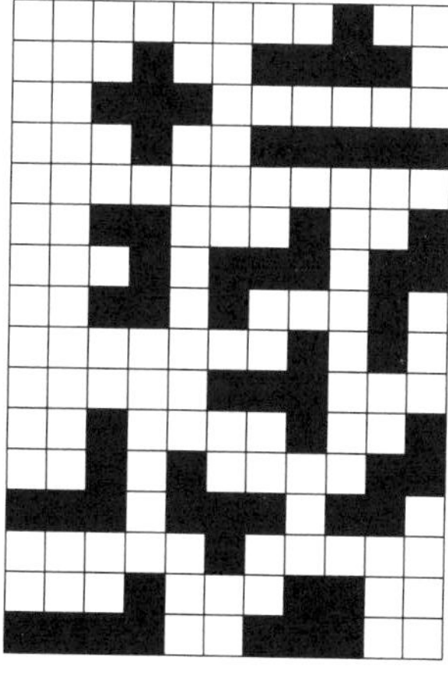

63

SOLUTIONS : LEVEL 4

64

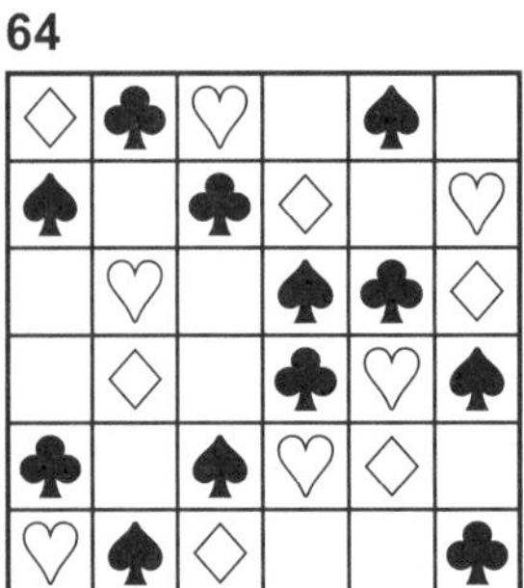

65

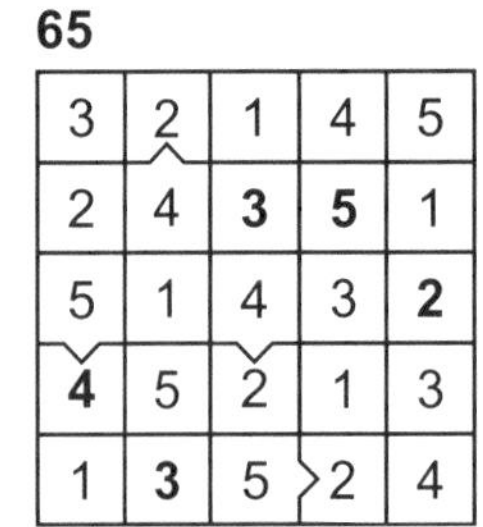

66

2	7	5		1	4	6	7		4	6	3	7
	2	2	4	0	1	5		4	5	0		0
5	5	6	8	0	2	1		3		9	1	2
8	4		9	3	4	5		3		9	2	3
9	3	5	7		2		1	3	2	7	3	
4	6	4		2		6	1	7		7		3
8	2		4	6	9	2	4	4	8		5	0
7		1		1	3	8		9		2	2	3
	3	6	8	8	9		3		9	3	1	4
7	4	3		1		5	0	4	5		4	1
2	9	2		5		6	1	4	3	8	5	7
3		8	5	5		1	2	7	2	8	4	
6	5	8	6		4	0	1	8		4	5	1

67

4	5	6	1	2	3
5	1	3	2	4	6
6	4	1	5	3	2
2	6	4	3	5	1
3	2	5	6	1	4
1	3	2	4	6	5

68

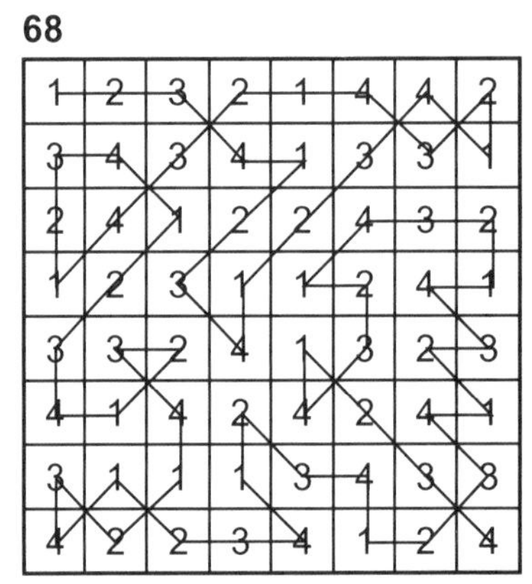

69

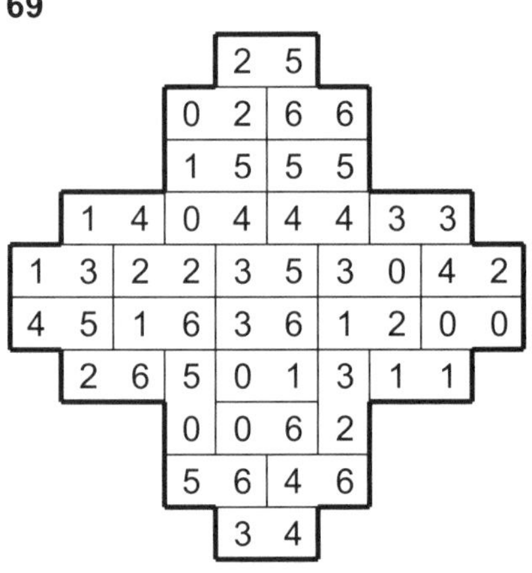

70

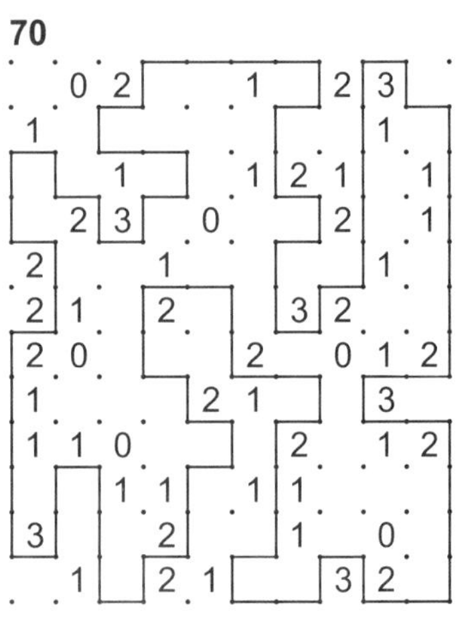

71

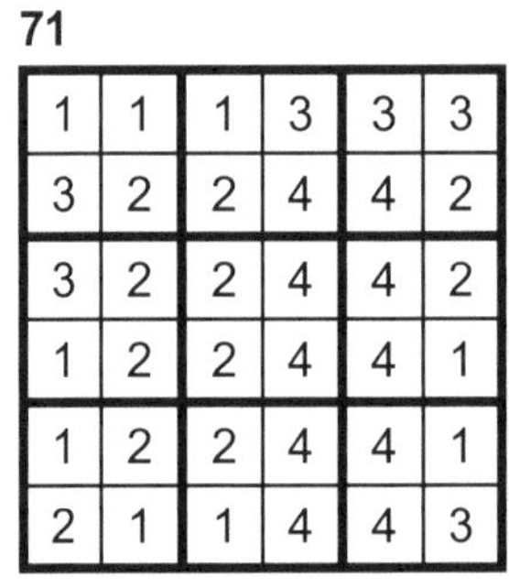

72

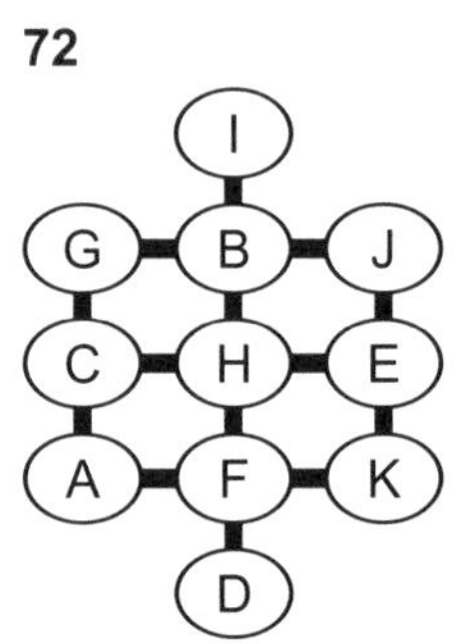

SOLUTIONS : LEVEL 4

73

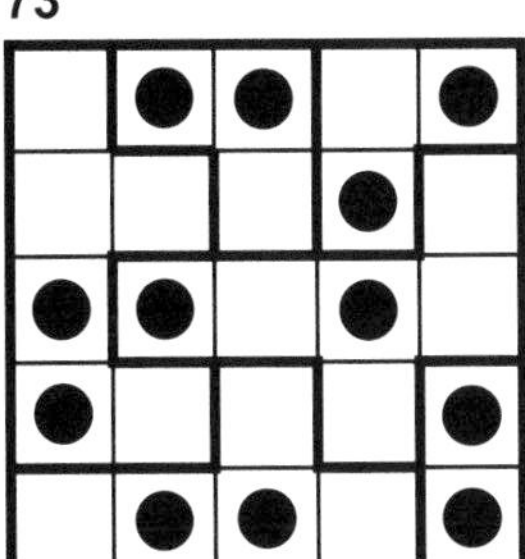

74

		○		○		○	
	○						○
	○		○				
				○			
				○			
	○			○			○

75

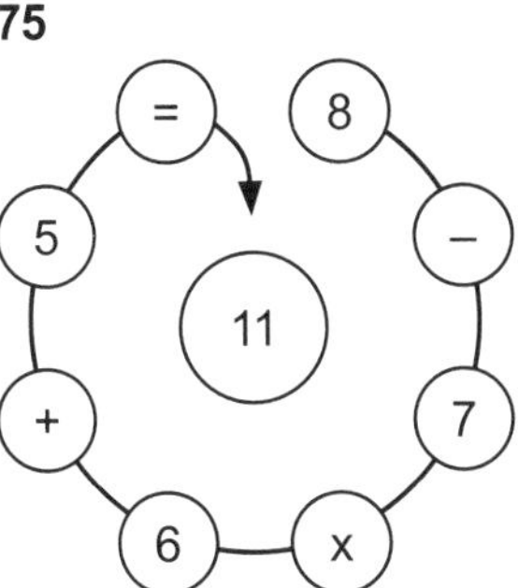

76

A	A	B	C	C	B
B	B	C	A	C	A
B	A	C	C	B	A
C	C	A	B	A	B
C	B	A	B	A	C
A	C	B	A	B	C

77

7	+	9	+	2	=	18
+		–		x		
1	x	6	x	8	=	48
–		x		+		
5	x	3	x	4	=	60
=		=		=		
3		9		20		

78

2E	3S	2E	2W	2S
1S	3E	2W	1N	2W
2S	2E	■	1W	1S
3E	1N	1S	2N	2W
1N	3N	1E	1E	3W

79

9			9		9	
4		5		4		2
7			9			
					2	
9		4				

80

23	34	38	39	48	**75**
72	42	32	25	47	39
67	**62**	42	24	25	37
25	63	47	**60**	23	39
22	16	**56**	60	63	40
48	40	42	49	**51**	27

81

							76
14	17	8	21	24	19	4	107
13	7	11	1	29	30	20	111
27	21	10	8	6	2	19	93
9	14	28	11	8	3	18	91
12	11	5	14	26	24	15	107
29	13	4	15	23	10	17	111
7	9	14	12	25	4	27	98
111	92	80	82	141	92	120	105

SOLUTIONS : LEVEL 5

1

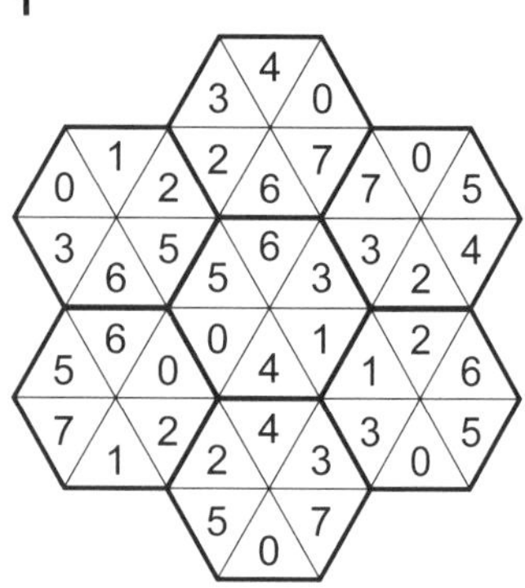

2

▲								
■		●		●				
■								
▼						◀	■	▶
		◀	■	▶				
●								▲
				▲				▼
		▲		▼				
		▼						●

3

☆2	◇4	⬡1	□5	○3
⬡3	☆5	□4	○2	◇1
□1	⬡2	○5	◇3	☆4
○4	□3	◇2	☆1	⬡5
◇5	○1	☆3	⬡4	□2

4

896 – Assign a number to each letter according to its place in the alphabet, so A=1, B=2, C=3, etc. Multiply this by the number in the same point of the star, and then by the central figure, to give the number in the opposite point of the star. P(16) x8=128x7=896.

5

A=53, B=135, C=80, D=10, E=118, F=188, G=215, H=90, I=128, J=403, K=305, L=218, M=708, N=523, O=1231.

6

	1		●	●	●	2		1	●
2	●		3			●			1
●	2	1		●	3	●	3		0
		1		1			●		0
0		●	2	2	1		2		
	3		●		●			●	
●	●					2		2	
	3	●	1		●	2	1		●
	4	4	4		3	●		1	
●	●	●	●	●	2			0	

7

The sum total of the values of the letter in the right squares is subtracted from the sum total of the values of the letters in the left squares to give the value of the letter in the central square. Thus the missing value is 26, so the missing letter is Z.

8

9

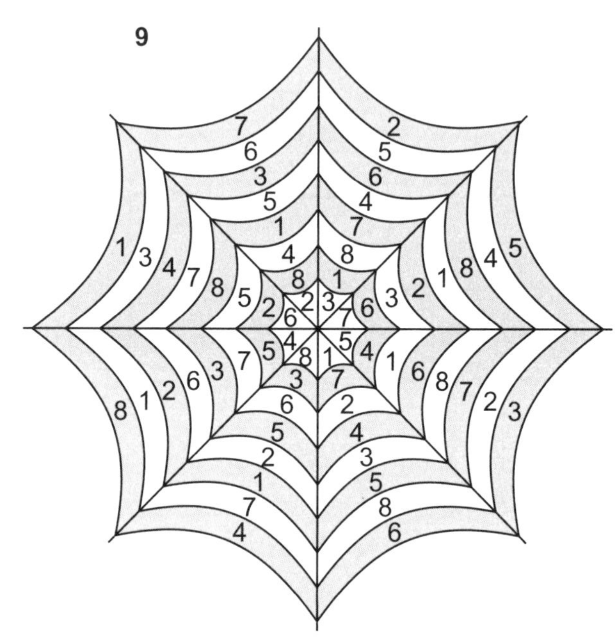

SOLUTIONS : LEVEL 5

10

♣		♡	♢		♠
♢	♣			♠	♡
	♡	♠	♣		♢
♠	♢	♣		♡	
♡		♢	♠	♣	
	♠		♡	♢	♣

11

4	5	**3**	**1**	2
1	4	5	2	3
3	2	4	5	1
5	1	**2**	3	4
2	**3**	1	4	**5**

12

5	0	7	1	■	3	6	6	■	3	5	9	7
0	■	2	1	■	6	■	9	2	3	5	■	5
7	8	2	■	6	4	4	4	■	8	9	■	3
■	3	3	9	1	4	■	8	1	3	3	2	0
6	2	■	5	■	8	8	1	■	■	■	0	■
5	2	7	9	9	3	■	2	5	8	6	3	6
4	■	4	5	6	■	■	■	1	2	3	■	4
6	3	0	0	0	5	■	2	0	3	3	9	2
■	3	■	■	■	3	2	5	■	4	■	3	4
1	3	6	7	8	3	■	4	9	1	9	3	■
1	■	2	4	■	7	0	2	3	■	7	8	9
4	■	7	4	1	1	■	5	■	2	0	■	8
6	7	1	5	■	8	2	6	■	3	8	8	7

13

4	1	6	5	3	2
2	3	4	6	5	1
6	4	1	3	2	5
3	2	5	4	1	6
1	5	3	2	6	4
5	6	2	1	4	3

14

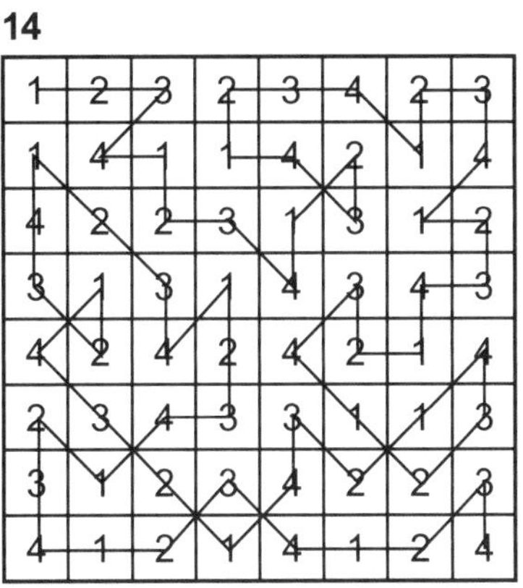

15

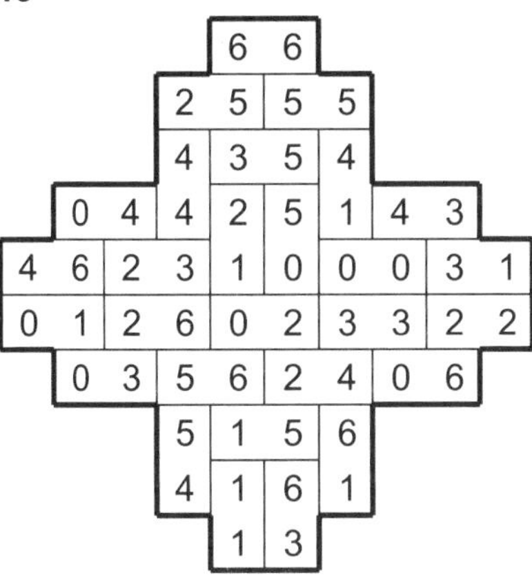

16

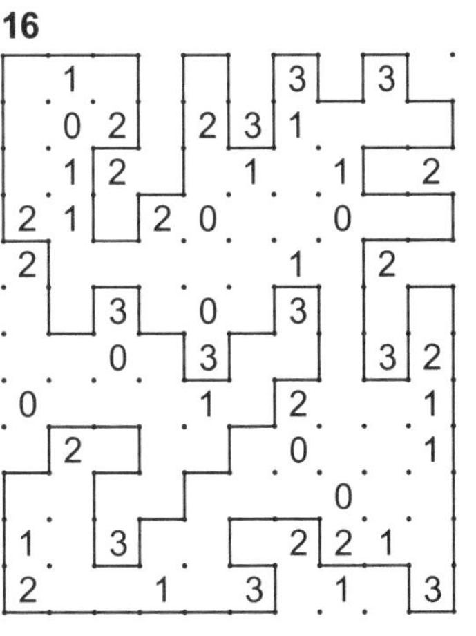

17

1	3	3	2	2	1
4	3	3	1	1	3
4	3	3	1	1	3
1	1	1	3	3	2
1	1	1	3	3	2
4	2	2	4	4	1

18

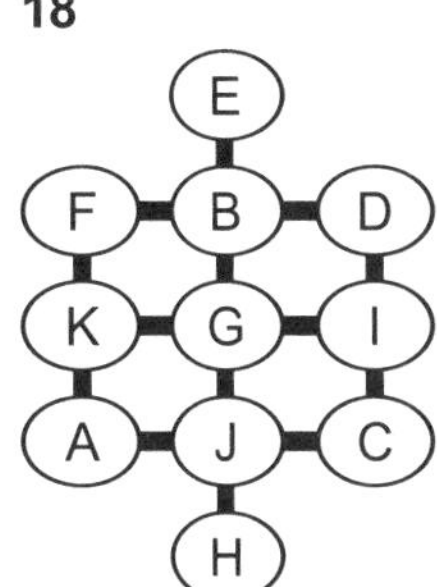

SOLUTIONS : LEVEL 5

19

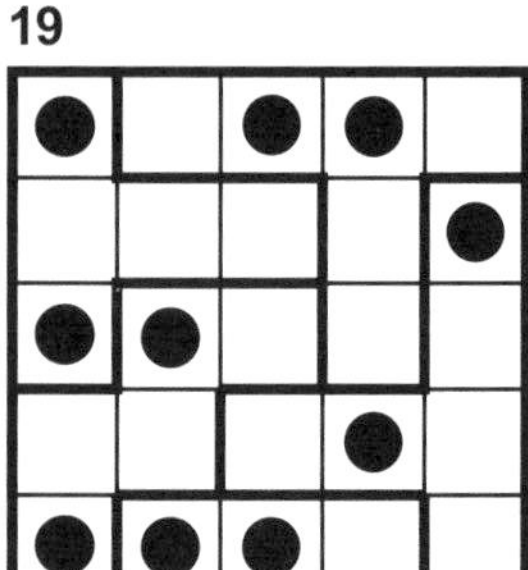

20

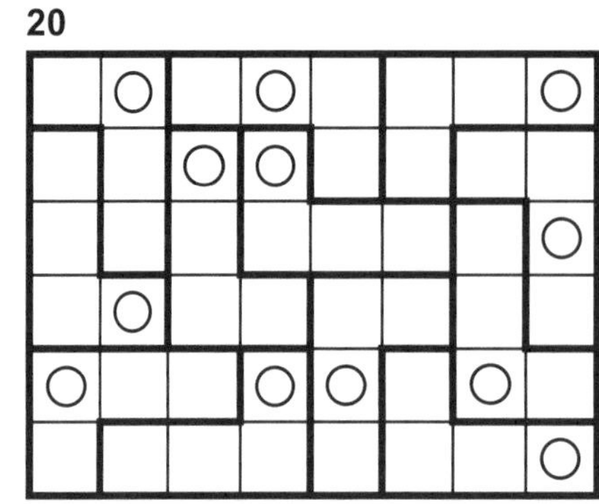

21

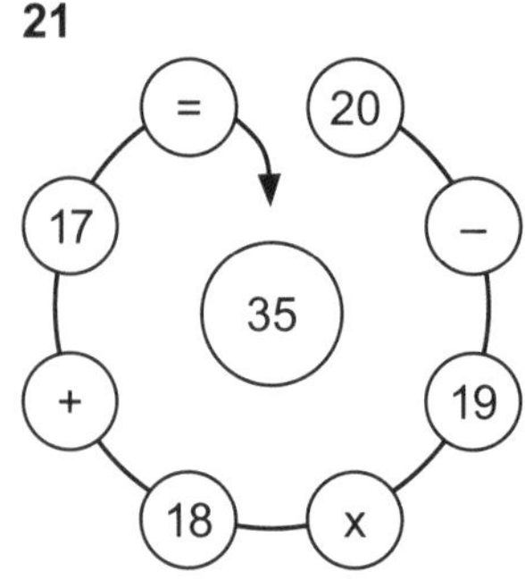

22

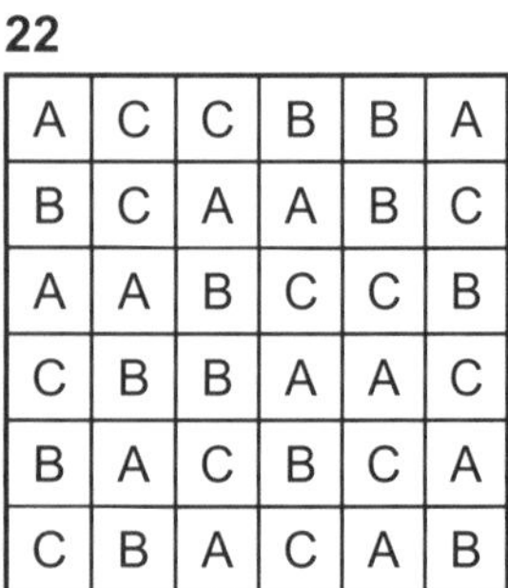

A	C	C	B	B	A
B	C	A	A	B	C
A	A	B	C	C	B
C	B	B	A	A	C
B	A	C	B	C	A
C	B	A	C	A	B

23

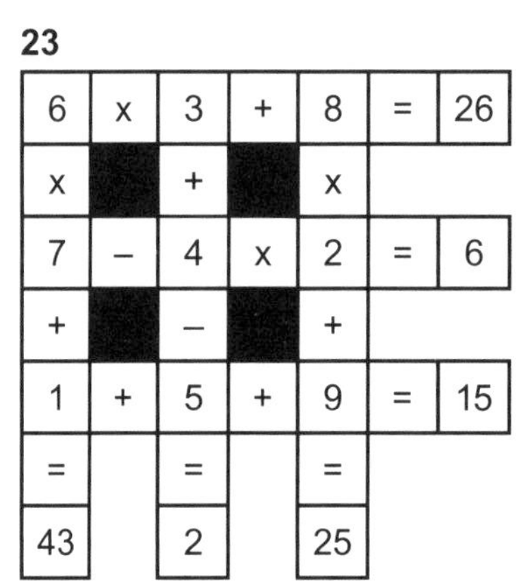

6	x	3	+	8	=	26
x	■	+	■	x		
7	–	4	x	2	=	6
+	■	–	■	+		
1	+	5	+	9	=	15
=		=		=		
43		2		25		

24

4E	4S	2S	2W	2W
2E	1W	2E	1N	2S
2S	1N	■	2W	4W
3N	1W	1W	**2N**	2W
3E	1E	2E	2N	2N

25

3				9		3
		1				
						1
		3		7		
4						7
		8				
8				9		

26

37	10	**38**	52	103	37
57	46	44	**31**	47	52
43	83	46	30	33	42
54	48	47	62	**21**	45
34	**64**	55	55	27	42
52	26	47	47	46	**59**

27

							119
14	17	29	3	6	13	19	101
2	1	12	26	11	24	8	84
30	18	15	7	4	28	5	107
22	9	13	24	20	16	10	114
7	16	26	18	12	11	20	110
27	12	17	30	25	5	9	125
10	15	23	26	6	14	21	115
112	88	135	134	84	111	92	92

SOLUTIONS : LEVEL 5

28

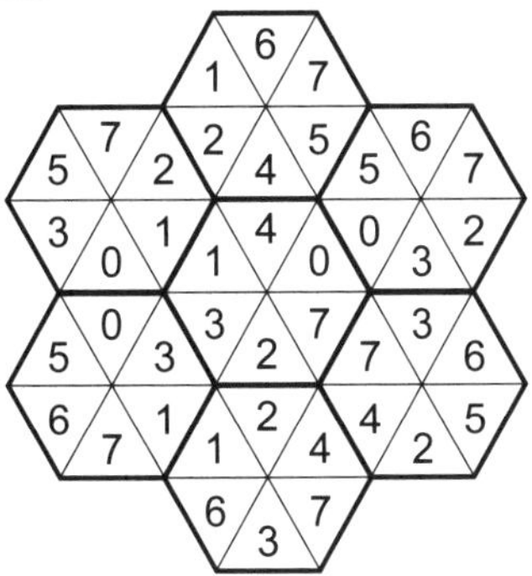

29

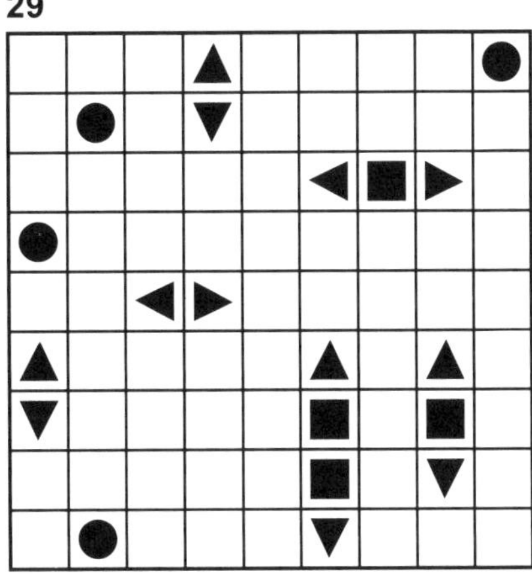

30

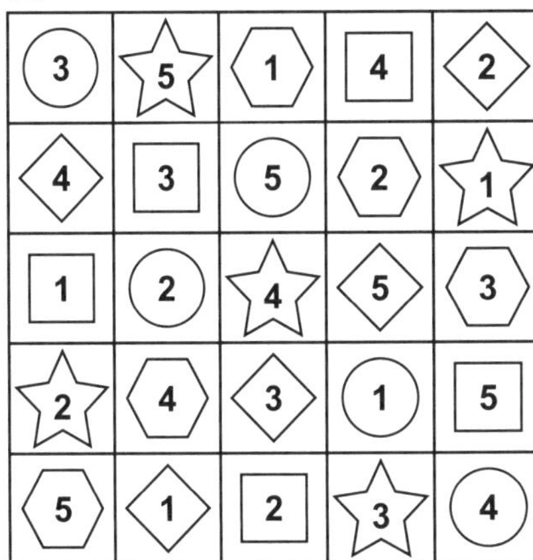

31

D – In the top row, all numbers are divisible by 8, in the middle row by 7, and in the bottom row by 6.

32

A=1, B=132, C=29, D=90, E=19, F=133, G=161, H=119, I=109, J=294, K=280, L=228, M=574, N=508, O=1082.

33

		●				●	4	●	2
0			4	4	●	4	●	●	
	3	●	●	●	●	3		2	
1	●	●	6	●				2	
		●	4	2		1	●	2	●
	1	2	●			2			
	0		1	2		●	3		
					●	●	3	●	2
			0		●			3	●
0					2	●	1		●

34

The value of the letter in the central square is half that of the sum total of the values of the letters in the other squares. Thus the missing value is 19, so the missing letter is S.

35

36

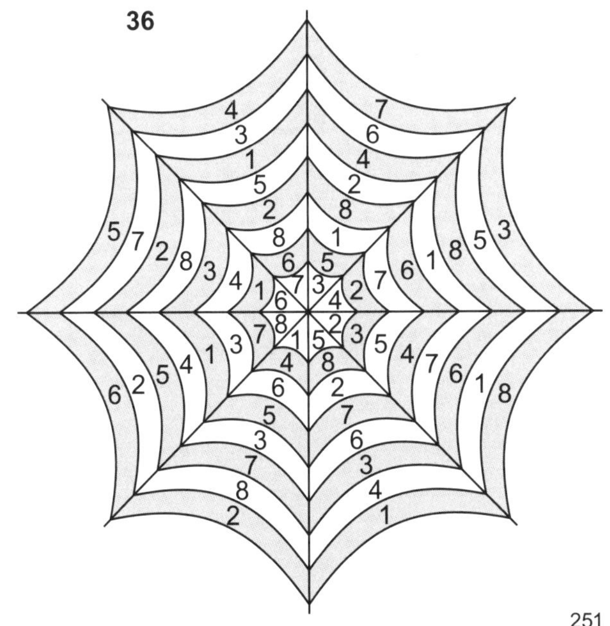

SOLUTIONS : LEVEL 5

37

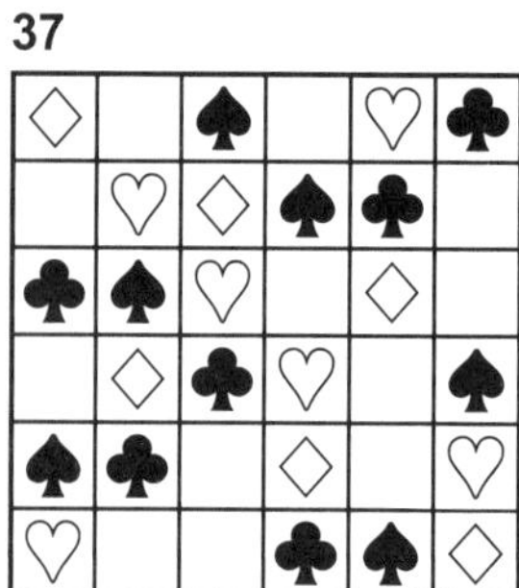

38

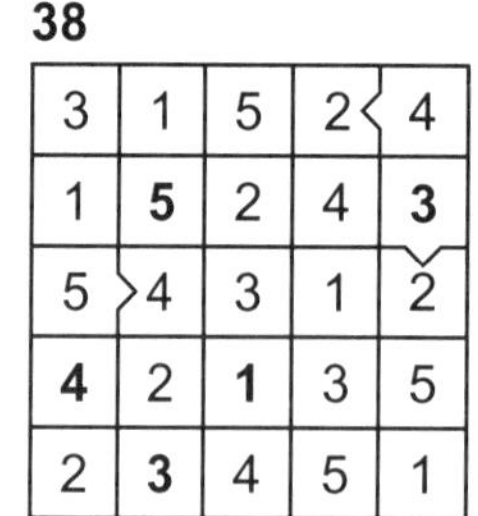

39

1	8	2		4	3	5		5	1	8	0	6
8		7	4	3	1	6		7	9	1		2
4	0	4		9	2	5	3	2		2	2	2
0		3		3		4	4	4			9	0
5	8	0	8		2	3		6	9	3	0	4
	9		1	2	2	4	5	6		8		4
	7	3	6		1		5		6	8	2	
1		9		2	1	6	5	5	9		2	
1	7	0	5	2		9	9		1	6	3	2
6	1			5	9	3		2		0		1
8	2	1		9	3	6	5	4		4	0	0
2		7	5	0		3	9	3	1	5		4
4	1	9	8	4		7	9	6		3	3	4

40

2	4	5	1	6	3
6	2	4	5	3	1
5	1	6	3	2	4
3	6	2	4	1	5
1	5	3	2	4	6
4	3	1	6	5	2

41

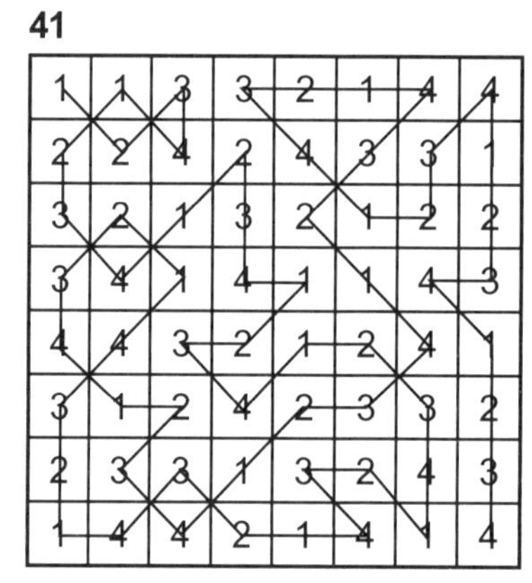

42

				3	5				
			2	5	6	6			
			4	1	3	2			
	2	3	3	0	3	2	5	3	
2	4	5	5	6	3	6	0	3	5
0	0	0	2	4	4	0	1	6	1
	1	6	1	4	0	4	4	0	
			5	6	2	6			
			1	2	4	5			
				1	1				

43

	2		1					3	
2	0			3		1		1	
			0	1	1	0		2	
					1			0	
2				1					
2		0			1			3	
2	0		2	2	1		2		1
	1		1			2	2		2
	2			1		3	2	2	
1		3	2		0	1	2		
		3		1			0	2	2
3	1					1	1		

44

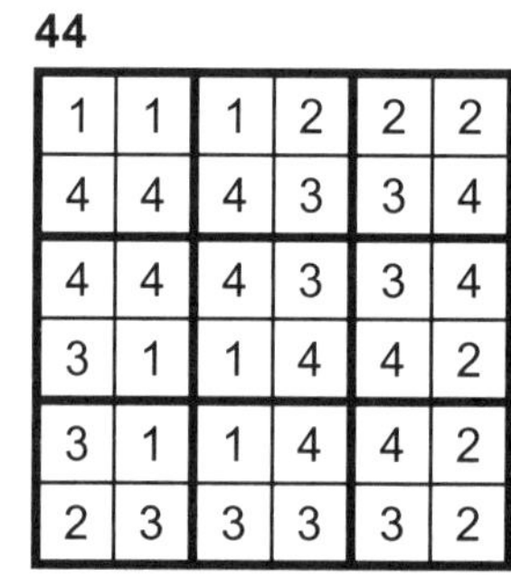

45

A – Each central number is twice the product of the other two numbers.

SOLUTIONS : LEVEL 5

46

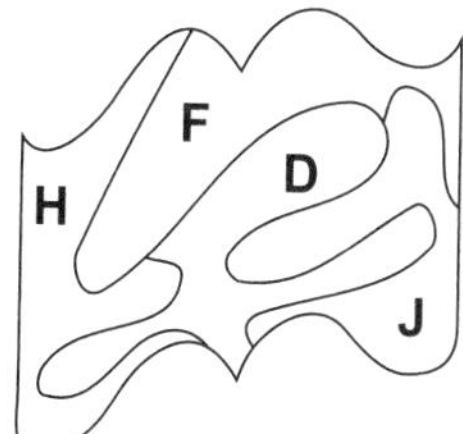

47

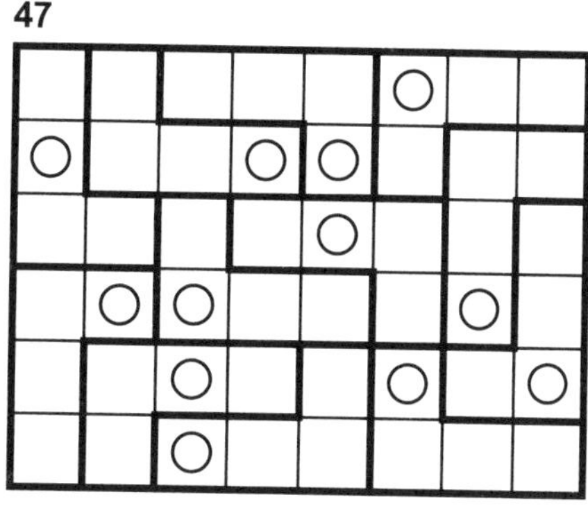

48

Circle = 3, cross = 8, pentagon = 7, square = 5, star = 1.

49

C	B	A	C	B	A
B	B	A	A	C	C
A	C	C	B	A	B
A	A	B	B	C	C
B	A	C	C	A	B
C	C	B	A	B	A

50

D – Assign a value to each letter according to its place in the alphabet. The number at the top is the sum total of these values.

51

4E	4S	1E	4S	4S
1E	1N	2E	1S	1S
2S	1E	■	3W	1S
2E	1W	3N	2W	1W
3N	2N	3N	3N	2W

52

24 – Each number is twice the number of straight lines in the shape surrounding it.

53

54 – From the top right corner, follow a clockwise path around and spiral towards the middle, deducting 3 from each number every time.

54

							90
14	20	16	24	30	19	4	127
6	17	9	11	29	15	21	108
22	1	5	17	19	29	15	108
2	13	27	22	14	8	7	93
18	20	5	7	23	6	21	100
19	3	13	12	11	23	16	97
22	6	26	3	7	14	10	88
103	80	101	96	133	114	94	114

SOLUTIONS : LEVEL 5

55

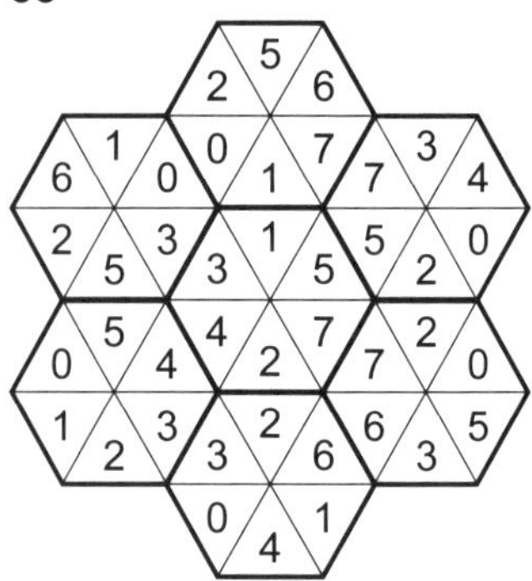

56

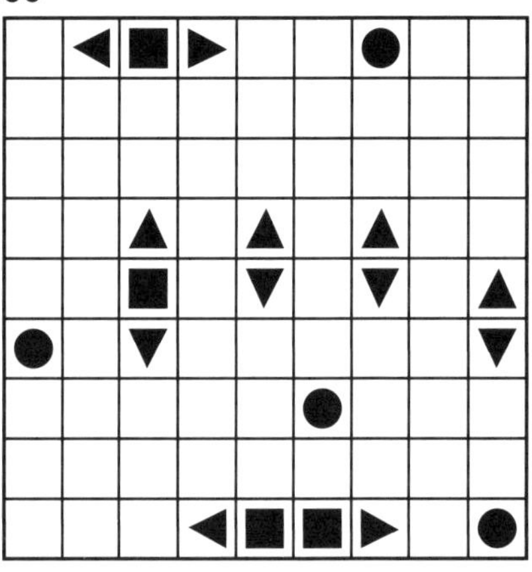

57

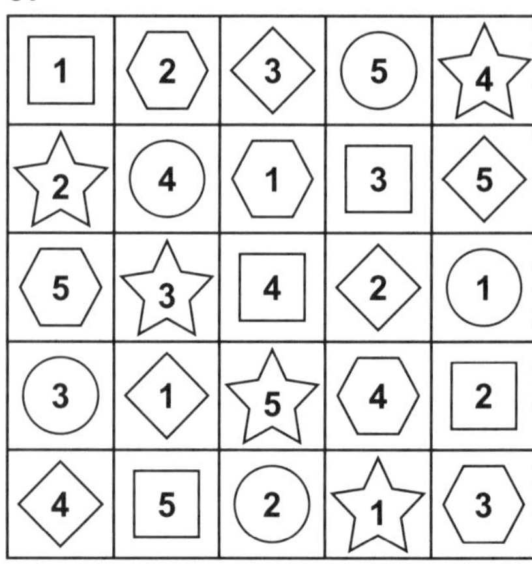

58

64 – The numbers in the outer points of the star are the cubes of the adjacent numbers in the central hexagon.

59

A=117, B=78, C=61, D=50, E=34, F=195, G=139, H=111, I=84, J=334, K=250, L=195, M=584, N=445, O=1029.

60

	0	1	●			1	2		2
			3			●	3	●	●
1		2	●	●		●			2
●		2	●	5		3	2	1	0
	4			●	●		●	1	
●	●	●	3	3	●	●			1
3		●	2	2	4	4	3	●	
1	●	2			●	●			1
1		2			●	●			
	1	●			2	2		0	

61

The value of the letter in the central square is one quarter of the sum total of the value of the letters in the outer four squares. Thus the missing value is 12, so the missing letter is L.

62

63

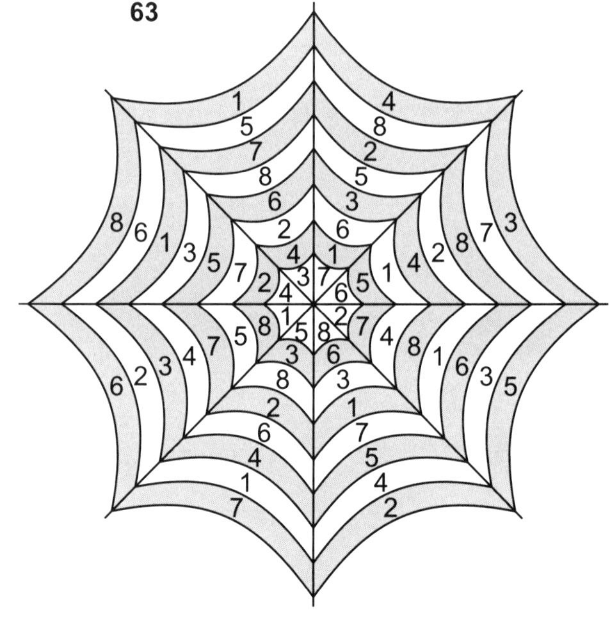

SOLUTIONS : LEVEL 5

64

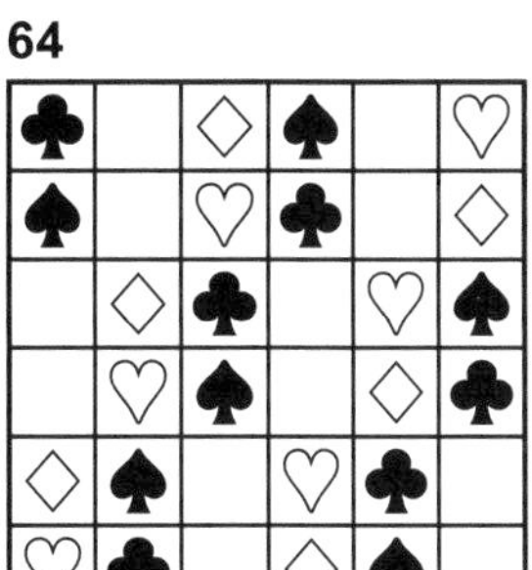

65

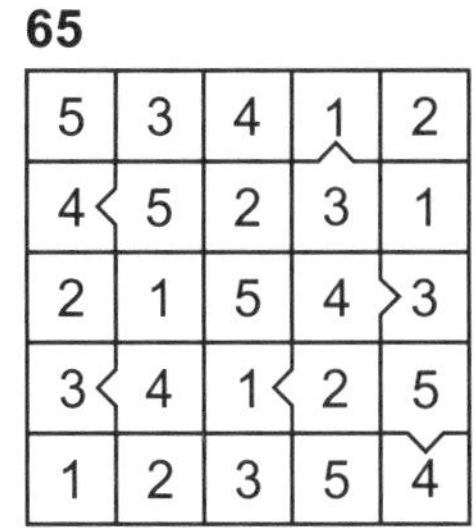

66

4	8	3		2	3	5		4	9	1	7	2
6	2	4		4	0	0	0	5		8	2	7
5	0	5	2	8		7		6	3	1	5	0
1		0		9	1	6	5	8		8	3	
7	9	6	3	9		8	9		5	0	3	1
	0		0		1	3	5	6	6			7
6	1	0	8	1	6		2	9	9	9	7	9
0			4	4	3	4	9		0		2	
8	1	6	8		7	4		1	2	2	2	4
	9	1		5	6	4	3	7		1		6
3	3	1	7	3		2		6	4	6	7	3
4	5	1		2	9	4	4	7		3	0	2
7	5	5	4	2		1	0	8		5	7	8

67

4	3	5	1	6	2
1	6	3	5	2	4
5	1	6	2	4	3
6	5	2	4	3	1
3	2	4	6	1	5
2	4	1	3	5	6

68

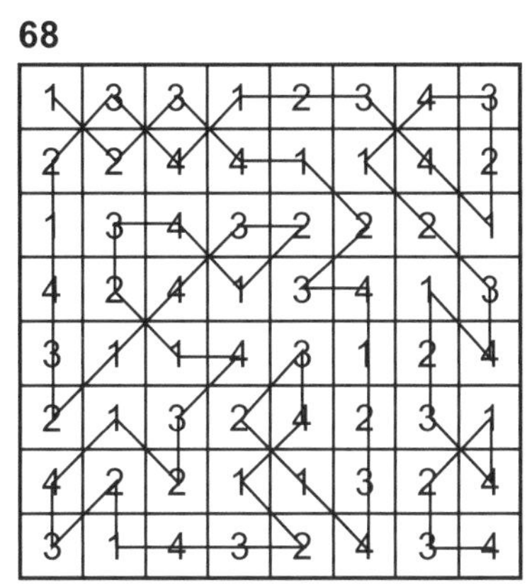

69

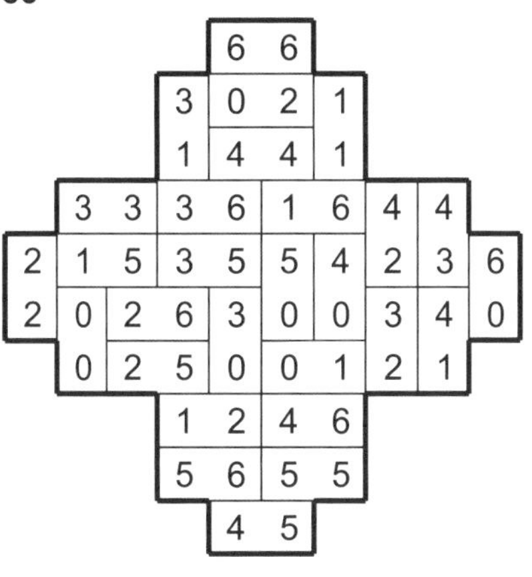

70

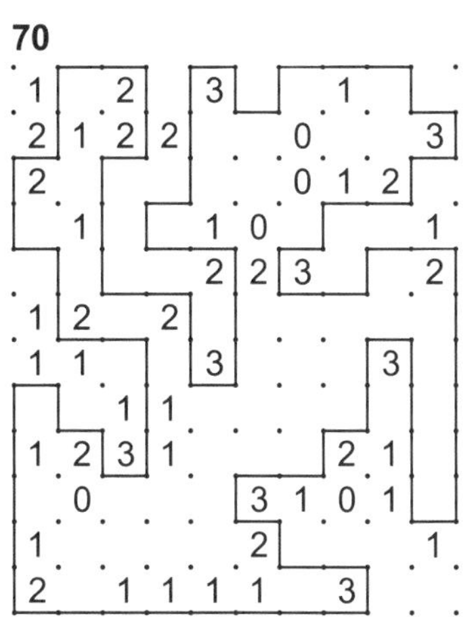

71

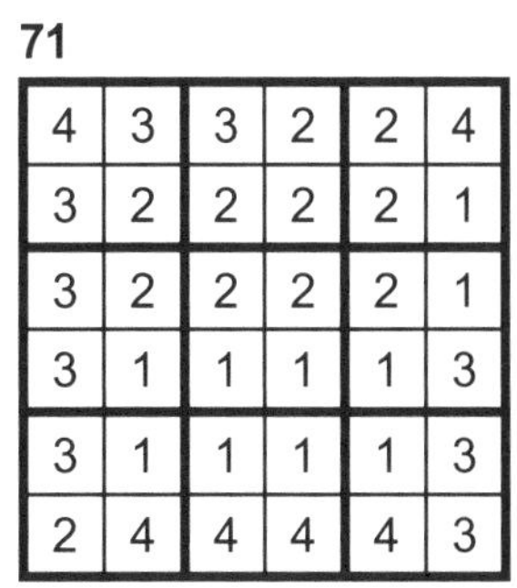

72

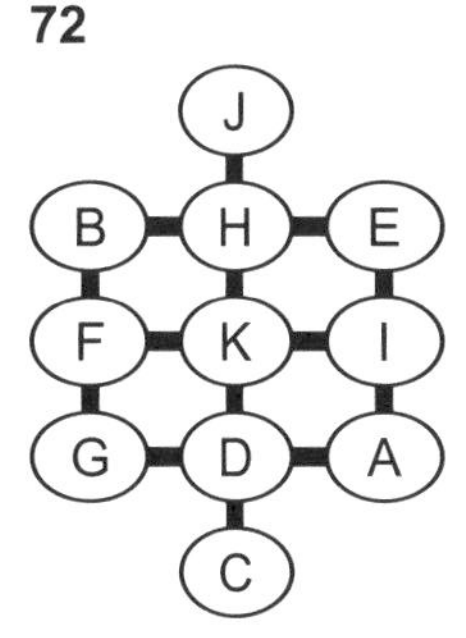

SOLUTIONS : LEVEL 5

73

	●		●	●
●			●	
	●	●	●	●
		●